THE RED BOOK OF UNITED STATES COINS

1971

A GUIDE BOOK
of
UNITED STATES COINS

24th Revised Edition

Fully Illustrated
Catalog and Valuation List — 1616 to Date

By R. S. YEOMAN

Including . . .

A BRIEF HISTORY OF AMERICAN COINAGE
EARLY AMERICAN COINS AND TOKENS
EARLY MINT ISSUES • REGULAR MINT ISSUES
PRIVATE STATE AND TERRITORIAL GOLD
SILVER AND GOLD COMMEMORATIVE ISSUES
PROOFS

CONDITION OF COINS

FAIR. Coin has sufficient design and letters to be easily identified. Excessive wear.

G. or **GOOD.** All of design, every feature and legend must be plain and date clear.

V. G. or **VERY GOOD.** Features all clear and bold. Better than good, but not quite fine.

F. or **FINE.** Obviously a circulated coin but little wear. Mint luster gone. All letters in LIBERTY and mottoes clear.

V. FINE or **VERY FINE.** Shows enough wear on high spots to be noticeable. Still retains enough luster to be desirable.

EX. FINE or **EXTREMELY FINE.** Slightly circulated with some luster but faint evidence of wear.

UNC. or **UNCIRCULATED.** New. Regular mint striking, but never placed in circulation. Older pieces may be tarnished or "toned."

PF. or **PROOF.** Coins with mirrorlike surface, specially struck for coin collectors. Also sandblast and matte proof. See Page 60.

Pre-1968 branch mint coins having a mirrorlike surface are not proofs but are first strikings of new dies.

IMPORTANT: Coins in any condition with defects, such as those which are bent, corroded, scratched, holed, nicked, stained, oxidized, mutilated, or have other imperfections, are worth less than if free of these defects. Flawless uncirculated coins are generally worth more than values quoted in this book.

THE SPANISH MILLED DOLLAR
The Coin of Our Nation's Founders

The Spanish milled dollar valued at eight reales, otherwise known as the "pillar dollar" and "piece of eight," has been given a place in romantic fiction unequalled by any other coin.

This time-honored piece, along with its fractional parts, such as two reales and four reales, was the chief coin of the American Colonists and was the forerunner of our own silver dollar and its fractional divisions, such as the quarter-dollar and half-dollar.

THE PURPOSE OF THIS BOOK

Coin values listed in the Guide Book are averaged from data supplied by contributors several months before publication. The coin market is so active in some categories that values can easily change during this period. Prices are shown as a guide and are not intended to serve as a price-list for any dealer's stock.

Prices rise because: 1. The trend of our economy is inflationary. 2. The number of collectors is increasing rapidly, while coin supplies remain stationary. 3. Dealers can procure their stock of coins only from collectors or other dealers, who expect a profit over and above what they originally paid.

Prices decline because: 1. Speculators buy and sell in large quantities, drawing in thousands of unwary persons looking for quick profits. When the average collector stops buying, the prices drop. 2. Hoards of coins suddenly are released from estates of deceased collectors or Federal Reserve vaults (as in the case of silver dollars) and the like. Such conditions usually adjust themselves within months or a few years.

Those who edit, contribute to, and publish this book, advocate the collecting of coins for pleasure and educational benefits. A secondary consideration is that of investment, the profits from which are realized over the long term based on intelligent purchases of the best grades of coins.

Neither the publisher, nor the editor, deals in coins; therefore, the values shown are not offers to sell but are included only as general information.

We thank all contributors to this edition.   R. S. YEOMAN

The Handbook of United States Coins, containing average prices dealers will pay for certain specified coins, is obtainable at hobby dealers for $1.50. A companion book, Buying and Selling U.S. Coins (paperback edition, $1.00), gives a capsule comparison of Guide Book and Handbook prices for coins n certain average grades.

QUANTITIES OF COINS STRUCK

Collectors are cautioned that mint reports are not always reliable for estimating the rarity of coins. In the early years of the mint, dies of previous years were often used until they became worn or broken.

It should also be emphasized that quantities reported, particularly for gold and silver, cover the number of coins struck and have no reference to the quantity reaching actual circulation. Many issues were deposited in the treasury as backing for paper currency and were later melted. There are other similar examples.

The rarity of gold pieces struck before 1834, particularly half eagles, can be traced to the fact that the gold content was reduced in 1834, making previous issues greater in value than face, causing melting and reminting.

The quantities reported by the mint of three dollar gold pieces from 1873 to 1877 and half cents from 1832 to 1836 are subject to doubt.

Coinage figures shown for 1964 through 1966 are for coins bearing those dates. Some of them were struck in more than one year and at various mints, both with and without mint marks.

Mint quantities are shown adjacent to each date throughout the book.

PROOF TOTALS ARE SHOWN IN PARENTHESES

CONTRIBUTORS TO THE TWENTY-FOURTH EDITION

KENNETH E. BRESSETT, Co-ordinating Editor

Robert F. Batchelder
A. E. Bebee
Philip E. Benedetti
Q. David Bowers
Walter Breen
Dan Brown
Malcolm O. E. Chell-Frost
Alan R. Cohen
Jerry Cohen
Ted Craige
B. M. Douglas
Ben Dreiske
Kurt Eckstein
Pete Foerster
Charles F. French
Dorothy Gershenson
Bernard Gimelson
Lawrence S. Goldberg
Gene L. Henry
Floyd O. Janney
Robert R. Johnson
A. M. Kagin
Paul Kagin
M. L. Kaplan

Mike Kliman
Abe Kosoff
Abner Kreisberg
Kenneth W. Lee
Lester Merkin
Bill Mertes
Roy A. Miller
Ken Nichols
Dean Oakes
Al C. Overton
Joe Person
Richard Picker
Elmer B. Ray
James Ruddy
Dick Rudolf
F. K. Saab
Earl C. Schill
Norman Shultz
Sidney W. Smith
Leonard W. Stark
Maurice A. Storck
R. E. Wallace
Harold E. Whiteneck
Gary Young

Credit is due:

Herbert Bergen, Harry X Boosel (1873), Hy Brown, Ronnie Carr, William L. Clark, George Fuld, Robert W. Julian, Hubert L. Polzer, Richard Rogers, Max M. Schwartz, Neil Shafer, Arlie Slabaugh, Holland Wallace and Leo A. Young for special data and service in connection with this book.

Those now deceased, but whose contributions have been a part of this book since early editions, include:

David M. Bullowa, Charles E. Green, Richard D. Kenney, Steve Kosoff, Franklyn H. Miller, Stuart Mosher, Gen. M. S. Newton, Earl Parker, Lewis M. Reagan, Herbert E. Rowold, Walter Thompson and Farran Zerbe.

Brief guides to grading are placed before each major coin type in this book. For those readers who desire more detailed descriptions of all coin grades, we recommend A GUIDE TO THE GRADING OF UNITED STATES COINS, by Martin R. Brown and John W. Dunn.

AN INTRODUCTION TO UNITED STATES COINS

Money of the Early Americans

The story of American money, which occupies a period of about three cen-
turies, began when the early settlers in New England carried on their fur
trade with the Indians through the use of wampum, which had been fashioned
from mussel shells in the form of "beads." Beaver skins, wampum, and in
Virginia, tobacco, soon became the common accepted media of exchange for
all other available commodities. The immigrants, in fact, had little use for
coined money at first, but when traders arrived from foreign lands, coins were
usually demanded in payment for goods. Any foreign coins were usually
accepted, such as French louis, English guineas, German thalers, Dutch
ducats, and various Spanish coins, including doubloons and particularly the
Spanish milled dollar, or piece of eight. The coin last mentioned remained
as a standard money unit throughout the entire colonial period. Even after
the Revolutionary War, the Spanish dollar and its fractional parts continued
to circulate in this country with official sanction until 1857. One real equaled
12½ cents and was known as a "bit." A quarter of the dollar thus became
known as "two bits," a term still in common use.

England consistently ignored the plight of the colonists and made no effort
to provide gold or silver coins, or a small-change currency for them. Although
coins known as "Hogge Money" were provided for the Sommer Islands,
now known as the Bermudas, about the year 1616, the first coins minted in
America were minted by John Hull in the Massachusetts Bay Colony. The
General Court of the colony granted him authority to begin coinage. Starting
in 1652 the Boston mint provided the famous N.E., pine tree, and similar
shillings, with their fractional parts, for the hardpressed colonists. Other
colonies tried similar projects but failed.

As time went on coins and tokens of many types were introduced and employed by the colonists in their daily course of business. Lord Baltimore in
Maryland was responsible for a series of silver pieces, which were probably
struck in England in 1659. Mark Newby introduced a piece known as St.
Patrick's Halfpence into the province of New Jersey in 1682. Coins dated
1722 to 1724, known as Rosa Americana and Hibernia coppers, were produced
by William Wood in England and were widely circulated in America. The
Carolina and New England Elephant tokens were current in the years following 1694. There were also a few issues of uncertain date and origin, such as
the New Yorke Token and the New England Stiver, which circulated among
the Dutch settlers and were probably sent over from Holland.

Enterprising American individuals were responsible for some of the copper
pieces that circulated during the eighteenth century. The Gloucester Token,
about which little is known, was one of these. John Higley of Granby, Connecticut, made an interesting series of threepence pieces during the period from
1737 to 1739. J. Chalmers, a goldsmith in Annapolis, Maryland, issued silver
shillings, sixpence, and threepence pieces in 1783. In 1787 Ephraim Brasher,
a New York goldsmith, struck a gold piece of the value of a doubloon (about
$16.00). Standish Barry of Baltimore, Maryland, made a curious silver token
threepence in 1790.

Still other tokens, struck in England, reached our shores in Revolutionary
times and were for the most part speculative ventures. These much-needed,
small-denomination coppers were readily circulated because of the great
scarcity of fractional coins. Included in this category were the Nova Constellatio coppers and the Bar cent.

During the period of confederation following the War of Independence,
still more English tokens were added to the great variety of coins and tokens
employed in the new nation. In 1787 the Nova Eboracs, known as New York

Coppers, the Georgius Triumpho, the Auctori Plebis, and later the Kentucky, Myddelton and Franklin Press tokens were introduced.

Another interesting series, important because of their close association with our first president, comprises those tokens bearing the portrait of Washington. They circulated during and after the Confederation.

Coinage of the States

The Articles of Confederation, adopted July 9, 1778, provided that Congress should have the sole right to regulate the alloy and value of coin struck by its own authority or by that of the respective states.

Each state, therefore, had the right to coin money, but Congress served as a regulating authority. New Hampshire was the first state to consider coinage, but few if any coins were placed in circulation. The only specimens known bear the date 1776.

Vermont, Connecticut, and New Jersey granted coining privileges to companies or individuals. Massachusetts erected its own mint in which copper coins were produced. A number of interesting varieties of these state issues, most of which were struck in fairly large quantities, can still be easily acquired, and form the basis for many present day collections of early American coins.

The Beginnings of United States Coinage

Throughout the Colonial years, Americans had become accustomed to the use of the Spanish dollar and its fractional parts, the real, the medio (half-real), etc. It was only natural, therefore, that when a national coinage was under consideration the dollar was mentioned most frequently. In earlier years currency statutes in many of the colonies had given first consideration to the Spanish dollar. Connecticut, Massachusetts, and Virginia, particularly, passed laws making Spanish coins a legal tender. The first issue of Continental paper money May 10, 1775, offers further evidence that the dollar was to be our basic money unit, for it provided that the notes should be payable in "Spanish Milled dollars or the value thereof in gold or silver."

The Assistant Financier of the Confederation, Gouverneur Morris, proposed a decimal coinage ratio, and his plan was incorporated in a report presented by Robert Morris, Superintendent of Finance, to the Congress, January 15, 1782. Plans for a mint were advanced, and a uniform national currency to relieve the confused money conditions was outlined. Morris's unit, 1/1440 of a dollar, was calculated to agree without a fraction with all the different valuations of the Spanish milled dollar in the various States. Although a government mint was approved February 21, 1782, no immediate action was taken. During 1784 Thomas Jefferson, then a member of the House of Representatives, brought in a report concerning the plan, and expressed disagreement with Morris' complicated money unit. He advocated the simple dollar unit because he believed the dollar was already as familiar and convenient a unit of value as the British pound. He favored the decimal system and remarked that, "The most easy ratio of multiplication and division is that of ten. President George Washington referred to it as 'a measure, which in my opinion, has become indispensibly necessary.' "

The Grand Committee in May 1785 recommended a gold five-dollar piece; a dollar of silver with fractional coins, of the same metal, in denominations of half, quarter, tenth, and twentieth parts of a dollar; and copper pieces valued at one-hundredth and one two-hundredth of a dollar.

In 1783 Robert Morris submitted a series of pattern pieces in silver which were designed by Dudley to carry out the decimal idea for United States money. These are known as the Nova Constellatio Patterns and consist of the "Mark" or 1,000 units, the "Quint" or 500 units, and the "Bit" or 100 units. The unit was to be a quarter grain of silver. This was not the first attempt at a dollar coin, for the Continental currency piece of dollar size, dated 1776, had been struck in such metals as brass, pewter, and silver. The variety in silver probably saw limited service as a dollar.

Congress gave formal approval to the basic dollar unit and decimal coinage ratio in its resolution of July 6, 1785, but other more pressing matters delayed further action. Not until the Constitutional Convention had placed the country on firm ground and the new nation had elected George Washington President, did the Congress again turn attention to the subject of currency, a mint, and a coinage system.

The Massachusetts cents and half-cents struck in 1787 and 1788 were the first official coins to bear a stated value in terms of decimal parts of the dollar unit in this country. The cent represented a hundredth part of a Spanish dollar.

The first federally authorized coin was the Fugio Cent, sometimes called the Franklin Cent, as he was supposed to have supplied the design and composed the legends. This piece, similar in design to the Continental Currency dollar of 1776, was privately struck in 1787 by contract with the Government.

Alexander Hamilton, then Secretary of the Treasury, reported his views on monetary matters January 21, 1791. He concurred in all essentials with the decimal subdivisions and multiples of the dollar contained in the earlier resolutions and urged the use of both gold and silver in our standard money.

Congress passed a resolution March 3, 1791, that a mint be established, and authorized the President to engage artists and procure machinery for the making of coins. No immediate steps were taken, but when Washington delivered his third annual address, he recommended immediate establishment of a mint.

On April 2, 1792, a bill was finally passed providing "that the money of account of the United States should be expressed in dollars or units, dismes or tenths, cents or hundredths, and milles or thousandths; a disme being the tenth part of a dollar, a cent the hundredth part of a dollar, a mille the thousandth part of a dollar . . ."

Denominations specified in the act were as follows:

	Value of	Grains Pure	Grains Standard
Gold Eagle	$10.00	247 - 4/8	270
Gold Half Eagle	5.00	123 - 6/8	135
Gold Quarter Eagle	2.50	61 - 7/8	67 - 4/8
Silver Dollar	1.00	371 - 4/16	416
Silver Half-Dollar	.50	185 - 10/16	208
Silver Quarter-Dollar	.25	92 - 13/16	104
Silver Disme (dime)	.10	37 - 2/16	41 - 3/5
Silver Half-Disme	.05	18 - 9/16	20 - 4/5
Copper Cent	.01	11 pennyweights	
Copper Half-Cent	.005	5½ pennyweights	

The word "pure" meant unalloyed metal; "standard" meant, in the case of gold, 11/12 fine or 11 parts pure metal to one part alloy, which was mixed with the pure metal to improve the wearing qualities of the coins. The fineness for silver coins was 1485/1664 or approximately 892.43 thousandths, in contrast with the gold coins of 22 karats, or 916⅔ thousandths fine.

The law also provided for free coinage of gold and silver coins at the fixed ratio of 15 to one, and a token coinage of copper cents and half-cents. Under the free coinage provision no charge was to be made for converting gold or silver bullion into coins "weight for weight." At the depositor's option, however, he could demand an immediate exchange of coins for his bullion, for which privilege a deduction of one-half of one per cent was to be imposed.

Washington appointed David Rittenhouse, a well-known philosopher and scientist, as the first Director of the Mint. A mint building was started nearly four months after the passage of the Act of April 2, 1792. It was located on Seventh Street near Arch in Philadelphia.

The first coin struck at the new mint was the half-disme. Fifteen hundred of these pieces were produced during the month of July 1792 before the mint was completed. Washington supplied some of his own private plate to the value of about one hundred dollars for these first mint coins. Dismes also were probably struck at this time or a short while later. The portrait on these pieces is presumed to have been modeled by Martha Washington.

Copper for cents and half-cents was covered in the Act of May 8, 1792 when the purchase of not over 150 tons was authorized. On September 11, 1792, six pounds of old copper were purchased, this being the first purchase of copper for coinage, which was probably used for the striking of patterns.

Planchets with upset rims for cents and half-cents were purchased from Boulton of Birmingham, England from 1798 to 1838.

Several pattern coins were prepared in 1792 before regular mint operations commenced. These included the silver center cent by Voigt, a smaller piece than that of regular issue. The small plug of silver, worth about three-quarters of a cent, was evidently intended to bring the intrinsic value of the coin up to the value of one cent and permit production of a coin of more convenient size. Alexander Hamilton had mentioned a year before that the proposed "intrinsic value" cent would be too large, and suggested that the amount of copper could be reduced and a trace of silver added. This pattern cent with a silver center may have been designed to conform to this recommendation.

The cents by Robert Birch are equally interesting. These patterns are identified by their legends which read "LIBERTY PARENT OF SCIENCE AND INDUSTRY" and "TO BE ESTEEMED BE USEFUL." The cent with an eagle on the reverse side belongs among the early patterns devised before regular issues were struck.

The first depositor of silver was the bank of Maryland, which sent $80,715.73½ in French coins to the mint July 18, 1794. Moses Brown, a Boston merchant, deposited the first gold in the form of ingots, February 12, 1795, amounting to $2,276.22, receiving silver coin in payment. The first coins transferred to the Treasurer consisted of 11,178 cents on March 1, 1793. The first return of coined silver was made on October 15, 1794, and the first gold coins were delivered July 31, 1795, 744 half-eagles.

File marks on early U. S. Coins are a mint process of weight adjustment.

Regular Mint Issues

Cents and half-cents exclusively were coined during the year 1793, and by 1799 approximately $50,000 in these coins had been placed in circulation. This amount proved insufficient for the requirements of commerce, and small denomination coins of the states and of foreign countries continued in use during the first few years of the nineteenth century.

One of the most serious problems confronting the commercial interests during the early years was the failure of the government to provide a sufficient volume of circulating coins. The fault, contrary to popular opinion at the time, did not lie with any lack of effort on the part of the mint. Other circumstances tended to interfere with the expected steady flow of new coinage into the channels of trade.

Free circulation of United States gold and silver coins was greatly hindered by speculators. For example, worn Spanish dollars of reduced weight and value were easily exchanged for U. S. silver dollars, which meant the export of most of the new dollars as fast as they were minted, and a complete loss to American trade channels.

Gold coins failed to circulate for similar reasons. The ratio of 15 to 1 between gold and silver was close to the world ratio when Hamilton recommended it, but by 1799 the ratio in European commercial centers had reached 15¾ to 1. At this rate the undervalued gold coins tended to flow out of the country, or were reduced for bullion. After 1800, therefore, United States gold coins were rarely seen in general circulation. As no remedy could be found, coinage of the Eagle and the silver dollar was suspended by President Jefferson in 1804 and 1806 respectively. It is generally conceded that the silver dollar was discontinued in 1804, although the last coins minted for the period were dated 1803.

Lacking gold coins and silver dollars, the half-dollar became the desirable coin for large transactions, bank reserves, and foreign payments. Until 1830, in fact, half-dollars circulated very little as they were mainly transferred from bank to bank. This will account for the relatively good supply of half-dollars of this period which are still available to collectors in better than average condition. A senate committee of 1830 reported that United States silver coins were considered so much bullion and were accordingly "lost to the community as coins."

There was only a negligible coinage of quarters, dimes, and half-dimes from 1794 to 1834. It has been estimated that there was less than one piece for each person in the country in the year 1830. This period has been described as one of nondescript currency made up of banknotes, underweight foreign gold coins, foreign silver coins of many varieties, and domestic fractional silver coins. Notes of "wildcat banks" flooded the country before 1830 and were much more common than silver coins.

On June 28, 1834, a new law was passed reducing the weight of standard gold, which had the effect of placing our money on a gold standard. Trade and finance were greatly benefited by this act, which also proved a boon to the gold mines of Georgia and North Carolina. Branch mints in Dahlonega, Georgia, and Charlotte, North Carolina, were established two or three years later to handle the newly-mined gold at the source. The Templeton Reid and Bechtler issues of private gold coins were struck in this area.

The law of January 18, 1837, completely revised and standardized the mint and coinage laws. Legal standards, mint charges, legal tender, mint procedure, tolerance in coin weights, accounting methods, a bullion fund, standardization of gold and silver coins to 900 thousandths fine, and other desirable regulations were covered by the new legislation. Results of importance to the collector were the changes in type for the various coin denominations and the resumption of coinage of the Eagle and silver dollar shortly thereafter.

The political and financial elements underwent a crisis at about this time. The familiar "Jackson Tokens" and fractional notes of banks and commercial establishments completely eclipsed the circulation of metallic currency. This was the era of "shinplasters."

The California gold discovery in 1848 was responsible for an interesting series of private, state, and territorial gold issues in the Western states, culminating in the establishment of a branch mint at San Francisco in 1854.

Two new regular gold issues were adopted in 1849. In that year the double Eagle and gold dollar joined our American family of coins. The California gold fields greatly influenced the world gold market, making the exportation of silver profitable. For example, the silver in two half-dollars was worth $1.03½ in gold. The newly introduced gold dollars soon took over the burden and hastened the disappearance of silver coins from trade channels. This was the situation when the new three-cent postage rate brought about the bill authorizing the coinage of the silver three-cent piece in 1851. This was our country's first subsidiary coin, for its value was intrinsically 86% of its face value, an expedient designed to prevent its withdrawal from circulation.

The three-dollar gold piece was authorized by the act of February 21, 1853. Never a popular or necessary coin, it nevertheless was issued regularly until 1889.

On February 21, 1853, fractional silver coins were made subsidiary resulting from the fact that the weight of all silver pieces, excepting the dollar, was reduced. As the coins were now worth less than their face value free coinage of silver was prohibited, and the mint was authorized to purchase its silver requirements on its own account using the bullion fund of the mint, and, according to law, "the profit of said coinage shall be, . . . transferred to the account of the treasury of the United States."

Arrows were placed at the date on all silver coins except three-cent pieces and dollars, and on the quarters and half-dollars rays were added on the reverse side to denote the change of weight. In 1854 the rays were removed, and in 1856 the arrows disappeared. Production of silver coins in large quantities during this period greatly relieved the demands on gold dollars and three-cent pieces. Consequently for the first time in our nation's history there was a sufficient supply of fractional coins in general circulation.

The law of 1857 was designed primarily to reform the copper coinage. No matter how interesting and valuable the large cents and half-cents may have become in the eyes of the modern collector, they were very unpopular with the people and cost the mint too much to produce.

The new law abolished the half-cent piece, and reduced the size and changed the design of the cent. The new eagle or white cent contained 88% copper and 12% nickel. Several hundred were stamped from dies bearing the date 1856, a quantity considered by many to be too large for a pattern issue. Yet, no authority for the issue existed before 1857. Other important effects of the law were the retirement of the Spanish silver coins from circulation, and dispersal of the new cents in such excessive quantities as to create a nuisance to business houses, particularly in the eastern cities. The Indian head device replaced the Eagle in 1859, and in 1864 thè weight of the cent was further reduced and its composition changed to a proportion of 95% copper and 5% tin and zinc. This bronze composition has been standard for our cent except for the year 1943. In 1962 the alloy was changed to 95% copper and 5% zinc.

Both Jefferson and Hamilton had contended in their day that the currency of money of small value benefits society. The history of our cent and its daily use proves the soundness of this principle.

Abundance turned to scarcity following the outbreak of the Civil War. Anticipation of a scarcity and depreciation of the paper money was sufficient to induce hoarding. The large volume of greenbacks in circulation caused a premium on gold, and subsidiary silver as a result of the sudden depreciation quickly vanished in the North. Resort was soon made to postage stamps for small change. All types of fractional notes were put out at this time by municipalities and the Government. "Postage currency" became widely used, and in 1863 a great variety of tokens appeared to help fill the vacuum. Like the tokens of 1837 they were of two general classes, tradesmen's coins and imitations of legal cents. The latter were usually produced at a profit, many of which were political or patriotic in character, with slogans typical of the times.

The Law of 1864, which effected changes in the cent, provided also for the new bronze two-cent piece. The act, moreover, provided legal tender status for these two coins up to ten times their value. The two-cent piece was the first coin to bear the motto IN GOD WE TRUST. The new coin was readily accepted by the people but proved an unnecessary denomination, going out of fashion and being discontinued only nine years later.

Secretary Chase had issued a great many currency notes of three-cent denomination early in 1865. The nickel interests seized upon this circumstance to fight for a new three-cent coin for redemption of the paper money. A law was quickly passed and signed by the president as of March 3, 1865, providing for a three-cent coin of 75-25 copper-nickel composition. Our country now possessed two types of three-cent pieces. The nickel three-cent piece was struck continuously until 1889; the three-cent silver until 1873.

The new copper-nickel alloy ratio was selected for the five-cent coin, adopted May 16, 1866, to be thereafter known as a "nickel." Again the people had a coin value available in two forms. The silver half-dime, like the three-cent piece, was retired from service in 1873.

The Carson City Mint was established in 1870 as a convenient depository for the miners in that area and operated until 1893.

The Law of March 3, 1871, was a redemption measure and was passed to provide a means for the disposal to the United States Treasury of millions of minor coins which had accumulated in the hands of postmasters, newsdealers, and others. Small-denomination coins as a result of this new law were placed on an equal footing and could be redeemed when presented in lots of twenty dollars.

There was a general revision of the coinage laws in 1873. Several years of study and debate preceded the final enactment. The legislative history of the bill occupies hundreds of pages of the Congressional Globe, and the result was considered by many a clumsy attempt and a failure. The law has sometimes been referred to as the "Crime of '73." One consequence of the bill, which achieved final enactment February 12, 1873, was the elimination of the silver dollar. In its stead the Trade dollar of greater weight was provided for use in commerce with the Orient in competition with the Mexican dollar. The legal tender provision, which unintentionally gave the trade dollar currency within our borders, was repealed the following year.

The charge for converting standard gold bullion into coin was reduced by the act to one-fifth of one per cent. The same rate was imposed on silver bullion for coining trade dollars only.

It may be a surprise to some collectors to learn that the silver dollar had not circulated to any great extent in the United States after 1803. The coin had been turned out steadily since 1840, but for various reasons such as exportation, melting, and holding in bank vaults, the dollar was virtually an unknown coin. The Law of 1873 in effect demonetized silver and committed our country to a gold standard. The silver mining interests came to realize what had occurred a little later, and the ensuing quarter century of political and monetary history was filled with their voluble protests. There was a constant bitter struggle for the return to bimetallism.

From an economic point of view the inadequate supply of gold was responsible for a gradual decline in prices throughout the world. This brought about a gradual business depression in our country, particularly in the South and Middle-West. Private silver interests influenced great sections of the West for bimetallism as a remedy for the failing price level. Authorities have concluded that a world-wide adoption of bimetallism would have improved economic conditions, but the United States alone proceeding to place its money on a double standard at the old 16 to 1 ratio would have led only to a worse situation.

Of particular importance to collectors, however, were those features of the Law of 1873 which affected the status and physical properties of the individual coins. The weight of the half-dollar, quarter, and dime, was slightly changed and arrows were placed at the date for the ensuing two years to indicate the difference in weight. Silver three-cent pieces, half-dimes, and two-cent pieces were abolished by the act, and the manufacture of minor coins was restricted to the Mint at Philadelphia.

The short-lived twenty-cent piece was authorized March 3, 1875. It was created for the Western states where the Spanish "bit" had become equivalent to a U. S. dime. The five-cent piece did not circulate there, so when a quarter was offered for a "bit" purchase, only a dime change was returned. However, it was confused with the quarter-dollar and was discontinued after 1878.

The Bland-Allison Act of February 28, 1878, gave the Secretary authority to purchase two to four million dollars worth of silver bullion each month to be coined into silver dollars. The coin, never popular, was produced in minimum quantities. This was not a bimetallic law, nor was it a free coinage act. Strictly speaking it was a subsidiary coinage law, called by some "a wretched compromise."

The North and East so disliked the silver dollar that they found their way back to the Treasury, mostly through tax payments. Secretary Manning transferred ownership to the people and removed them from Treasury holdings by the simple expedient of issuing silver certificates in small bills to effect a wide circulation.

The Bland-Allison Act was repealed in 1890 and the Sherman Act took its place. Under this new law 4,500,000 ounces of silver per month could be paid for with Treasury Notes that were to be legal tender, and redeemable in gold or silver dollars coined from the bullion purchased. Important in this case was the fact that the notes were constantly being redeemed for gold which was mainly exported. The measure was actually a government subsidy for the silver miners and as such it was marked for failure, and was hastily repealed. The Bland-Allison Act and the Sherman Act gave a total of 570 million silver dollars to our monetary stocks.

The "Gold Standard Act" of 1900 gave our country a single standard, but reaffirmed the fiction that the silver dollar is a standard coin. It still enjoys unlimited, legal tender, but is as much a subsidiary coin, practically speaking, as the dime, for its value in terms of standard gold, even before the gold surrender executive order, was far below its face value.

The lapse in coinage after 1904 and until 1921 was due to lack of bullion. Legislation authorizing further metal supplies for silver dollars was not forthcoming until 1918 when the Pittman Act provided silver for the new dollars.

The dollar issued from 1921 to 1935 was a commemorative peace coin, which might easily have been a half dollar. The peace dollar, in fact, was issued without congressional sanction, under the terms of the Pittman Act, which referred to the bullion and in no way affected the design.

Before the first world war the value of gold was equal to the value of gold coined into money. In order to encourage a steady flow of gold to the mints the government (with the exception of the period 1853-1873) had adopted a policy of gratuitous coinage. The cost of converting gold into coin had generally been considered an expense chargeable to the government.

In practice the mint made fine bars for commercial use or mint bars for coinage at its discretion. The bars in later years were stored in vaults and gold or silver certificates issued in place of the coins.

On March 6, 1933 an order was issued by the President prohibiting banks from paying out gold and gold certificates without permission, and gold currency was thus kept for reserve purposes. Gold imports and newly mined domestic gold must now be sold to the government. Gold may not be hoarded, and there is no free domestic gold market.

Under the Coinage Act of 1965, the composition of dimes, quarters and half dollars was changed to eliminate or reduce the silver content of these coins. The "clad" dimes and quarters are composed of an outer layer of copper-nickel (75% copper and 25% nickel) bonded to an inner core of pure copper. The clad half dollar has an outer layer of 80% silver bonded to an inner core of 21% silver, with a total content of 40% silver.

By the Law of September 26, 1890, changes in designs of United States coins cannot be made oftener than once every twenty-five years. Since that date, there have been design changes in all denominations and there have been many gold and silver commemorative issues. These factors are largely responsible for the ever increasing interest in coin collecting.

COINS AND TOKENS OF THE
ENGLISH-AMERICAN COLONIES

★ Star Throughout Colonial Section Indicates That Facsimiles Exist.

Copies of certain early American issues were made to provide facsimiles of rare issues that would otherwise be unobtainable. A star has been placed adjacent to such early American coins or tokens, together with the fabricator's name for which corresponding copies are known.

The specimens illustrated are the genuine specimens.

SOMMER ISLANDS (Bermuda)

This coinage, the first struck for the English-American colonies, was issued about 1616. The coins were known as "Hogge Money" or "Hoggies."

The pieces were made of brass or a similar substance lightly silvered, in four denominations; shilling, sixpence, threepence and twopence, represented by Roman numerals. The hog is the main device and appears on the obverse side of each. SOMMER ISLANDS is inscribed within beaded circles. The reverse shows a full-rigged galleon with the flag of St. George on each of four masts.

The islands were named, during this early period, for Sir George Somers who was shipwrecked there in 1609 while enroute to the Virginia Plantation. Shakespeare's "The Tempest" was supposedly based on this incident.

The Bermuda Islands, as they are known today, were named for Juan Bermudez who is believed to have stopped there in 1515. A few hogs which he carried for delivery to the West Indies were left behind. When Somers and his party arrived many years later, the islands were over-run with the beasts, and they served as a welcome source of food for the members of the expedition.

Shilling: Small sail —
    Fair: $300 G.: $475 F.: $975
Shilling: Large sail —

Sixpence: Small portholes —

Sixpence: Large portholes —
    Fair: $275 G.: $400 F.: $850
Threepence —

Twopence —
    Fair: $300 G.: $500 F.: $975

Shilling   ★Dickeson

Sixpence   Large Portholes   Small Portholes

Threepence   Twopence

[13]

MASSACHUSETTS
New England

The earliest medium of exchange in the New England settlements was wampum. The General Court of Massachusetts in 1637 ordered "that wampampege should passe at 6 a penny for any sume under 12 d." Wampum consisted of shells of various colors ground to the size of a grain of corn. A hole was drilled through each piece so they could be strung on leather thongs for convenience and adornment.

Corn, pelts and bullets were frequently offered in lieu of coins, which were almost non-existent. Currency brought over from England, Holland and other countries tended to flow back across the Atlantic for much needed supplies. The colonists thus thrown on their own resources dealt with the friendly Indians in kind. In 1661 the law authorizing wampum as legal tender was repealed.

Agitation for a standard coinage reached its height in 1651. England, with a civil war between the Puritans and Royalists on her hands, ignored the colonists, who took matters into their own hands in 1652.

The General Court in 1652 ordered the first metallic currency in the English Americas (the Spaniards had established a mint in Mexico City in 1535), the silver N.E. shillings, and fractional denominations. Silver bullion was procured principally from the West Indies. Joseph Jenks made the die for the first impression at Iron Works (Saugus, Massachusetts), just outside of Boston where the mint was located. John Hull was appointed mint-master; his assistant was Robert Sanderson (or Saunderson). Mint-master Hull received one shilling threepence for every twenty shillings coined as his compensation. This fee was adjusted several times during his term as mint-master.

Note: Early American coins in select condition (V. Fine, Ex. Fine, etc.) are much higher priced as these coins are scarce in these higher grades.

NE Shilling (1652)   ★Wyatt

NE Sixpence (1652)   ★Wyatt   NE Threepence (1652)

	Good	Fine
NE Shilling	$950.00	$2600.00
NE Sixpence	——	——
NE Threepence (2 known)	——	——

WILLOW TREE PIECES

The simplicity of the design on the N.E. coins invited counterfeiting and clipping of the edges. Therefore, they were soon replaced by the Willow, Oak and Pine Tree Series.

The "tree" coins were minted about thirty years without change of date; Charles II disapproved of the issues, and mintages dated 1652 could not be easily proven to be unauthorized.

The coinage was abandoned in 1682; a proposal to renew coinage in 1686 was rejected by the General Court.

Willow Tree Shilling (1653-1660)

Willow Tree Sixpence (1653-1660)   Willow Tree Threepence (1653-1660)

	Fair	Good	Fine
Willow Tree Shilling...............................	$600.00	$950.00	$2850.00
Willow Tree Sixpence..........................	——	——	——
Willow Tree Threepence (3 known).............	——	——	——

OAK TREE PIECES

Oak Tree Shilling (1660-1667) ★Wyatt   Oak Tree Sixpence (1660-1667)
Various Die Varieties

Oak Tree Shilling............................	100.00	200.00	350.00
Oak Tree Sixpence..........................	100.00	225.00	375.00

OAK TREE PIECES

★ Wyatt

Oak Tree Threepence (1660-1667)   Oak Tree Twopence (1662)

Fair $100   Good $200   Fine $350   Fair $80   Good $175   Fine $300

PINE TREE PIECES
Various Die Varieties

★Tatham

Pine Tree Shilling — Large Planchet (1667-1674)

The first pine tree coins were stamped on wide thin planchets. The later issues were narrower and thicker in imitation of English coins.

Pine Tree Shilling — Small Planchet (1675-1682)

Pine Tree Sixpence ★Wyatt   Pine Tree Threepence ★Wyatt

	Fair	Good	Fine	V. Fine
Pine Tree Shilling, Large Planchet	$85.00	$165.00	$325.00	$475.00
Pine Tree Shilling, Small Planchet	75.00	150.00	265.00	425.00
Pine Tree Sixpence	80.00	160.00	285.00	425.00
Pine Tree Threepence	75.00	150.00	265.00	390.00

GOOD SAMARITAN SHILLING

Although this piece was formerly thought to be a pattern for the 1652 shillings, recent findings show that the known specimens are all fabrications. Three different varieties are known. The most common type was made by Thomas Wyatt, about 1856. The variety pictured here is somewhat older and is probably unique.

Good Samaritan Shilling (Unique)................................ ———

MARYLAND

In 1658 Cecil, the second Lord Baltimore and "Lord Proprietor of Maryland," began an issue of coinage. These pieces were made in England.

There were four denominations: shillings, sixpence, fourpence (groat) in silver, and the small copper penny (denarium). The silver coins show the bust of Cecil Calvert (Lord Baltimore) on the obverse, and the Baltimore family arms with the values in Roman numeral form and the legend CRESCITE ET MULTIPLICAMINI (Increase and be multiplied) on the reverse. The obverse of the penny is similar, but the reverse has a ducal coronet with two pennants and the inscription DENARIUM, TERRAE-MARIAE (Penny, Maryland). Numerous die varieties and patterns exist in this series.

Lord Baltimore Shilling

Fourpence (Groat)

Sixpence

Penny (denarium)

★Idler

	Fair	Good	Fine
Shilling.................................	$275.00	$550.00	$1,100.00
Sixpence.................................	175.00	400.00	775.00
Fourpence.................................	275.00	550.00	1,100.00
Penny (Copper) (Ex. Rare).................	—	—	—

ST. PATRICK OR MARK NEWBY HALFPENCE
NEW JERSEY

Mark Newby, who came from Dublin, Ireland, in November 1681, brought some halfpence pieces believed by numismatists to have been struck in Dublin in 1678. These were called St. Patrick Halfpence.

The coin received wide currency in the New Jersey Province, having been authorized to pass as legal tender by the general assembly in May 1682.

These have a brass insert at the crown so that when the coin was struck it would appear as though it were a golden crown. On some pieces this insert has been removed or does not show.

There was also a smaller piece known as a farthing. These copper pieces exist in many die varieties. The obverses show a crowned king kneeling playing a harp. The legend FLOREAT REX (May the King prosper) is separated by a crown. The reverse side of the halfpence shows St. Patrick with a crozier in his left and a trefoil in his right hand, surrounded by people. At his left is a shield. The legend is ECCE GREX (Behold the flock).

The farthing reverse shows St. Patrick driving away reptiles and serpents, as he holds a Metropolitan cross in his left hand. The legend reads QUIESCAT PLEBS (May the people be at ease). Numerous die variations exist.

St. Patrick
Halfpence

St. Patrick
Farthing

	Good	Fine
St. Patrick Halfpence	$ 85.00	$175.00
St. Patrick Farthing	50.00	100.00
St. Patrick Farthing, Silver	400.00	700.00

COINAGE OF WILLIAM WOOD
ROSA AMERICANA AND HIBERNIA COINS

William Wood, an Englishman, obtained a patent from George I to make copper tokens for Ireland and the American Colonies.

The first pieces struck were undated; others bear the dates 1722, 1723, 1724 and 1733. The Rosa Americana pieces were issued in three denominations, twopence, penny and halfpennies, and were intended for America. This type had a full-blown rose on the reverse with the words ROSA AMERICANA UTILE DULCI (American Rose — the useful with the pleasant).

The obverse, common to both Rosa Americana and Hibernia pieces, shows the head of George I and the legend GEORGIUS D:G: MAG: BRI: FRA: ET. HIB: REX. (George, by the Grace of God, King of Great Britain, France and Ireland). Rosa Americana tokens were not well received by the American Colonists.

ROSA AMERICANA

	Good	Fine	Ex. F.
Twopence (No Date).........................	$35.00	$90.00	$150.00
Twopence (No Date) Motto without Label (3 known)	——	——	——

1722 Twopence, Period after REX..............	35.00	90.00	150.00
1722 Twopence, No Period after REX	35.00	90.00	150.00

1722 Penny UTILE DULCI.....................	25.00	65.00	125.00
1722 Penny VTILE DVLCI.....................	20.00	55.00	110.00

1722 Halfpenny D. G. REX ROSA AMERI.			
UTILE DULCI............................	35.00	75.00	150.00
1722 Halfpenny DEI GRATIA REX UTILE DULCI ...	30.00	45.00	120.00
1722 Halfpenny VTILE DVLCI.................	——	——	——

ROSA AMERICANA

	Good	Fine	Ex. F.
1723 Twopence	$30.00	$85.00	$140.00

| 1723 Penny | 27.50 | 70.00 | 120.00 |

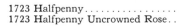

| 1723 Halfpenny | 27.50 | 70.00 | 120.00 |
| 1723 Halfpenny Uncrowned Rose | —— | —— | —— |

| 1724 Twopence (Pattern) | —— | —— | —— |

ROSA AMERICANA

	Fine	Ex. Fine
1724 Penny...	——	——
1724 Penny (Undated) ROSA: SINE: SPINA. (3 known).....	——	——

★A. S. Robinson

	Fine	Ex. Fine
1733 Twopence (Pattern) Proof........................	——	——

The 1733 twopence is a pattern piece and bears the bust of George II facing to the left. Issued by the successors to the coinage patent, since William Wood had died in 1730.

HIBERNIA OR WOOD'S COINAGE

The type intended for Ireland had a seated figure with a harp on the reverse side and the word HIBERNIA. Denominations struck were halfpenny and farthing with dates 1722, 1723 and 1724. Hibernia coins were unpopular in Ireland, so most of them were sent to the American Colonies.

	First Type	Second Type	1723 over 22	
			Good	Fine	Ex. F.
1722 Farthing, D. G. REX (Ex. Rare)............			——	——	——
1722 Halfpenny, First Type, Harp at Left.......			$15.00	$40.00	$ 95.00
1722 Halfpenny, Second Type, Harp at Right....			15.00	60.00	110.00
1723 over 22 Halfpenny......................			15.00	60.00	125.00
1723 Halfpenny.............................			10.00	25.00	65.00

HIBERNIA COINS

1723 Hibernia Farthing   1724 Hibernia Halfpenny

	Good	Fine	Ex. F.
1723 Hibernia Farthing — DEI. GRATIA. REX.....	$15.00	$35.00	$70.00
1723 Hibernia Farthing — D.G.REX. (Ex. Rare)...	——	——	——
1724 Hibernia Halfpenny......................	15.00	45.00	90.00
1724 Hibernia Farthing........................	25.00	50.00	110.00

COINAGE OF THE STATES

NEW HAMPSHIRE

New Hampshire was the first of the states to consider the subject of coinage following the Declaration of Independence.

William Moulton was empowered to make a limited quantity of coins of pure copper authorized by the State House of Representatives March 13, 1776. Although patterns were prepared, it is generally believed that they were not approved. Little of the proposed coinage was ever actually circulated.

★Betts   ★ Copley

	V. Good
1776 New Hampshire Copper.....................................	——
1776 New Hampshire Copper, WM in Center (3 known)..........	——
1776 New Hampshire Copper, Engraved Type (Unique)..........	——

[22]

VERMONT

Reuben Harmon, Jr., of Rupert, Vermont, was granted permission to coin copper pieces on June 15, 1785. The well-known Vermont cents were first produced in that year.

Harmon's mint was located in the northeast corner of Rupert near a stream known as Millbrook. Col. William Cooley, a New York goldsmith, made the dies.

	Good	Fine
1785 Cent IMMUNE COLUMBIA......	$350.00	$750.00

	Good	Fine
1786 Cent Baby Head......	$55.00	$175.00

	Good	Fine
1785 Cent VERMONTS......	35.00	110.00
1786 Cent Bust Left.......	40.00	135.00

	Good	Fine
1785 Cent VERMONTIS.....	50.00	150.00
1787 Cent Bust Left.......	————	————

	Good	Fine
1786 Cent VERMON-TENSIUM.......	35.00	110.00
1787 Cent (Several Varieties)........	25.00	65.00

[23]

VERMONT

	Good	Fine
1787 Cent BRITANNIA...	$20.00	$70.00

Reverse of this coin is usually weak.

	Good	Fine
1788 Cent (Several varieties*)....	$22.50	$70.00
1788 Cent VERMON AUƆTORI......	——	——
1788 Cent *ET LIB* *INDE........	65.00	175.00

*Typical 1788 Variety

	Good	Fine
1788 Cent GEORGIVS III REX.......	$45.00	$125.00

Most Vermont pieces are struck on poor and defective planchets. Well struck coins on clean planchets command higher prices.

NEW YORK

There are no records to show that coinage was authorized for New York following the Revolutionary War. The only coinage laws passed were those regulating coins already in use.

A firm composed of ten individuals became associated in 1787 for the purpose of striking copper coins, at Newburgh. The establishment was called a "Manufactory of hardware," but the operations there were conducted in secret and looked upon as illegal.

Members of the firm included Reuben Harmon, Jr., who operated the mint at Rupert, Vermont; James F. Atlee, a die engraver and others.

The articles of agreement offer an interesting sidelight on the trade in tokens of that day. Reuben Harmon and William Cooley were listed as co-partners "in such trades and merchandizing and in the coinage of copper for the state of Vermont, Connecticut and New York, for their most benefit advantage and profit."

Perhaps many of the pieces now classified as Connecticut coins, the Vermon Auctori with the Britannia reverse and the counterfeit George III halfpence were products of this "hardware manufactory."

The Nova Eborac (New York) issues are supposed to have been struck in England as a speculative venture.

Cents attributed to New York during the period of 1786 and 1787 include the following:

NEW YORK

1786 NON VI VIRTUTE VICI

(Believed to be Head of Washington.)

	Good	Fine	V. Fine
Cent	$425	$750	$1300

★Robinson

★Bolen

	Good	Fine	V. Fine
1787 Excelsior Cent, Eagle on Globe Facing Right	$200.00	$500.00	$975.00
1787 Excelsior Cent, Eagle on Globe Facing Left	185.00	400.00	850.00

1787 Cent
Large Eagle on Reverse

Arrows and Branch
Transposed (Ex. Rare) ———

1787 George Clinton Cent

	Good	Fine	V. Fine
Cent	$475	$900	$1600

★Bolen

1787 Indian N.Y. Arms

	Good	Fine	V. Fine
Cent	$425	$850	$1400

★Bolen

NEW YORK

1787 Indian Cent
Reverse Eagle
on Globe

Good	$ 475.00
Fine	900.00
V. Fine	1600.00

★Bolen

1787 Indian Cent
with George III
Reverse (2 known)

1787 IMMUNIS COLUMBIA
Eagle Reverse

Good	$ 85.00
Fine	130.00
V. Fine	225.00
Ex. Fine	450.00

THE NOVA EBORACS

1787
NOVA EBORAC
Reverse Seated
Figure Facing Left

Fair	$ 7.50
Good	35.00
Fine	75.00
V. Fine	125.00

1787
NOVA EBORAC
Reverse Seated
Figure Facing Right

Fair	$ 7.50
Good	35.00
Fine	75.00
V. Fine	125.00

NEW YORK

1787 NOVA EBORAC
Small Head

Good	$160.00
Fine	360.00
V. Fine	600.00

1787 NOVA EBORAC
Large Head

Fair	$ 12.50
Good	75.00
Fine	170.00
V. Fine	300.00

CONNECTICUT

Authority for establishing a mint was granted to Samuel Bishop, Joseph Hopkins, James Hillhouse and John Goodrich in 1785.

Available records indicate that the Connecticut Cents were turned out under a sub-contract by Samuel Broome and Jeremiah Platt, former New York merchants who operated two mint houses, one at Morris Cove and the other at Westville. Abel Buel was the principal die-sinker.

1785 Cent
Bust Facing Right

Good	$10.00
Fine	30.00
V. Fine	60.00

1785 Cent
African Head

Good	$20.00
Fine	55.00
V. Fine	90.00

1785 Cent
Bust Facing Left

Good	$ 35.00
Fine	100.00
V. Fine	175.00

CONNECTICUT

1786 Cent
ETLIB INDE

Good.............$ 30.00
Fine............... 67.50
V. Fine............ 130.00

1786 Cent
Large Head Facing Right

Good.............$ 35.00
Fine............... 90.00
V. Fine........... 160.00

1786 Cent
Mailed Bust Facing Left

Good..............$17.00
Fine................ 40.00
V. Fine............. 70.00

1786 Cent
Mailed Bust Facing Left
Hercules Head

Good...........$ 15.00
Fine............ 37.50
V. Fine......... 100.00

1786 Cent
Draped Bust

Good...........$ 30.00
Fine............ 70.00
V. Fine......... 125.00

CONNECTICUT

1787 Cent
Small Head Facing Right
ETLIB INDE

Good . . . . $ 35.00
Fine 75.00
V. Fine 135.00

1787 Cent
Mailed Bust Facing Left
IND ET LIB

Good . . . . $ 30.00
Fine 75.00
V. Fine 135.00

1787 Cent
Muttonhead
Variety

Good . . . . $ 25.00
Fine 65.00
V. Fine 100.00

	Good	Fine	V. Fine
1787 Cent, Mailed Bust Facing Left	$ 10.00	$ 30.00	$ 55.00
1787 Cent, Similar, Laughing Head Variety	10.00	30.00	55.00
1787 Cent, Similar, Hercules Head (see 1786)	100.00	200.00	——

1787 Cent, Similar, Horned Bust Variety	10.00	30.00	55.00
1787 Cent, Similar, CONNECT Variety	30.00	75.00	125.00

1787 Cent, Draped Bust Facing Left	7.50	20.00	35.00
1787 Cent, Similar, AUCIORI Variety	12.50	35.00	65.00

CONNECTICUT

	Good	Fine	V. Fine
1787 Cent, Similar, AUCTOPI Variety............	$12.50	$35.00	$65.00
1787 Cent, Similar, AUCTOBI Variety............	12.50	35.00	75.00
1787 Cent, Similar, CONNFC Variety............	10.00	27.50	55.00
1787 Cent, Similar, CONNLC Variety............	25.00	70.00	95.00
1787 Cent, Similar, FNDE Variety..............	12.50	35.00	65.00
1787 Cent, Similar, ETLIR Variety.............	10.00	30.00	55.00
1787 Cent, Similar, ETIIB Variety.............	12.50	37.50	75.00

1788 Cent, Mailed Bust Facing Right...........	15.00	40.00	80.00
1788 Cent, Similar, Small Head...............	45.00	110.00	160.00

1788 Cent, Mailed Bust Facing Left............	17.50	37.50	85.00
1788 Cent, Mailed Bust Left CONNLC...........	20.00	45.00	85.00

1788 Cent, Draped Bust Facing Left...........	15.00	35.00	55.00
1788 Cent, Similar, CONNLC Variety...........	30.00	60.00	95.00
1788 Cent, Similar, INDL ET LIB Variety........	20.00	50.00	80.00

MASSACHUSETTS

MASSACHUSETTS PINE TREE COPPER

Nothing is known regarding the origin of the Pine Tree pattern cent dated 1776. The obverse has a crude pine tree with an animal resembling a dog at its base; Inscription, MASSACHUSETTS STATE. The reverse has a figure probably intended to represent the Goddess of Liberty, seated on a globe and holding a liberty cap and staff. A dog sits at her feet. The legend LIBERTY AND VIRTUE surrounds the figure.

★Copley

1776 Cent (Unique). . . . .   ———

MASSACHUSETTS HALFPENNY

This pattern piece is sometimes called the " Janus Copper." There are three heads facing left, front and right on the obverse with the inscription STATE OF MASSA. ½ D. The reverse shows the Goddess of Liberty, seated resting against a globe facing right, inscribed GODDESS LIBERTY 1776.

★Copley

1776 Halfpenny, 3 Heads on Obverse (Unique). . . . .   ———

An "Act for establishing a mint for the coinage of gold, silver and copper" was passed by the Massachusetts General Court October 17, 1786. The next year the Council directed that the design should incorporate "the figure of an Indian with a bow and arrow and a star at one side, with the word 'Commonwealth,' the reverse, a spread eagle with the words 'of Massachusetts A.D. 1787'."

A Mr. Joshua Witherle was placed in charge of the mint, where he soon began coining the Massachusetts cents. There resulted many varieties, the rarest being that with arrows in the right talon. Half cents with similar devices and legends were also struck in 1787 and 1788.

Most of the dies for these coppers were made by Joseph Callender. Jacob Perkins of Newburyport probably engraved some of the dies.

The mint was abandoned early in 1789 as the venture was unprofitable to the Commonwealth.

MASSACHUSETTS

	Obverse	Arrows in Eagle's Right Talon	in Left Talon			
			Good	Fine	V. F	E. F.
1787 Cent, Arrows in Right Talon (Ex. Rare)..						
1787 Cent, Arrows in Left Talon.............			$15.00	$27.50	$50.00	$85.00
1787 Cent, Horn (Die Break) from Eagle's Head			15.00	30.00	55.00	90.00

1787 Half Cent

Good..................	$17.50
Fine...................	30.00
V. Fine................	55.00
Ex. Fine...............	95.00

1788 Cent
Period after Massachusetts

Good..............	$12.50
Fine..............	25.00
V. Fine...........	45.00
Ex. Fine..........	80.00

No period after Massachusetts

Good..............	$15.00
Fine..............	30.00
V. Fine...........	50.00
Ex. Fine..........	90.00

★Evanson

1788 Half Cent

Good............	$ 20.00
Fine............	35.00
Very Fine........	60.00
Ex. Fine........	110.00

★Evanson

NEW JERSEY

On June 1, 1786, the New Jersey Colonial legislature granted to Thomas Goadsby, Albion Cox and Walter Mould authority to coin some three million coppers weighing six pennyweight and six grains apiece, not later than June 1788, on condition that they delivered to the Treasurer of the State, "one-tenth part of the full sum they shall strike and coin," in quarterly installments. These coppers were to pass current at 15 to the shilling.

In an operation of this kind the contractors purchased the metal and assumed all expenses of coining. The difference between these expenses and the total face value of the coins issued represented the profit.

Later Goadsby and Cox asked authority to coin two-thirds of the total independently. Their petition was granted November 22, 1787. Mould was known to have produced his coins at Morristown, while Cox (and probably Goadsby) operated in Elizabethtown.

The series offers many varieties. The obverse shows a horse's head with plow and the legend NOVA CAESAREA (New Jersey). The reverse has a United States shield and legend E PLURIBUS UNUM (One composed of many).

1786 Cent
IMMUNIS COLUMBIA
Obverse
Shield Reverse

Good..———   Fine..———

Eagle Reverse

Good..——— Fine..———

1786 (No Date) Cent, Washington Obverse............. ——— ———
1786 Cent, Eagle Obverse............................... ——— ———
1786 Cent, Washington Obv.-Eagle Rev. (Unique)....... ——— ———

1786 Cent
Date Under Plow Handle
Good ———   Fine ———

1786 Cent
No Coulter
Good $60.00   Fine $150.00

[33]

NEW JERSEY

	Good	Fine	V. Fine
1786 Cent, Narrow Shield	$12.50	$35.00	$50.00
1786 Cent, Wide Shield	17.50	40.00	60.00
1786 Cent, Similar, Bridle Variety	17.50	40.00	60.00

Pluribs Variety
Large Planchet

Small Planchet

Outlined Shield

1787 Cent, Pronounced Outline to Shield	12.50	30.00	45.00
1787 Cent, Small Planchet, Plain Shield	10.00	25.00	40.00
1787 Cent, Large Planchet, Plain Shield	10.00	25.00	40.00
1787 Cent, Similar, PLURIBS Variety	22.50	50.00	85.00

Serpent Head

Fox Variety

1787 Cent, Serpent Head Variety	22.50	50.00	85.00
1788 Cent, Horse's Head Facing Right	10.00	25.00	40.00
1788 Cent, Similar, Running Fox before Legend	22.50	50.00	85.00

| 1788 Cent, Horse's Head Facing Left | 42.50 | 90.00 | 135.00 |

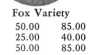

TOKENS AND PATTERN COINS
THE CONTINENTAL DOLLAR

The Continental Dollars were probably a pattern issue only and never reached general circulation. It was the first silver dollar size coin ever proposed for the United States. The dies were engraved by someone whose initials were E. G. (possibly Elisha Gallaudet). Some of them have his signature "EG FECIT" on the obverse. The coins were probably struck in Philadelphia.

Varieties are caused by differences in the spelling of the word CURRENCY and the addition of EG FECIT. These coins were struck in silver, pewter and brass, those in silver probably having done service as a dollar. Pewter coins in original bright uncirculated condition are worth an additional premium.

"CURRENCY"   "CURENCY"

★Dickeson

Copies were struck in various metals for the 1876 Centennial Exposition in Philadelphia.

	Good	Fine	Ex. F.	Unc.
1776 CURENCY — Brass (2 Varieties)....	——	——	——	——
1776 CURENCY — Pewter..............	$200.00	$400.00	$650.00	$1,200
1776 CURENCY — Silver...............	——	——	——	——
1776 CURENCY — Pewter.............	225.00	425.00	700.00	1,300
1776 CURENCY — Pewter, EG FECIT....	250.00	450.00	725.00	1,400
1776 CURENCY — Silver, EG FECIT.....	——	——	——	——
1776 CURRENCEY — Pewter...........	——	——	——	——

NOVA CONSTELLATIO PATTERNS (Silver)

These Nova Constellatio pieces undoubtedly represent the first patterns for a coinage of the United States. They were designed by Benjamin Dudley for Gouverneur Morris to carry out his ideas for a decimal coinage system. The 1000 unit designation he called a "mark," the 500 a "quint." These denominations, together with the smaller 100 unit piece, were designed to standardize the many different coin values among the several states. These pattern pieces represent the first attempt at a decimal ratio, and were the forerunners of our present system of money values. Neither the proposed denominations nor the coins advanced beyond the pattern stage. The pieces are all dated 1783 and are extremely rare. There are two types of the "quint."

NOVA CONSTELLATIO PATTERNS (Silver)

MARK

QUINT Type 1   Reverse   QUINT Type 2

★Set of
Mickley
Electrotypes

Bit 100 Units

1783 MARK (1000), Silver (Unique)...................	——	——
1783 QUINT (500), Silver — Type 1 (Unique)..........	——	——
1783 QUINT (500), Silver — Type 2 (Unique)..........	——	——
1783 BIT (100), Silver (2 known)......................	——	——

NOVA CONSTELLATIO COPPERS

The Nova Constellatio pieces were struck supposedly by order of Gouverneur Morris who had been Assistant Financier of the Confederation. The tokens were turned out in fairly large quantities in the years 1783 and 1785. There are a number of varieties of the 1783 and 1785 issues which are similar to the patterns heretofore described. No official records have been found stating where, or by whom the Nova Constellatio coppers were manufactured. Evidence indicates that they were struck in Birmingham from dies made there by Thomas Wyon, and imported for American circulation as a private business venture by Gouverneur Morris.

NOVA CONSTELLATIO COPPERS

1783 Cent "CONSTELLATIO" Pointed Rays Small U.S.

Good.................$12.50
Fine.................. 25.00
Ex. Fine.............. 65.00

1783 Cent "CONSTELLATIO" Pointed Rays, Large U.S.

Good.................$12.50
Fine.................. 35.00
Ex. Fine.............. 82.50

1783 Cent "CONSTELATIO" Blunt Rays

Good..............$12.50
Fine................. 30.00
Ex. Fine............ 80.00

1785 Cent "CONSTELATIO" Blunt Rays

Good.................$ 17.50
Fine.................. 35.00
Ex. Fine.............. 120.00

	Good	Fine	Ex. F.
1785 Cent, CONSTELLATIO Pointed Rays........	$10.00	$25.00	$65.00
1786 Cent........................(Ex. Rare)	——	——	——

IMMUNE COLUMBIA CENTS

★Edwards

These are considered experimental or pattern pieces. No laws describing them are known. There are several types with the seated figure of Justice device. These dies were possibly the work of James F. Atlee.

1785 Cent, Copper...... ———
1785 Cent, Silver........ ———

1785 Cent, Extra Star in Border
    Copper, CONSTELLATIO
G...$300 Fine..$600 V.F...$875
    Copper, CONSTELATIO,
Blunt Rays.....(2 known) ———
Gold..........(Ex. Rare) ———
A gold specimen in the National Coin Collection was acquired from Stickney in exchange for an 1804 dollar.

1785
George III Obverse
Good..$350.00   Fine..$700.00
1785
Vermon Auctori Obverse
Good..$350.00   Fine..$750.00

FRENCH COLONIES
Copper Sou or Nine Deniers

	V. Good	Fine
1721 French Colonies, Sou, Mint Mark B for Rouen...........	$37.50	$65.00
1721 French Colonies, Sou, Mint Mark H for Rochelle.........	25.00	35.00
1722 French Colonies, Sou, Mint Mark H....	17.50	30.00
1722 over 1........	25.00	35.00

1767 French Colonies, Sou
Good...............$ 20.00
Fine.................. 50.00
Ex. Fine.............. 110.00

FRENCH COLONIES

1767 French Colonies, Sou
Counterstamped RF for
Republic

Good................... $10.00
Fine.................... 30.00
Ex. Fine.............. 70.00

For greater coverage of French
Colonial Coins see Charlton's
Standard Catalogue of Canadian
Coins, Tokens and Paper Money.

CONFEDERATIO CENTS

The Confederatio Cents are usually classed as experimental or pattern pieces. This will explain why the die with the CONFEDERATIO legend was combined with other designs such as bust of George Washington, Libertas et Justitia of 1785, Immunis Columbia of 1786, the "New York Excelsiors," Inimica Tyrannis Americana and others. There were in all thirteen dies struck in fourteen combinations. Some of the dies were believed to have been made by Thomas Wyon of Birmingham, England, whereas others may have been the work of James Atlee, or the New Jersey coiners.

There are two types of the Confederatio reverse. In one instance the stars are contained in a small circle; in the other larger stars are in a larger circle.

1785 Cent, Stars in Small
Circle

Fine............... ———
V. Fine............ ———

★Bolen

Typical Obverse Types

1785 Stars in Large Circle

Fine............ ———
V. Fine........ ———

Reverse

BRASHER'S DOUBLOONS

Perhaps the most famous piece brought out before the establishment of the mint at Philadelphia was that produced by a well-known goldsmith and jeweler, Ephraim Brasher, next door neighbor of George Washington, in New York.

Brasher produced a gold piece weighing about 408 grains, approximately equal in value to a Spanish doubloon (about $16.00).

The punch-mark EB appears in either of two positions as illustrated. This mark is found on coins of other countries as well, and probably was so used by Brasher as evidence of his approval of their value.

*Robinson

	V. Fine
1787 Doubloon, Punch on Breast, Gold (Unique)	———
1787 Doubloon, Punch on Wing, Gold	———
1787 So-called Half Doubloon (Unique)	———

The half doubloon is struck from the usual doubloon dies, but on a smaller, cut down planchet.

AMERICAN TOKENS

Struck in America or England by Order of American Merchants
GLOUCESTER TOKENS

According to S. S. Crosby, in his book "The Early Coins of America" this piece appears to have been intended as a pattern for a shilling, a private coinage by Richard Dawson of Gloucester (county?), Virginia. The only specimens known are struck in brass, none in silver.

The denomination XII indicates that a silver coinage (one shilling) was planned but never issued. Known specimens are imperfect and a full description cannot be given.

The building may represent a warehouse or some public building, possibly a court house. The legend on the reverse may have been designed to read GLOUCESTER COURT HOUSE VIRGINIA.

1714 Shilling (2 known) Brass............................... ———

HIGLEY OR GRANBY COPPERS

John Higley owned a private copper mine near Granby, Connecticut. He worked the mine as an individual, smelting his own ore and making his own dies for the coins that he issued.

The Higley coppers were never officially authorized. All the tokens were made of pure copper. There were seven obverse and four reverse dies. The first issue, in 1737, bore the legend THE VALUE OF THREEPENCE. After a time the quantity exceeded the local demand, and a protest arose against the value of the piece. Higley, a resourceful individual, promptly created a new design, still with the Roman III, but with the inscription VALUE ME AS YOU PLEASE. On the reverse appeared the words I AM GOOD COPPER.

(Electrotypes and Casts Exist)

★Bolen

		Good	V. Good
1737 THE • VALVE • OF • THREE • PENCE. — 3 Hammers — CONNECTICVT		$700.00	$975.00
1737 THE • VALVE • OF • THREE • PENCE. — 3 Hammers — I • AM • GOOD • COPPER		700.00	975.00

1737 VALUE • ME • AS • YOU • PLEASE — 3 Hammers — I • AM • GOOD • COPPER		650.00	900.00
1737 VALVE • ME • AS • YOU • PLEASE — 3 Hammers — I • AM • GOOD • COPPER		(Ex. Rare)	

(1737) VALUE • ME • AS • YOU • PLEASE — Broad Axe — J • CUT • MY • WAY • THROUGH		900.00	1150.00
(1737) Similar, Wheel Design (Unique)		——	——
1739 VALUE • ME • AS • YOU • PLEASE — Broad Axe — J • CUT • MY • WAY • THROUGH		950.00	——

J. CHALMERS
Annapolis, Maryland

J. Chalmers, a goldsmith, struck a series of silver tokens at Annapolis in 1783. The shortage of change and the refusal of the people to use underweight cut Spanish coins, or "bits," prompted the issuance of these pieces.

The shilling with rings on the reverse is very rare. The common type shilling has two clasped hands on the obverse. The reverse shows two doves pulling what appears to be a worm.

The sixpence has a star within a wreath on the obverse, and a cross with hands clasped on the reverse. The threepence has the clasped hands on the obverse side, and the reverse shows a branch encircled by a wreath.

	Good	Fine
1783 Shilling — Birds, Long Worm	$210.00	$440.00
1783 Shilling — Birds, Short Worm	180.00	400.00
1783 Shilling — Rings (Ex. Rare)		

	Good	Fine
1783 Sixpence, Small Date	375.00	750.00
1783 Sixpence, Large Date	300.00	675.00
1783 Threepence	250.00	500.00

STANDISH BARRY, BALTIMORE, MARYLAND

Standish Barry, a Baltimore silversmith, circulated a silver threepence in 1790. He was a watch and clockmaker, engraver and later a silversmith. The tokens were believed to have been an advertising venture at a time when small change was scarce. The precise date, July 4, 90, on this piece may indicate that Barry intended to commemorate Independence Day, but there are no records to substantiate this belief. The head shown on the obverse is probably that of George Washington. The legend BALTIMORE TOWN JULY 4, 90 appears in the border. STANDISH BARRY THREE PENCE is on the reverse.

1790 Threepence...

THE BAR CENT

The Bar Cent is undated and of uncertain origin.

It has thirteen parallel and disconnected bars on one side. On the other side is the large Roman USA monogram.

The significance of the design is clearly defined by its extreme simplicity. The separate thirteen states (bars) unite into a single status as symbolized by the interlocking letters (USA).

This coin is believed to have been issued at the same time as the Nova Constellatio coppers by Thomas Wyon at Birmingham, England, for America. It first circulated in New York during November, 1785. The design was supposedly copied from an old Continental button.

*Bolen (A is under S)

	Good	Fine	Ex. Fine
Undated (about 1785) Bar Cent...............	$160.00	$250.00	$500.00

THE MOTT TOKEN

This was one of the first tradesman's tokens issued in America. Manufactured in England, they were issued by Messrs. Mott of New York in 1789. The firm was composed of William and John Mott, located at 240 Water Street, a fashionable section of New York at that time.

	Good	Fine	Ex. Fine
1789 Mott Token, Thick Planchet..............	$30.00	$55.00	$120.00
1789 Mott Token, Thin Planchet..............	40.00	70.00	175.00
1789 Mott Token, entire edge engrailed........	——	——	——

TALBOT ALLUM & LEE CENTS

Talbot, Allum & Lee, engaged in the India trade and located at 241 Pearl Street, New York, placed a large quantity of English-made coppers in circulation during 1794 and 1795. ONE CENT appears on the 1794 issue, and the legend PAYABLE AT THE STORE OF——— on the edge. The denomination is not found on the 1795 reverse but the edge legend was changed to read: WE PROMISE TO PAY THE BEARER ONE CENT.

TALBOT ALLUM & LEE CENTS

1794 Cent NEW YORK
V. Good.............$ 15.00
V. Fine............... 42.50
Unc.................. 120.00

1794 Cent without NEW YORK
V. Good............. 100.00
V. Fine............. 350.00
Unc................. ———

1795 Cent
V. Good............$10.00
V. Fine............ 30.00
Unc............... 75.00

ANGLO-AMERICAN TOKENS
Supposedly of English Origin — Speculative Ventures
CAROLINA and NEW ENGLAND ELEPHANT TOKENS

Although no law is known authorizing coinage for Carolina, two very interesting pieces known as Elephant Tokens were current with the date 1694. These copper coins were of halfpenny denomination. The reverse reads GOD PRESERVE CAROLINA AND THE LORDS PROPRIETERS. 1694.

The second and more common variety has the last word spelled PROPRIETORS. The correction was made on the original die, for the E shows plainly beneath the O. The elephant's tusks nearly touch the milling on the second variety.

The Elephant Pieces were probably struck in England and perhaps intended only as tokens, or, as we might say today, as an advertising stunt to enliven interest in the Carolina Plantation.

Like the Carolina Tokens, the New England Elephant Tokens were believed to have been struck in England as a promotional piece to increase interest in the American Colonies. Some of these tokens were said to have been struck in brass.

NEW ENGLAND

★Robinson

1694 NEW ENGLAND..(Ex. Rare)

CAROLINA ELEPHANT TOKENS

Good   Fine

1694 PROPRIETERS (Ex. Rare)........................

★Bolen

1694 PROPRIETORS................................... $375.00 $750.00

The London Token, an early historian states, was produced during the great plague raging in London. The legend on this piece relates directly to that crisis. It has also been stated that the London Token was to have been current in Tangier, Africa, but was never used in that locality. No date appears on this coin.

	V. Good	V. Fine	Ex. Fine
(1694) Halfpenny GOD PRESERVE LONDON (Thick Planchet)......................	$40.00	$75.00	$120.00
(1694) Halfpenny GOD PRESERVE LONDON (Thin Planchet).......................	60.00	95.00	150.00
(1694) Halfpenny GOD PRESERVE LONDON (Diagonals in center of shield)...........	90.00	160.00	275.00
(1694) Halfpenny, similar. Variety with sword in second quarter of shield instead of first...	——	——	——
(1694) Halfpenny LON DON....................	135.00	225.00	350.00

VIRGINIA HALFPENNY

In 1773, George III issued this halfpenny. There are also known to have been a few specimens struck on a larger planchet with a wide milled border, known as pennies.

The Virginia piece of 1774 known as a shilling may have been a pattern piece for a halfpenny.

	Halfpenny		Penny	
		Good	Fine	Unc.
1773 Halfpenny, Period after GEORGIUS.........		$10.00	$30.00	$ 70.00
1773 Halfpenny, No period after GEORGIUS......		15.00	50.00	125.00
1773 "Penny"..Proof				850.00

Virginia
Shilling
1774

1774 Shilling...Proof ——

GEORGIUS TRIUMPHO TOKEN

Although the head shown on this token bears a strong resemblance to that upon some coins of George III, many collectors consider the Georgius Triumpho (Triumphant George) a token intended to commemorate the successful termination of the Revolutionary War — a triumph justly claimed for Washington.

The reverse side shows the Goddess of Liberty behind a framework of thirteen bars and fleur de lis. She holds an olive branch in her right hand and staff of liberty in her left. VOCE POPOLI (By the Voice of the People) 1783.

	Good	Fine	V. Fine
1783 GEORGIUS TRIUMPHO.....................	$30.00	$75.00	$115.00

AUCTORI PLEBIS TOKEN

This token is sometimes included with the coins of Connecticut as it greatly resembles issues of that state. The coin was struck in England, maker unknown, for use in America.

1787 AUCTORI PLEBIS

Good	$ 30.00
Fine	75.00
V. Fine	110.00

KENTUCKY TOKEN

These tokens were struck in England about 1792-94. Each star in the triangle represents a state, identified by its initial letter. These pieces are usually called Kentucky Cents because the letter K (for Kentucky) happens to be at the top. Some of the edges are plain; others are engrailed with an oblique reeding, and some have the edge lettered: "PAYABLE IN LANCASTER LONDON OR BRISTOL," or "PAYABLE AT BEDWORTH NUNETON OR UNKIET."

	V. Good	V. Fine	Unc.
Cent, (1792-96) Plain Edge	$20.00	$35.00	$125.00
Cent, Engrailed Edge	65.00	160.00	400.00
Cent, Lettered Edge			
PAYABLE AT BEDWORTH, etc.	—	—	—
Cent, Lettered Edge			
PAYABLE IN LANCASTER, etc.	30.00	50.00	135.00
Cent, Lettered Edge			
PAYABLE BY I. FIELDING, etc.	—	—	—

MYDDELTON TOKENS

These tokens were from the establishment of Boulton and Watt near Birmingham, England. They are unsurpassed in beauty and design by any piece issued for American circulation.

1796 Myddelton Token (Copper), Proof $1150.00

1796 Myddelton Token (Silver), Proof.. 1050.00

COPPER COMPANY OF UPPER CANADA

The reverse of this piece, according to S. S. Crosby, properly belongs upon another token and was apparently intended for Canadian circulation, or it was used to give the coin creditability.

Proof
1796 Bronze.......$350.00

NORTH WEST COMPANY TOKEN

Used among fur traders throughout western Canada, Oregon and Washington. The token was good for one beaver.

1820 North West Token,
   Brass......V. Good $300.00
1820 North West Token,
   Copper............V. Rare

All but one known specimen are holed.

MISCELLANEOUS TOKENS
THE NEW YORKE TOKEN

Although only three or four specimens of this piece were known to S. S. Crosby, the authority on early American coins, a number have since been discovered. From an account in the Historical Magazine for 1861, he infers that this token is of Dutch origin. The following is quoted from the magazine article mentioned.

"The style in which it is executed is more Dutch than English; and as the only existing specimen has been preserved in Holland, it is probable that the dies were originally cut there. . . . There is no date upon the token; but it evidently belongs to the period between 1664, when the name New Yorke was first adopted, and 1710, after which it was rarely spelled with an e. It should probably be referred to the latter part of this period, for the currency of the colonies was then in a very unsettled state, and the amount in circulation was not adequate to the wants of trade. . . .

"Without venturing to claim that this coin contains the earliest display of the American eagle, we think it unquestionably deserves to be considered the earliest New York token."

	Good	Fine
UNDATED Brass	$425.00	$750.00
Pewter	—	—

NEW ENGLAND STIVER

This token was believed to have originated in Holland and to have been used by Dutch merchants in New Amsterdam for small change. The obverse shows two lions; the upper facing left and the lower inverted facing right.

There has been considerable conjecture concerning the significance of the letters on the obverse side. One interpretation is that they stand for "I Stiver Von Connecticut." Another suggestion has it that they were the initials of a Dutch Trader, as I. S. Van C.

There is no clue to the date of the issue. Crosby judges the time as "that of the seventeenth century."

It is possible that this is a fantasy coin.

UNDATED (1650) (Unique). . . . .   ———

AMERICAN PLANTATIONS TOKEN

These tokens struck in nearly pure tin were the first authorized coinage for the British colonies in America. Bright, unblemished specimens are more valuable.

★19th Century
Restrikes
Exist

	Good	Fine	Unc.
(1688) James II Plantation Token, 1/24 PART REAL — Tin.	$35.00	$60.00	$170.00
(1688) James II Plantation Token, 1/24 PART REAL — Tin. Sidewise 4 in 24.	———	———	———

NORTH AMERICAN TOKEN

This piece was struck in Dublin, Ireland. The obverse shows the seated figure of Hibernia facing left. The date of issue is believed to have been much later than that shown on the token.

Like many Irish tokens, this issue found its way to America in large quantities and was readily accepted owing to a scarcity of small change.

	Good	Fine
1781.	$10.00	$20.00

FRANKLIN PRESS CENT

This piece is an English token but has often been associated with Benjamin Franklin, and has accordingly been placed in American collections.

1794 Franklin Press Cent

Good	Fine	Unc.
$20.00	$50.00	$100.00

HIBERNIA-VOCE POPULI

These coins, struck in the year 1760, were prepared by one Roche, of King Street, Dublin, who was at that period engaged in the manufacture of buttons for the army, for which he held a contract with home government. Like other Irish tokens, many of these pieces found their way to Colonial America. The piece dated 1700 is probably a die-cutter's error. It no doubt circulated in Colonies with numerous other counterfeit halfpence and "Bungtown Tokens."

Halfpenny 1700

Halfpenny 1760

VOOE POPULI

1760 Farthing

	Good	Fine
1700 Halfpenny	——	——
1760 Halfpenny	$15.00	$37.50
1760 Halfpenny VOCE POPULI	27.50	70.00
1760 Farthing Lg. Letters	70.00	175.00
1760 Farthing Sm. Letters	——	——

PITT TOKENS

William Pitt, who endeared himself to America, is the subject of these pieces, probably intended as commemorative medalets. The halfpenny served as currency during a shortage of regular coinage. Mr. Smithers of Philadelphia struck the coins. The reverse legend refers to Pitt's efforts to have the stamp act repealed. The Pitt farthing-size token, found in brass or copper, is rare.

	Good	Fine	Ex. Fine
1766 Halfpenny	$35.00	$90.00	$175.00
1766 Farthing	——	——	——

RHODE ISLAND SHIP TOKEN

Although this medal has a Dutch inscription, the spelling and design indicate an English or Anglo-American origin. Specimens are known in brass, copper, tin and pewter.

1778-1779 Rhode Island Ship Token

Wreath below ship......
V.F.$110.00 E.F.$225.00

No Wreath below ship...
V.F.$100.00 E.F.$200.00

VLUGTENDE below ship. V.F. —— E.F. ——

★Grant

THE CASTORLAND MEDAL

This piece is dated 1796 and relates to a settlement of Frenchmen known as Castorland in Carthage, New York, at the time of the French Revolution.

1796 Silver Original (Reeded edge)............................... ——
1796 Copper Original (Reeded edge, unbroken dies)............... ——

Copy dies are still available and have been used for restriking throughout the years.

WASHINGTON PIECES

An interesting series of coins and tokens was struck during the period from 1783 to 1795, bearing the portrait of George Washington. The likenesses in most instances were faithfully reproduced and were designed to please Washington. Some of these pieces were of English origin.

The legends generally signify a strong unity among the states and a marked display of patriotism which pervaded the new nation during that period. We find among these tokens an employment of what were soon to become our official coin devices, namely, the American eagle, the United States shield and stars. The one cent value is used in several instances, while on some of the English pieces the halfpenny value will be found. Several pieces were intended to be patterns for half dollars.

Small Military Bust

	Good	Fine	V. Fine
Plain edge...	$12.50	$20.00	$50.00
Engrailed edge...	20.00	30.00	80.00

Large Military Bust →
Point of bust is close to W.
10.00   17.50   35.00

WASHINGTON PIECES

1783 Draped Bust No Button
Good.................$ 10.00
Fine................. 17.50
V. Fine.............. 35.00
1783 Draped Bust with Button
Good................. 30.00
Fine................. 47.50
V. Fine.............. 90.00

1783 Draped Bust, Copper Restrike, plain edge..............Proof 120.00
1783 Draped Bust, Copper Restrike, engrailed edge..........Proof 50.00
1783 Draped Bust, Silver Restrike, engrailed edge..........Proof 150.00

UNITY STATES

Good..............$10.00
Fine............... 30.00
V. Fine............ 50.00

Undated (1783)
Double Head
Cent

Good...............$15.00
Fine............... 40.00
V. Fine............ 60.00

Ugly Head

1784 Ugly Head.....(Ex. Rare)

Presumably of American origin.

1791 Cent
Small Eagle

Lettered edge —
UNITED STATES OF
AMERICA

Good........$ 32.50
Fine.......... 75.00
Unc...........200.00

WASHINGTON PIECES

1791 Cent
Large Eagle

Lettered edge —
UNITED STATES OF
AMERICA

Good........	$ 30.00
Fine........	65.00
Unc.........	175.00

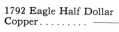

1791 Liverpool
Halfpenny

Lettered edge

Good...........	$175.00
Fine...........	350.00
Unc...........	750.00

1792 Eagle Half Dollar
Copper......... ———

1792 Eagle Half Dollar
Silver.......... ———

1792 Eagle Half Dollar
Gold.......... ———

1792 Cent
"WASHINGTON —
PRESIDENT"

Fine
Plain edge....... $625.00
Lettered edge.... ———

Undated
(1792) Cent
"WASHINGTON
BORN VIRGINIA"

Fine
Copper...... $525.00
Silver........ ———
(Restrike of obverse by
Albert Collis, 1960.)

WASHINGTON PIECES

★ Idler

1792 Half Dollar, Silver
Good........... ——
Fine........... ——
1792 Half Dollar, Copper
Good..........$400.00
Fine........... 900.00
1792 Half Dollar, Copper
Ornamented edge —
(Circles and Squares)
Good —— Fine ——
1792 same Silver——

1792 Half Dollar, Large
Eagle (Unique).. ——

1792 Cent
Roman Head

Lettered edge —
UNITED STATES OF
AMERICA

Proof......... ——

1793 Ship
Halfpenny

Lettered Edge

Good...........$20.00
Fine............. 40.00
V. Fine........... 90.00
Plain edge (Rare)..——

1795 GRATE CENT —
Large Buttons

	Reed. Edge	Let'd Edge
Good.....	$ 20.00	$120.00
V. Fine...	40.00	225.00
Unc......	110.00	435.00

Small Buttons
Good.......	50.00
V. Fine.....	100.00
Unc........	250.00

WASHINGTON PIECES
LIBERTY AND SECURITY HALFPENNY

	Good	Fine	Ex. F.
1795 Halfpenny, Plain Edge	——	——	——
1795 Halfpenny, London Edge	$25.00	$50.00	$100.00
1795 Halfpenny, Birmingham Edge	32.50	65.00	160.00
1795 Halfpenny, Asylum Edge	65.00	165.00	250.00

LIBERTY AND SECURITY PENNY
Undated (1795)

Good	$35.00
Fine	60.00
Unc	150.00

Dated 1795 . . . . . . ——

SUCCESS TOKENS

	Good	Fine
SUCCESS Token, Large Plain, or Reeded Edge	$35.00	$85.00

	Good	Fine
SUCCESS Token, Small Plain, or Reeded Edge	$35.00	$85.00

NORTH WALES HALFPENNY

	Good	Fine
1795 NORTH WALES Halfpenny, brass	$40.00	$100.00
Copper, lettered edge	——	——
Copper, two stars each side of harp	——	——

THE FUGIO CENTS

The first coins issued by authority of the United States were the "Fugio" cents. Entries in the Journal of Congress supply interesting information about proceedings relating to this coinage.

"Saturday, April 21, 1787. . . .

"That the board of treasury be authorized to contract for three hundred tons of copper coin of the federal standard, agreeable to the proposition of Mr. James Jarvis, ... That it be coined at the expense of the contractor, etc."

On Friday, July 6, 1787, there was "Resolved, that the board of treasury direct the contractor for the copper coinage to stamp on one side of each piece the following device, viz: thirteen circles linked together, a small circle in the middle, with the words 'United States,' round it; and in the centre, the words 'We are one'; on the other side of the same piece the following device, viz: a dial with the hours expressed on the face of it; a meridian sun above on one side of which is the word 'Fugio,' (The meaning is, 'time flies') and on the other the year in figures '1787' below the dial, the words 'Mind Your Business.' "

The legends have been credited to Benjamin Franklin by many, and the coin, as a consequence, has been referred to as the Franklin Cent.

These cents were coined in New Haven, Conn., and it has been suggested, also in New York City, Rupert, Vt. and elsewhere. Most of the copper used in this coinage came from military stores. It is believed to have been the copper bands which held together the powder kegs sent to us by the French. The dies were made by Abel Buel of New Haven.

We list below major varieties, some of considerable rarity:

WITH CLUB RAYS
1787

	Good	Fine	Unc.
Club Rays, rounded ends......................	$40.00	$100.00	——
Club Rays, concave ends to rays:			
FUCIO (C instead of G) (Ex. Rare).............	——	——	——
Club Rays, concave ends, FUGIO..............	——	——	——

WITH POINTED RAYS
1787

	Good	Fine	Unc.
UNITED above, STATES below (Rare)............	——	——	——
UNITED STATES at sides of circle................	25.00	50.00	$150.00

THE FUGIO CENTS

	Good	Fine	Unc.
STATES UNITED at sides of circle. Cinquefoils (small, five bladed clover design) on label	$20.00	$40.00	$125.00
STATES UNITED. Eight-pointed stars on label	30.00	75.00	——
STATES UNITED. Label with raised rims (simply two concentric circles). Large letters in WE ARE ONE.	40.00	95.00	——

Note: The preceding types with pointed rays have regular obverses punctuated with four cinquefoils.

Obv. no cinquefoils. Cross after date.

Rev. UNITED STATES	60.00	125.00	——
Same Obv., Rev. STATES UNITED	60.00	125.00	——
Same Obv., Rev. label with raised rims. (Ex. Rare)	——	——	——

American Congress   New Haven Restrike

Copper Pattern. Same obv.; reverse with rays and AMERICAN CONGRESS. (Ex. Rare)	——	——	——
New Haven Restrikes. Narrow rings on reverse.			
Gold (2 known)	——	——	——
Silver	——	——	200.00
Copper	——	——	80.00
Brass	——	——	75.00

New Haven Restrikes were struck from dies discovered by the fourteen-year-old C. Wyllys Betts in 1858 on the site of the Broome & Platt Store in New Haven, Conn., where the originals were made. Three pairs of dies were found and are still extant.

BIBLIOGRAPHY — Early American Coins

Crosby, S. S., Early Coins of America . . . . 1875 (Reprints 1945, 1965)
Dickeson, Dr. M. W., American Numismatic Manual 1859
Maris, Dr. Edward, New Jersey Cents . . . . 1881 (Reprint 1925)
Miller-Ryder, The State Coinage of New England 1920
Nelson, Philip, The Coinage of William Wood (1722-1733) 1903
Newman, Eric, Secret of Good Samaritan Shilling 1959
Noe, Sydney P., The New England and Willow Tree Coinages
    of Massachusetts 1943
Wurtzbach, Carl, Massachusetts Colonial Silver Money 1937

FIRST UNITED STATES MINT ISSUES

Many members of the House favored a representation of the president's head on the obverse of each coin. Others considered the idea a monarchical practice. Washington is believed to have expressed disapproval of the use of his portrait on our coins.

The majority considered a figure emblematic of Liberty more appropriate and the Senate finally concurred in this opinion. Robert Birch was an engraver employed at designing proposed devices for our coins. He engraved the dies for the disme and half-disme. He has also been associated with a large copper cent of unusual design, which is known as the Birch Cent.

DISME

	Good	Fine	Unc.
1792 Silver			
(3 Known)....	——	——	——
1792 Copper.....	——	——	——

HALF DISME

	Good	Fine	V. Fine
1792 Silver.....	$575	$950	$1600
1792 Copper (Unique)			

1792 SILVER CENTER CENT

	Fine	Ex. Fine
1792 Silver Center Cent.	——	——
1792 Cent,		
No Silver Center.....	——	——

1792 BIRCH CENT (Very Rare)
Copper...................... ——

G.W. Pt. Below Wreath
White Metal (Unique)

1792 PATTERN QUARTER DOLLAR

Copper.......(2 Known)
White Metal...(Unique)

MINTS AND MINT MARKS

Coins struck at Philadelphia (except 1942 to 1945 five-cent pieces) do not carry a mint mark. The mint mark is found only on coins struck at the branch mints. It is a small letter, usually found on the reverse side. The Lincoln cent is one exception to the rule. All coins minted after 1967 have the mint mark on the obverse. The letters that signify the various mints are as follows:

"C" for Charlotte, North Carolina (on gold coins only).
"CC" for Carson City, Nevada.
"D" for Dahlonega, Georgia (gold coins only, 1838 to 1861).
"D" for Denver, Colorado (from 1906 to date).
"O" for New Orleans, Louisiana.
"P" for Philadelphia, Pennsylvania.
"S" for San Francisco, California.

Location of Mint Marks

The mint mark is of utmost importance to collectors because of the fact that the coinage at the branch mints has usually been much smaller than at Philadelphia and many of the branch mint pieces are very scarce.

½¢, 1¢ through 1907, 2¢, 3¢ nickel, 5¢ nickel through 1911 — all coined at Philadelphia, no mint mark.

1¢ — Indian 1908-09, below wreath. Lincoln, below date.

3¢ silver — all Philadelphia, no mint mark, except 1851O: reverse side at right.

Half Dimes — above or below wreath bow.

Nickels — 1912, below dot left of CENTS. Buffalo, below FIVE CENTS. Jefferson (nickel) 1938-64, right of building. Jefferson (silver alloy) 1942-45, above building. Starting 1968, between date and shoulder.

Dimes — through 1916 Barber, above or below wreath bow. Mercury, right of ONE. Roosevelt 1946-64, left of torch base. Starting 1968, above date.

Twenty Cents — below eagle.

Quarter Dollars — through 1916, below eagle. 1917-30, between foot and left star. 1932-64, below wreath. Starting 1968, right of hair ribbon.

Half Dollars — 1838-39, above date. 1840-1915, below eagle. 1916-early 1917, below TRUST. Late 1917-1947, on reverse below pine branch. 1948-63, above bell beam. 1964, below claw holding laurel. Starting 1968, above date.

Dollars & Trade dollars — through 1921, below eagle. After 1921, above tip of eagle's tail.

Gold (all) — 1838-39, above date. 1840-1907 Liberty head, below wreath or eagle. $2½, 5, 10 after 1907, left of arrow point. $20 after 1907, above date.

PROOF COINS

A "proof" is a specimen striking of coinage for presentation, souvenir, exhibition, or numismatic purposes. Pre-1968 proofs were made only at the Philadelphia Mint. Current proofs are made only at the San Francisco Assay Office.

The term "proof" refers to the method of manufacture and not the condition of a coin. Regular production coins in mint state have coruscating, frosty lustre, soft details, and minor imperfections. Proof coins can usually be distinguished by their sharpness of detail, high wire edge, and extremely brilliant, mirrorlike surface. All proof coins are originally sold by the mint at premium prices.

Very few proof coins were made prior to 1855. Because of their rarity and infrequent sales, they are not all listed in this catalog.

Frosted proofs were issued prior to 1936. These have a brilliant mirror-like field with contrasting dull or frosted design and lettering. With modern proofs the first 15-20 coins struck from new proof dies are also frosted, but this feature is lost as soon as the dies are repolished.

Matte proofs have a granular "sandblast" surface instead of the mirror finish. Matte proof cents, nickels, and gold coins were issued from 1908 to 1916; a few 1921 and 1922 silver dollars were also struck this way.

Brilliant proofs have been issued from 1936 to date. These have a uniformly brilliant mirrorlike surface and sharp, high relief details.

"Proof-like" coins are occasionally seen. These are specimens from the first few impressions of regular coinage dies from any mint. They are not true proofs, but may have most of the characteristics of a proof coin and generally command a premium. Collectors should beware of coins that have been buffed to look like proofs; a magnifying glass will reveal myriad hair lines and lack of detail.

How A Proof Coin Is Made . . .

Selected dies are inspected for perfection and are highly polished and cleaned. They are again wiped clean or polished after every 15 to 25 impressions and are replaced frequently to avoid imperfections from worn dies. Coinage blanks are polished and cleaned to assure high quality in striking. They are then hand fed into the coinage press one at a time, each blank receiving two blows from the dies to bring up sharp, high relief details. The coinage operation is done at slow speed with extra pressure. Finished proofs are individually inspected and are handled by gloves or tongs. They also receive a final inspection by packers before being sonically sealed in special plastic cases.

MODERN PROOF COINS

After a lapse of twenty years, proof coins were struck at the Philadelphia Mint from 1936 to 1942 inclusive. In 1942, when the composition of the five-cent piece was changed, there were two types of this denomination available to collectors. The striking of proof coins was temporarily suspended from 1943 to 1949, and again from 1965 to 1967; during the latter period special mint sets were struck. Proof sets were resumed in 1968. They are delivered from the mint only during the year of issue.

RECENT PROOF SETS — Cent — Nickel — Dime — Quarter — Half

Figures in parentheses represent the total number of full sets minted.

1936 (3,837)............\$875.00	1956 (669,384)............ \$11.00
1937 (5,542)............. 350.00	1957 (1,247,952)............ 7.00
1938 (8,045)............. 180.00	1958 (875,652)............ 16.00
1939 (8,795)............. 145.00	1959 (1,149,291)............ 9.00
1940 (11,246)............. 110.00	1960 with sm. date 1¢
1941 (15,287)............. 95.00	(1,691,602 both kinds).. 25.00
1942 with both	1960 with lg. date 1¢........ 7.00
nickels (21,120)........ 115.00	1961 (3,028,244)............ 4.50
1950 (51,386)............. 105.00	1962 (3,218,019)............ 4.50
1951 (57,500)............. 70.00	1963 (3,075,645)............ 4.75
1952 (81,980)............. 37.50	1964 (3,950,762)............ 8.00
1953 (128,800)............. 27.50	1968S (3,041,509)......... 9.00
1954 (233,300)............. 17.50	1969S (2,934,631)......... 8.00
1955 (378,200)............. 25.00	1970S..................... 8.00

SPECIAL MINT SETS

1965 (2,360,000)............\$3.75	1967 (1,863,344)...........\$ 4.50
1966 (2,261,583)............ 3.75	

UNITED STATES REGULAR ISSUES

HALF CENTS — 1793-1857

From the standpoint of face value the half cent is the smallest coin struck by the United States. All half cents are scarce, but the series has never enjoyed the popularity of some of the other series, hence the more common dates are reasonably priced.

There were various intermissions in coinage, and during most of the period 1836 to 1849 the coinage was very small, causing a very noticeable lapse in the series for the average collector. While 1796 is the rarest date, the originals and restrikes of 1831, 1836 and 1840 through 1849 are difficult to obtain.

The half cent was authorized to be coined April 2, 1792. Originally the weight was to have been 132 grains, but this was changed to 104 grains by the Act of January 14, 1793, before coinage commenced. The weight was again changed January 26, 1796 by presidential proclamation in conformity with the Act of March 3, 1795 to 84 grains. Coinage was discontinued by the Act of February 21, 1857.

LIBERTY CAP TYPE 1793-1797

FAIR—Clear enough to identify.

GOOD—Outline of bust clear, no details. Date readable. Reverse lettering incomplete.

VERY GOOD—Some hair details. Reverse lettering complete.

FINE—Most of hair detail shows.

VERY FINE—Hair near ear and forehead worn, other areas distinct.

Head Facing Left 1793

	Quan. Minted	Fair	Good	V. Good	Fine	V. Fine
1793	35,334	$135.00	$250.00	$350.00	$650.00	$1100.00

Head Facing Right 1794-1797

| 1794 | 81,600 | 45.00 | 80.00 | 110.00 | 190.00 | 310.00 |

HALF CENTS

Pole to Cap   Punctuated Date   No Pole to Cap

	Quan. Minted	Fair	Good	V. Good	Fine	V. Fine
1795 Lettered Edge, with Pole.......	25,600	$ 40.00	$ 65.00	$ 90.00	$160.00	$275.00
1795 Let. Edge, Punctuated Date....		40.00	65.00	90.00	160.00	275.00
1795 Plain Edge, Punct. Date....	109,000	40.00	65.00	90.00	160.00	275.00
1795 Pl. Edge, no Pole		40.00	65.00	90.00	160.00	275.00
1796 with Pole*.........5,090		450.00	900.00	1500.00	2500.00	3500.00
1796 no Pole............1,390		600.00	1500.00	2150.00	3250.00	4750.00

*A deceptive copy of this coin was made by Edwards.

1797 Plain Edge

1797 1 Above 1, Plain Edge

1797 Lettered Edge All Kinds........119,214	110.00	225.00	350.00	550.00	950.00
1797 Plain Edge.............	37.50	60.00	90.00	150.00	265.00
1797 1 above 1, Plain Edge....	30.00	52.50	80.00	135.00	250.00

DRAPED BUST TYPE 1800-1808

FAIR—*Clear enough to identify.*
GOOD—*Bust outline clear, no details, date readable. Reverse lettering worn and incomplete.*
VERY GOOD—*Some drapery shows. Date and legends complete.*
FINE—*Shoulder drapery and hair over brow worn smooth.*
VERY FINE—*Only slight wear in above areas. Slight wear on reverse.*

1800...............211,530	5.00	10.00	14.00	22.50	37.50

HALF CENTS

	Quan. Minted	Fair	Good	V. Good	Fine	V. Fine
1802, 2 over 0, rev. of 1800	14,366	$100.00	$225.00	$325.00	$750.00	$1150.00
1802, 2 over 0, new rev.		45.00	90.00	135.00	220.00	375.00
1803	97,900	5.00	10.00	14.00	22.50	35.00

Plain 4   Crosslet 4   Stemless Wreath   Stems to Wreath

1804 Plain 4, Stems		10.00	18.00	27.50	35.00	70.00
1804 Pl. 4, Stemless		5.00	7.50	11.00	17.50	30.00
1804 Cr. 4, Stems	1,055,312	5.00	9.00	12.00	18.50	32.50
1804 Cr. 4, Stemless		5.50	9.50	13.00	21.00	35.00
1804 "Spiked Chin"		6.00	10.00	16.00	25.00	38.50

1804 "Spiked Chin" Variety   Small 5   Large 5

1805 Sm. 5, Stemless		5.00	8.50	12.00	20.00	35.00
1805 Small 5, Stems	814,464	30.00	52.50	85.00	165.00	260.00
1805 Large 5, Stems		5.00	8.50	12.00	20.00	35.00

Small 6   Large 6   1808 over 7   Normal Date

1806 Small 6, Stems		12.00	30.00	47.50	80.00	127.50
1806 Sm. 6, Stemless	356,000	5.00	9.00	12.00	18.00	32.50
1806 Large 6, Stems		5.00	9.00	12.00	18.00	32.50
1807	476,000	5.00	9.00	12.00	19.00	35.00
1808 over 7	400,000	22.00	37.50	52.50	95.00	190.00
1808 Normal Date		5.25	9.25	13.00	20.00	37.50

CLASSIC HEAD TYPE 1809-1836

FAIR—Worn, but clear enough to identify.

GOOD—LIBERTY only partly visible on hair band. Lettering, date, stars, worn but visible.

VERY GOOD—LIBERTY entirely visible on hair band. Lower curls worn.

FINE—Only part wear on LIBERTY and hair at top worn in spots.

VERY FINE—Lettering clear-cut. Hair only slightly worn.

HALF CENTS

<table>
<tr><td></td><td>1809 Circle Inside O</td><td colspan="5">1809 Normal Date</td></tr>
</table>

	Quan. Minted	Good	V. Good	Fine	V. Fine	Unc.
1809 Circle inside 0..	⎫	$10.50	$15.00	$25.00	$42.50	$140.00
1809, 9 over 6.......	⎬ 1,154,572	10.50	15.00	25.00	42.50	140.00
1809 Normal Date..	⎭	8.50	12.00	18.50	27.00	110.00
1810.................215,000		12.00	18.00	32.00	50.00	300.00
1811................. 63,140		37.50	50.00	85.00	135.00	600.00
1811 Restrike, Rev. of 1802...			Very Rare			
1825................. 63,000		8.00	11.00	16.50	25.00	80.00
1826................. 234,000		8.00	11.00	16.50	25.00	75.00

13 Stars

12 Stars

		Good	V. Good	Fine	V. Fine	Unc.
1828 13 Stars........	⎫ 606,000	7.00	10.00	14.00	20.00	60.00
1828 12 Stars........	⎭	10.00	15.00	22.00	40.00	160.00
1829................487,000		7.00	10.00	14.00	21.00	75.00

Original Large Berries

Restrike Small Berries

	Quan. Minted	V. Good	Fine	V. Fine	Unc.	Proof
1831 Original (Beware of altered date)....... 2,200					———	1100.00
1831 Restrike Large Berries (Rev. of 1836)..........						875.00
1831 Restrike Small Berries (Rev. of 1852)..........						
1832...............154,000*		10.00	14.00	20.00	67.50	650.00
1833...............120,000*		10.00	14.00	20.00	67.50	425.00
1834...............141,000*		10.00	14.00	20.00	67.50	450.00
1835...............398,000*		10.00	14.00	20.00	67.50	485.00
1836 Original................						700.00
1836 Restrike (Rev. of 1852)..						

*The figures given here are thought to be correct, although official mint records give the same quantities for 1833-36 rather than 1832-35.

HALF CENTS

No half cents were struck in 1837. Because of the great need for small change, however, a large number of tokens similar in size to current half cents and large cents were issued privately by businessmen who needed them in commerce. One of the most popular pieces is listed and illustrated below.

	Good	V. Good	Fine	V. Fine
1837 Token (not a coin)	$15.00	$25.00	$37.50	$75.00

BRAIDED HAIR TYPE 1840-1857

	Proof		Proof
1840 Original	$600.00	1845 Original	$700.00
1840 Restrike	550.00	1845 Restrike	625.00
1841 Original	600.00	1846 Original	625.00
1841 Restrike	850.00	1846 Restrike	575.00
1842 Original	700.00	1847 Original	600.00
1842 Restrike	500.00	1847 Restrike	500.00
1843 Original	600.00	1848 Original	725.00
1843 Restrike	525.00	1848 Restrike	525.00
1844 Original	650.00	1849 Original - Small Date . . .	800.00
1844 Restrike	650.00	1849 Restrike - Small Date . .	650.00

GOOD—Some of LIBERTY shows and beads partly distinct.
VERY GOOD—Beads uniformly distinct. Hairlines show in spots.
FINE—Hairlines above ear worn. Beads sharp.
VERY FINE—Lowest curl shows wear, hair otherwise distinct.

Brilliant or Red Uncirculated Half Cents Are Worth More Than Prices Shown.

	Quan. Minted	Small Date V. Good	Fine	V. Fine	Large Date Unc.	Proof
1849 Large Date	39,864	$15.00	$20.00	$32.50	$110.00	
1850	39,812	13.00	18.00	27.50	75.00	
1851	147,672	11.00	15.00	22.00	60.00	
1852 Original						
1852 Restrike						625.00
1853	129,694	11.00	17.00	23.00	62.50	
1854	55,358	11.00	17.00	23.00	67.50	425.00
1855	56,500	11.00	17.00	23.00	67.50	400.00
1856	40,430	12.00	19.00	26.50	70.00	425.00
1857	35,180	19.00	28.50	40.00	100.00	450.00

BIBLIOGRAPHY

Crosby, S. S., United States Coinage of 1793 (Cents and Half Cents). 1897. Reprint 1933.
Frossard, Ed., U. S. Cents and Half Cents 1793-1857. 1879.
Gilbert, Ebenezer, The United States Half Cents. 1916.

LARGE CENTS — 1793-1857

Laws affecting large cents were the same as half cents. The weights of cents are twice those of the half cents. Proofs are known to exist of some dates; all are rare.

FLOWING HAIR, CHAIN TYPE REVERSE 1793

FAIR—Date and devices clear enough to identify.
GOOD—Lettering worn but readable. Bust has no detail.
VERY GOOD—Date and lettering distinct, some details of head visible.
FINE—About half of hair, etc. details show.
VERY FINE—Ear visible. Most of details can be seen.

| Normal Obverse | AMERI. Reverse | Periods on Obverse | AMERICA Reverse |

	Quan. Minted	Fair	Good	V. Good	Fine	V. Fine
CHAIN TYPE	36,103					
1793 AMERI. in legend		$200.00	$365.00	$575.00	$950.00	$1750.00
1793 AMERICA		165.00	300.00	500.00	800.00	1400.00
1793 Period after date and LIBERTY		180.00	300.00	500.00	800.00	1300.00

FLOWING HAIR, WREATH TYPE REVERSE 1793

These cents might be more easily identified if they were called single-bow Wreath Cents. The Liberty Cap Cents also have wreaths but the stems are tied with a double bow knot. There are other differences to be seen on the Wreath type cents such as a bolder relief to the head of Liberty, more loosely flowing hair and a three-leaf sprig above the date. Some types have the vine and bars, and one variety has ONE HUNDRED FOR A DOLLAR on the edge.

| Wreath Type | | Strawberry Leaf Var. |

		Fair	Good	V. Good	Fine	V. Fine
WREATH TYPE	63,353					
1793 Edge has vine and bars		125.00	240.00	375.00	600.00	1150.00
1793 Lettered edge, one leaf on edge		140.00	250.00	400.00	675.00	1175.00
1793 Lettered edge, double leaf edge		150.00	260.00	410.00	700.00	1175.00
1793 Strawberry leaf variety			Ex. Rare			

[66]

LARGE CENTS
LIBERTY CAP TYPE 1793-1796

	Quan. Minted	Fair	Good	V. Good	Fine	V. Fine
1793 Liberty cap.......	11,056	$300.00	$475.00	$725.00	$1500.00	$2500.00
1794 (Many varieties).		19.00	35.00	55.00	90.00	185.00
1794 Head of 1793....	918,521	35.00	60.00	90.00	175.00	300.00
1794 Head of 1795....		20.00	40.00	60.00	110.00	200.00
1794 No fraction bar..		25.00	50.00	80.00	135.00	235.00

"Jefferson Head"	ONE CENT in Center of Wreath	ONE CENT High in Wreath

		Fair	Good	V. Good	Fine	V. Fine
1795 Jeff. hd. (not regular issue)		140.00	240.00	325.00	500.00	865.00
1795 Lettered edge, ONE CENT in center of wreath	82,000	25.00	50.00	75.00	135.00	220.00
1795 Lettered edge, ONE CENT high............		45.00	90.00	125.00	215.00	340.00
1795 Plain edge, ONE CENT high............	456,500	15.00	30.00	57.50	90.00	135.00
1795 Plain edge, ONE CENT in center of wreath		15.00	30.00	57.50	90.00	135.00
1795 Reeded edge............				Very Rare		
1796 Lib. cap.........	109,825	25.00	50.00	75.00	110.00	215.00

DRAPED BUST TYPE 1796-1807

FAIR—*Clear enough to identify.*
GOOD—*Lettering worn, but clear; date clear. Bust lacks details.*
VERY GOOD—*Drapery partly visible. Less wear in date and lettering.*
FINE—*Hair over brow is smooth, some detail showing elsewhere.*
VERY FINE—*Hairlines slightly worn. Hair over brow better defined.*

LARGE CENTS

	Draped Bust Type	Reverse of 1796		LIHERTY Variety		
	Quan. Minted	Fair	Good	V. Good	Fine	V. Fine
1796 Draped bust....	363,375	$23.00	$42.00	$70.00	$100.00	$225.00
1796 LIHERTY error..		27.50	57.50	90.00	150.00	275.00

Gripped or
Milled Edge

		Stems		Stemless		
1797 Stems on wreath						
All kinds........	897,510	10.00	16.00	25.00	42.50	80.00
1797 Stemless wreath.........		25.00	47.50	82.50	135.00	240.00
1797 Crudely gripped or						
milled edge. Rev. of 1796.		15.00	25.00	45.00	80.00	140.00
1797 Plain edge. Rev. of 1796..		16.00	27.50	47.50	90.00	150.00

1798 Over 97	Small Date	Large Date

Reverse of 1796
Single Leaves at Tops
of Both Branches

Wide Date

1798 over 97.........		15.00	25.00	45.00	90.00	145.00
1798 Small date......		7.00	12.00	19.00	35.00	70.00
1798 Large date......		7.00	15.00	22.50	37.50	75.00
1798 Rev. of 1796,	979,700					
wide date........		16.00	27.50	47.50	85.00	200.00
1798 Rev. of 1796,						
narrow date.....		Very Rare				

9 over 8	Normal Date	Chip on Reverse

1799 over 98.........	904,585	200.00	385.00	650.00	1250.00	2350.00
1799 Normal date.....		185.00	340.00	585.00	1100.00	2100.00

Genuine coins identified by the chip in the reverse die (see arrow).

LARGE CENTS

1800 Over 1798

Normal Date

	Quan. Minted	Fair	Good	V. Good	Fine	V. Fine
1800 over 1798...... ⎫		$7.50	$14.00	$21.00	$40.00	$75.00
1800 over 179....... ⎬ 2,822,175		7.00	12.50	18.50	35.00	70.00
1800 Normal date... ⎭		6.00	11.00	16.50	27.00	57.50

Normal Dies

1801
Reverse 3 Errors

Error 1/000

$\frac{1}{100}$ Over $\frac{1}{000}$

	Fair	Good	V. Good	Fine	V. Fine
1801 Normal dies, blunt 1's All kinds.......1,362,837	7.00	11.00	20.00	35.00	60.00
1801 First 1 perfect...........	7.00	15.00	22.50	40.00	75.00
1801 3 errors, 1/000, one stem and IINITED......	17.50	32.50	55.00	110.00	200.00
1801 Fraction 1/000..........	9.00	19.00	30.00	55.00	100.00
1801 Fraction 1/100 over 1/000	11.00	22.00	35.00	65.00	130.00

Normal Dies

Stemless Wreath, Double Fraction Bar

	Fair	Good	V. Good	Fine	V. Fine
1802 Normal dies All kinds.......3,435,100	5.00	9.00	13.50	22.50	50.00
1802 Stemless wreath, single fraction bar.......	6.00	11.00	17.00	32.50	57.50
1802 Stemless wreath, double fraction bar......	6.00	11.00	20.00	37.50	65.00
1802 Fraction 1/000..........	7.00	14.00	25.00	45.00	80.00

1803 Small Date

Small Fraction

Large Fraction

	Fair	Good	V. Good	Fine	V. Fine
1803 Sm. date, sm. fraction (blunt 1) All kinds 2,471,353	6.00	10.00	15.00	25.00	60.00
1803 Sm. date, lg. fraction (blunt 1 in date)........	6.00	10.00	15.00	25.00	60.00
1803 Lg. date, sm. fraction (pointed 1 in date).......	80.00	115.00	165.00	300.00	475.00
1803 Lg. date, lg. fraction (pointed 1 in date).......	40.00	65.00	110.00	185.00	325.00
1803 Stemless wreath.........	10.00	16.50	30.00	50.00	80.00
1803 1/100 over 1/000........	10.00	20.00	35.00	65.00	110.00

LARGE CENTS

1804 with
broken dies
(see arrows)

On all genuine 1804 Cents
the O of the date is in line
with the O in OF on the
reverse of the coin.

	Quan. Minted	Fair	Good	V. Good	Fine	V. Fine
1804 Normal dies						
All kinds.........756,838		$125.00	$185.00	$285.00	$450.00	$825.00
1804 Broken obv. die.........		125.00	185.00	285.00	450.00	825.00
1804 Broken obv. & rev. dies..		125.00	185.00	285.00	450.00	825.00

RESTRIKE OF 1804 CENT

A fake 1804 was manufactured
from discarded mint dies. An
altered 1803 die was used for the
obverse and a die of the 1820
cent used for the reverse. They
were struck about the year 1860
to satisfy the demand for this
rare date. Known as the "restrike," it was a patchwork job
and is easily distinguished from a genuine 1804 cent.

1804 Restrike of 1860...................................Unc. $150.00

Blunt 1 in Date   Pointed 1

1804 Blunt 1 in date.. } 941,116	6.00	12.00	15.00	25.00	52.50
1805 Pointed 1 in date }	7.00	13.00	18.00	32.50	60.00
1806.................348,000	12.00	22.50	37.50	67.50	115.00

1807
Over 6

"Comet" Variety

Small Fraction   Large Fraction

1807 Large 7 over 6					
All kinds........727,221	7.00	11.00	18.00	30.00	60.00
1807 Small 7 over 6, blunt 1...	45.00	75.00	115.00	210.00	340.00
1807 Small fraction...........	6.00	10.00	17.00	30.00	55.00
1807 Large fraction...........	6.00	10.00	17.00	30.00	55.00
1807 "Comet" variety					
(die break behind head)..	9.00	16.50	27.50	55.00	115.00

LARGE CENTS

CLASSIC HEAD TYPE 1808-1814

FAIR—Details clear enough to identify.

GOOD—Legends, stars, date worn, but plain.

VERY GOOD—LIBERTY all readable. Ear shows. Details worn but plain.

FINE—Hair on forehead and before ear nearly smooth. Ear and hair under ear sharp.

VERY FINE—All hairlines show some detail. Leaves on rev. show slight wear.

1808 to 1814 — This group does not compare in sharpness and quality to those struck before (1793-1807), nor to those struck after (1816 on). The copper used was "softer," having less alloy. This impaired the wearing quality of the series. For this reason collectors find greater difficulty in obtaining these dates in choice condition.

13 Stars

First star missing (caused by die defect)

	Quan. Minted	Fair	Good	V. Good	Fine	V. Fine
1808 13 stars	} 1,109,000	$ 9.00	$15.00	$ 27.50	$ 50.00	$ 95.00
1808 12 stars		10.00	16.50	32.50	52.50	110.00
1809	222,867	37.50	65.00	115.00	175.00	325.00

1810 Over 9

Normal Date

1810 over 9	} 1,458,500	8.00	15.00	25.00	40.00	70.00
1810 Normal date		8.00	13.00	22.50	35.00	65.00

1811 Over 10

Normal Date

1812 Large Date

1811 over 10	} 218,025	34.00	50.00	75.00	130.00	250.00
1811 Normal date		34.00	50.00	75.00	125.00	240.00
1812 Small date	} 1,075,500	7.00	12.00	17.50	32.50	60.00
1812 Large date		7.00	12.00	17.50	32.50	60.00
1813	418,000	12.50	25.00	35.00	70.00	110.00

1814 Plain 4

1814 Crosslet 4

1814 Plain 4	} 357,830	7.00	12.50	20.00	32.50	57.50
1814 Crosslet 4		7.00	12.50	20.00	32.50	57.50

LARGE CENTS
CORONET TYPE

Red to bright red uncirculated large cents (not cleaned) command higher prices.

GOOD—*Head details partly visible. Even wear in date and legends.*
VERY GOOD—*LIBERTY, date, stars, legends clear. Part of hair cord visible.*
FINE—*All hairlines show. Hair cords show uniformly.*
VERY FINE—*Hair cords only slightly worn. Hairlines only partly worn, all well defined.*

	Quan. Minted	Good	V. Good	Fine	V. Fine	Unc.
1816.................	2,820,982	$5.50	$8.50	$11.50	$22.50	$110.00

1817 Wide Date   1817 Close Date   1817 15 Stars

		Good	V. Good	Fine	V. Fine	Unc.
1817 Wide date.....		5.00	7.50	10.00	18.50	100.00
1817 Close date.....	}3,948,400	5.00	7.50	10.00	18.50	100.00
1817 15 stars.......		7.50	12.50	22.50	37.50	160.00
1818...............3,167,000		5.00	7.50	10.00	17.50	100.00

1819 Large Date   1819 Small Date   1819 Over 18

1819 over 18........		6.00	9.50	15.00	22.50	200.00
1819 Large date.....	}2,671,000	6.00	9.00	12.50	20.00	110.00
1819 Small date.....		6.00	9.00	12.50	20.00	110.00

1820 Over 19   1820 Small Date   1820 Large Date

1820 over 19 All kinds.	4,407,550	6.00	9.00	12.50	20.00	150.00

LARGE CENTS

	Quan. Minted	Good	V. Good	Fine	V. Fine	Unc.
1820 Small date.............		$5.00	$7.50	$12.50	$17.50	$120.00
1820 Large date.............		5.00	7.50	12.50	17.50	120.00

1821 Wide Date

1821 Close Date

	Quan. Minted	Good	V. Good	Fine	V. Fine	Unc.
1821 Wide date.......	} 389,000	12.50	20.00	35.00	65.00	400.00
1821 Close date......		16.00	30.00	50.00	80.00	475.00

1822
Wide Date

1822
Close Date

	Quan. Minted	Good	V. Good	Fine	V. Fine	Unc.
1822 Wide date.....	} 2,072,339	5.00	8.00	12.00	22.50	175.00
1822 Close date.....		5.00	8.00	12.00	22.50	200.00

1823 Over 22

1823 Normal Date

	Quan. Minted	Good	V. Good	Fine	V. Fine	Unc.
1823 over 22........	} 855,730	22.50	35.00	57.50	110.00	1300.00
1823 Normal date....		30.00	42.50	75.00	145.00	2100.00
1823 Restrike, from broken obverse die.						120.00

LARGE CENTS

1824 Over 22   1824 Wide Date   1824 Close Date

	Quan. Minted	Good	V. Good	Fine	V. Fine	Unc.
1824 over 22		$12.50	$20.00	$32.50	$60.00	$400.00
1824 Wide date	}1,262,000	7.00	9.50	16.50	32.50	240.00
1824 Close date		7.00	9.50	16.50	32.50	240.00

1825 Small A's   1825 Large A's

1825 Small A's	}1,461,100	6.00	8.00	14.50	27.50	200.00
1825 Large A's		6.00	8.00	14.50	27.50	200.00

1826 Over 25   1826 Close Date

1826 over 25 (Trace						
of 5 inside 6) ..		10.00	25.00	40.00	62.50	225.00
1826 Wide date	}1,517,425	6.00	8.50	13.50	24.00	140.00
1826 Close date		6.00	8.50	13.50	24.00	140.00

LARGE CENTS

	Quan. Minted	Good	V. Good	Fine	V. Fine	Unc.
1827	2,357,732	$5.00	$7.00	$11.00	$17.50	$135.00

1828
Small Date

1828
Large Date

		Good	V. Good	Fine	V. Fine	Unc.
1828 Small date	} 2,260,624	10.00	15.00	22.50	37.50	250.00
1828 Large date		5.00	7.50	11.50	21.00	135.00

1829 Small Letters　　　1829 Large Letters

		Good	V. Good	Fine	V. Fine	Unc.
1829 Small letters . . .	} 1,414,500	7.00	11.00	15.00	30.00	185.00
1829 Large letters . . .		5.00	7.50	11.00	19.00	125.00
1830 Small letters . . .	} 1,711,500	12.00	22.00	40.00	77.50	300.00
1830 Large letters . . .		5.00	7.00	10.00	17.00	140.00
1831 Small letters . . .	} 3,359,260	4.75	6.50	8.50	13.50	120.00
1831 Large letters . . .		4.75	6.50	8.50	13.50	140.00
1832 Small letters . . .	} 2,362,000	5.00	6.75	10.00	16.50	120.00
1832 Large letters . . .		5.00	6.75	10.00	16.50	120.00
1833 Small letters . . .	} 2,739,000	4.50	6.25	8.75	14.50	105.00
1833 Large letters . . .		4.50	6.25	8.75	14.50	105.00

LARGE CENTS

Large Date, Large Stars   Small Date, Large Stars   Large Date, Small Stars

	Quan. Minted	Good	V. Good	Fine	V. Fine	Unc.
1834 Lg. date, lg. stars, lg. let. on rev. All kinds	1,855,100	$6.50	$11.75	$18.50	$29.00	$120.00
1834 Sm. date, lg. stars, sm. let. on rev.		5.50	8.00	14.00	21.00	105.00
1834 Lg. date, sm. stars, sm. let. on rev.		6.50	10.75	17.00	29.00	135.00

GOOD—*Considerably worn. LIBERTY readable.*
VERY GOOD—*Hairlines smooth but visible, outline of ear clearly defined.*
FINE—*Hairlines at top of head and behind ear worn but visible. Braid over brow plain, ear clear.*
VERY FINE—*All details more sharp. Hair over brow shows only slight wear.*

Large Date, Large Stars   Small Date, Small Stars   Type of 1836

1835 Lg. date, lg. stars All kinds	3,878,400	6.50	10.50	16.00	27.00	110.00
1835 Sm. date, sm. stars		6.50	10.50	16.00	27.00	110.00
1835 Type of 1836		5.00	7.25	12.50	16.00	110.00

1836	2,111,000	5.00	7.00	12.00	18.50	125.00

LARGE CENTS

1837
Plain Hair
Cord

1837
Beaded
Hair
Cord

	Quan. Minted	Good	V. Good	Fine	V. Fine	Unc.
1837 Plain hair cord, sm. let. All kinds	5,558,300	$6.50	$9.50	$16.00	$27.00	$135.00
1837 Plain hair cord, lg. let.		4.50	6.00	9.25	14.50	90.00
1837 Beaded hair cd., sm. let.		4.50	6.00	9.25	14.50	90.00
1838	6,370,200	4.50	5.75	8.75	13.00	85.00

1839 over 36

Line Under
CENT
No Center
Dot

1839 over 36, line under CENT; No ctr. dot. All kinds	3,128,661	100.00	145.00	225.00	350.00	———

Type of
1838

Silly Head
Variety

1839 Type 1838, line under CENT	8.00	11.75	20.00	32.50	150.00
1839 Silly head, line under CENT; no center dot	11.00	15.00	25.00	36.00	200.00

Booby Head Variety, No Line Under CENT

1839 Booby head, no line	7.50	11.00	17.50	27.50	165.00
1839 Type of 1840, no line	8.00	12.00	24.00	30.00	165.00

1839 Type of 1840

LARGE CENTS
BRAIDED HAIR TYPE

1840
Small Date

1840
Large Date

	Quan. Minted	Good	V. Good	Fine	V. Fine	Unc.
1840 Small date..... }	2,462,700	$6.00	$8.00	$11.00	$16.00	$105.00
1840 Large date..... }		6.00	8.00	11.00	16.00	115.00
1841................	1,597,367	6.00	8.00	13.00	19.00	110.00

1842
Small Date

1842
Large Date

1842 Small date..... } 2,383,390	5.00	7.50	10.00	16.00	95.00
1842 Large date..... }	5.00	7.50	10.00	16.00	95.00

1843
Obverse of
1842

1843
Reverse of
1842

1843 Obv. and rev. of 1842-All kinds...2,428,320	5.50	8.00	11.50	18.00	105.00
1843 Obv. of 1842, rev. of 1844.	20.00	32.50	57.50	85.00	500.00

1843
Obverse of
1844

1843
Reverse of
1844

1843 Obv. and rev. of 1844....	6.50	10.00	15.00	25.00	160.00

LARGE CENTS

1844

1844
Over
81

	Quan. Minted	Good	V. Good	Fine	V. Fine	Unc.
1844 Normal date...	} 2,398,752	$4.50	$ 6.00	$ 8.75	$14.00	$95.00
1844 over 81 (error).		7.00	10.00	13.50	30.00	150.00
1845................	3,894,804	4.25	5.75	7.50	11.00	77.50

1846
Small
Date

1846
Tall
Date

1846 Small date.....	3.50	4.50	5.75	9.50	70.00
1846 Medium date.. } 4,120,800	3.50	4.50	5.75	9.50	70.00
1846 Tall date......	4.50	5.50	8.00	14.00	90.00
1847................6,183,669	3.50	4.50	5.75	9.50	70.00

1851 Over 81

1848................6,415,799	3.50	4.50	5.75	9.00	65.00
1849................4,178,500	3.50	4.50	5.75	9.00	65.00
1850................4,426,844	3.50	4.50	5.75	9.00	65.00
1851 Normal date... } 9,889,707	3.00	4.00	5.00	8.00	62.50
1851 over 81 (error).	7.50	11.00	15.00	37.50	200.00
1852................5,063,094	3.00	4.00	5.00	8.00	62.50
1853................6,641,131	3.00	4.00	5.00	8.00	62.50
1854................4,236,156	3.00	4.00	5.00	8.00	62.50

LARGE CENTS

1855
Upright 5's

1855
Slanting 5's

Original sketches of Engraver James B. Longacre's work reveal that slanting 5's were a peculiarity of his work. The upright 5's were probably the work of an apprentice.

	Quan. Minted	Good	V. Good	Fine	V. Fine	Unc.
1855 Upright 5's						
All kinds........1,574,829		$4.25	$5.25	$7.50	$11.00	$72.50
1855 Slanting 5's.............		4.25	5.25	7.50	11.00	72.50
1855 Slanting 5's, knob on ear .		7.00	9.00	12.00	28.00	120.00

1856
Upright 5

1856
Slanting 5

		Good	V. Good	Fine	V. Fine	Unc.
1856 Upright 5.....	}2,690,463	4.00	5.00	7.00	10.50	72.50
1856 Slanting 5.....		4.00	5.00	7.00	10.50	72.50

1857
Small Date

1857
Large Date

		Good	V. Good	Fine	V. Fine	Unc.
1857 Small date......	}333,456	29.00	37.00	45.00	60.00	155.00
1857 Large date......		23.50	29.00	37.00	47.00	140.00

BIBLIOGRAPHY

Crosby, S. S., The Cents and Half Cents of 1793.
Hays, W. W., The Cents of 1794.
Gilbert-Elder, The Cents of 1796.
Doughty, Francis W., United States Cents.
Clapp, Geo. H., Cents of 1798 and 1799.
Newcomb, H. R., United States Copper Cents 1816-1857.
Sheldon, Wm. H., Penny Whimsy (1793-1814).

FLYING EAGLE CENTS — 1856-1858

Copper-Nickel or "White" Cents

The Act of February 21, 1857 provided for the coinage of the small cent, and made uncurrent the coins of other countries, particularly the Spanish and Mexican dollars. The new cents weighed 72 grains. Composition, 88% copper, 12% nickel.

THE 1856 FLYING EAGLE CENT

The 1856 Eagle Cent was not an authorized mint issue, as the law governing the new size coin was enacted after the date of issue. It is believed that about 1000 of these pieces were struck. They are usually referred to as patterns.

1858 Large Letters

1858 Small Letters

The 1858 cent is found in two major varieties. The A and M in the word AMERICA are joined in the large letter variety, and separated in the small letter variety. The reverse design of the eagle cents is dominated by a wreath of corn, wheat, cotton and tobacco.

1858 Over 7 Cent ⟶

GOOD—All details worn, but readable.
VERY GOOD—Feather details and eye of eagle are evident, but worn.
FINE—Eagle head details and feather tips sharp.
EXTRA FINE—Slight wear, all details sharp.

	Quan. Minted	Good	V.G.	Fine	V.F.	E.F.	Unc.	Proof
1856	(1,000)	$ 625	$ 775	$ 950	$1,175	$1,450	$2,000	$2,500
1857	17,450,000	4.50	5.50	8.00	12.00	21.00	115.00	2,150
1858 All kinds - 24,600,000 (Proofs L.L. 80; S.L. 200)								
Lg. Letters		5.00	6.25	9.25	15.00	27.50	130.00	2,100
1858 8 over 7						——	——	
1858 Sm. letters		5.00	6.25	9.25	15.00	27.50	130.00	2,100

INDIAN HEAD CENTS — 1859-1864

Copper-Nickel

The small cent was redesigned in 1859, and a representation of an Indian girl was adopted as the obverse device. The 1859 reverse was also changed to represent a laurel wreath. In 1860 the reverse only was modified to display an oak wreath with a small shield at the top. The weight and composition of the coin was not changed.

GOOD—*No LIBERTY visible.*

VERY GOOD—*At least half of LIBERTY readable.*

FINE—*LIBERTY completely visible.*

VERY FINE—*Slight but even wear on LIBERTY.*

EXTRA FINE—*LIBERTY sharp. All other details sharp. Only slight wear on ribbon end.*

Without shield at top of wreath on reverse 1859 only

With shield on reverse 1860 to 1909

	Quan. Minted	Good	V.G.	Fine	V.F.	E.F.	Unc.	Proof
1859	36,400,000	$2.75	$3.75	$ 7.00	$11.00	$20.00	$82.50	$600.00
1860 (1,000)	20,566,000	2.25	3.25	6.00	9.00	15.00	60.00	460.00
1861 (1,000)	10,100,000	6.25	8.50	13.00	17.00	25.00	85.00	525.00
1862 . .(550)	28,075,000	1.85	2.50	4.00	5.50	9.00	26.50	315.00
1863 . .(460)	49,840,000	1.60	2.25	3.75	5.25	8.00	25.00	300.00
1864 . .(300)	13,740,000	4.25	6.00	10.00	14.00	21.00	52.50	590.00

1864-1909 Bronze

During the year 1864 the alloy of the cent was changed to 95 per cent copper and five per cent tin and zinc. The weight was reduced to 48 grains, resulting in a thinner coin than the "White" Cents. The design remained unchanged. The first 1864 bronze cents did not have the designer's initial L on the bonnet ribbon. Later in the year the letter appeared on only a small quantity. The initial appeared on all dates of Indian Cents thereafter. Consult the illustration details.

1864 Bronze
Indian Head Cent With "L"

If the coin is turned slightly (so Indian faces observer) the highlighted details of the "L" will appear to better advantage. The point of the bust is pointed on the variety with "L"; rounded without "L." The "L" is the initial of the engraver, Longacre.

SMALL CENTS

Closed 3   Open 3

Select brilliant Unc. and Proof small cents command higher prices.

	Quan. Minted	Good	V.G.	Fine	V.F.	E.F.	Unc.	Proof
1864 (No L on ribbon)								
..(150)	39,233,714	$1.75	$3.25	$6.50	$11.00	$18.00	$52.50	$775.00
1864 (L on ribbon must show)								
....(20)	Unknown	13.00	23.50	45.00	65.00	85.00	225.00	———
1865..(500)	35,429,286	1.75	2.75	4.75	7.50	13.75	40.00	325.00
1866..(725)	9,826,500	7.50	12.00	22.50	37.50	55.00	125.00	325.00
1867..(625)	9,821,000	8.00	11.75	22.00	34.00	52.50	125.00	300.00
1868..(600)	10,266,500	7.50	12.00	22.50	37.50	55.00	135.00	315.00
‡1869 over 8	6,420,000	40.00	55.00	80.00	150.00	250.00	675.00	
1869..(600)		12.50	22.00	47.50	72.50	105.00	280.00	535.00
1870 (1,000)	5,275,000	12.00	20.00	36.00	52.50	70.00	150.00	340.00
1871..(960)	3,929,500	16.00	25.00	45.00	60.00	85.00	180.00	400.00
1872..(950)	4,042,000	18.00	30.00	52.50	75.00	105.00	250.00	480.00
1873 All kinds 11,676,500								
1873 Closed 3 (1100)...		4.00	6.75	12.50	20.00	32.50	75.00	255.00
1873 Open 3..........		4.00	6.75	12.50	20.00	32.50	75.00	
1874..(700)	14,187,500	3.75	6.00	12.50	20.00	32.50	75.00	225.00
1875..(700)	13,528,000	3.75	6.00	12.50	20.00	32.50	75.00	225.00
1876 (1,150)	7,944,000	6.00	9.00	17.50	27.50	40.00	87.50	200.00
1877..(510)	852,500	80.00	120.00	180.00	265.00	425.00	750.00	1,100
1878 (2,350)	5,799,850	6.25	9.50	18.50	27.50	40.00	87.50	155.00
1879 (3,200)	16,231,200	1.50	2.35	5.00	7.25	12.50	35.00	70.00
1880 (3,955)	38,964,955	.90	1.35	3.25	5.00	8.00	25.00	52.50
1881 (3,575)	39,211,575	.90	1.35	3.25	5.00	8.00	25.00	52.50
1882 (3,100)	38,581,100	.90	1.35	3.25	5.00	8.00	25.00	52.50
1883 (6,609)	45,598,109	.80	1.25	3.00	4.50	7.50	21.50	50.00
1884 (3,942)	23,261,742	1.50	2.50	4.75	7.50	11.00	32.50	60.00
1885 (3,790)	11,765,384	3.25	5.00	9.00	14.00	22.50	50.00	80.00
1886 (*Var. 1) All kinds								
(4,290)	17,654,290	1.85	2.85	5.25	9.25	15.00	40.00	67.50
1886 (**Var. 2).......		1.85	2.85	5.25	9.25	15.00	40.00	67.50
1887 (2,960)	45,226,483	.40	.80	1.90	3.25	5.75	19.50	52.50
1888 (4,582)	37,494,414	.45	.85	2.00	3.35	6.00	20.00	50.00
1889 (3,336)	48,869,361	.40	.80	2.00	3.10	5.75	19.50	52.50
1890 (2,740)	57,182,854	.40	.80	1.85	3.00	5.50	18.50	52.50
1891 (2,350)	47,072,350	.40	.80	1.85	3.00	5.50	18.50	52.50
1892 (2,745)	37,649,832	.45	.85	2.00	3.10	5.75	19.50	55.00
1893 (2,195)	46,642,195	.40	.80	1.85	3.00	5.25	20.00	52.50
1894 (2,632)	16,752,132	1.50	3.50	6.25	9.00	14.50	37.00	75.00
1895 (2,062)	38,343,636	.35	.75	1.50	2.65	5.00	18.00	53.50
1896 (1,862)	39,057,293	.35	.75	1.75	2.75	5.00	20.00	55.00
1897 (1,938)	50,466,330	.35	.70	1.50	2.40	4.50	19.50	54.00
1898 (1,795)	49,823,079	.35	.70	1.50	2.40	4.50	19.00	54.00

‡Do not confuse with recut variety.
*1886 Variety 1. Last feather points between I and C.
**1886 Variety 2. Last feather points between C and A.

SMALL CENTS

	Quan. Minted	Good	V.G.	Fine	V.F.	E.F.	Unc.	Proof
1899 (2,031)	53,600,031	$ .30	$ .65	$1.25	$2.10	$4.00	$16.50	$54.00
1900 (2,262)	66,833,764	.30	.50	.95	1.75	3.25	11.50	52.00
1901 (1,985)	79,611,143	.30	.50	.85	1.50	3.15	9.25	52.00
1902 (2,018)	87,376,722	.30	.50	.85	1.50	3.15	9.25	52.00
1903 (1,790)	85,094,493	.30	.50	.85	1.50	3.15	9.25	52.00
1904 (1,817)	61,328,015	.30	.50	.85	1.50	3.15	9.25	52.00
1905 (2,152)	80,719,163	.30	.50	.85	1.50	3.15	9.25	52.00
1906 (1,725)	96,022,255	.30	.50	.85	1.50	3.15	9.25	52.00
1907 (1,475)	108,138,618	.30	.50	.85	1.50	3.15	9.25	52.00
1908 (1,620)	32,327,987	.40	.60	1.00	1.75	3.50	11.00	57.50
1908S........	1,115,000	15.00	18.50	23.50	30.00	43.00	100.00	
1909 (2,175)	14,370,645	.75	1.10	1.75	2.60	5.00	13.00	65.00
1909S........	309,000	60.00	67.50	77.50	100.00	150.00	260.00	

LINCOLN TYPE, WHEAT EARS REVERSE 1909-1959

Victor D. Brenner designed this cent which was issued to commemorate the
hundredth anniversary of Lincoln's birth. The designer's initials VDB appear
on a limited quantity of cents of 1909. The San Francisco mint produced the
smallest issue before the initials were removed, creating the scarcest though not
the highest priced Lincoln Head Cent. The initials were restored, in 1918, to
the obverse side as illustrated below. This type cent was the first to have
the motto "In God We Trust."

Select brilliant uncircu-
lated cents command
higher prices.

Cents with well-struck
mint marks are also
worth more.

Matte
Proof

1909 V.D.B.

(420)	27,995,000	.80	1.00	1.25	1.60	2.15	5.25	365.00
1909S, V.D.B.	484,000	97.50	110.00	120.00	130.00	145.00	200.00	

GOOD—*Date worn but apparent. Lines in wheat ears missing.
Full rims.*

VERY GOOD—*Half of lines show in upper wheat ears.*

FINE—*Wheat lines worn but visible.*

VERY FINE—*Cheek and jaw bones worn but separated. No worn
spots on wheat ears.*

EXTRA FINE—*Slight wear. All details sharp.*

No
V. D. B.
on
Reverse

1909 (2,198)	72,702,618	.15	.25	.40	.65	1.35	5.75	82.00
1909S........	1,825,000	20.00	23.00	26.00	30.00	40.00	65.00	
1910 (2,405)	146,801,218	.15	.20	.30	.60	1.25	7.25	90.00
1910S........	6,045,000	2.75	3.50	4.25	6.50	9.50	40.00	
1911 (1,733)	101,177,787	.15	.20	.30	.85	1.50	8.50	90.00
1911D......	12,672,000	1.25	1.85	3.00	5.75	10.00	32.00	
1911S........	4,026,000	6.75	8.00	9.25	12.50	18.00	50.00	
1912 (2,145)	68,153,060	.15	.25	.45	1.25	2.35	11.50	97.50
1912D......	10,411,000	1.25	2.00	3.90	8.00	15.00	45.00	
1912S........	4,431,000	3.75	4.50	6.00	9.00	16.00	45.00	
1913 (2,848)	76,532,352	.15	.20	.40	1.10	2.00	11.00	100.00
1913D......	15,804,000	.85	1.25	2.10	5.00	10.00	40.00	
1913S........	6,101,000	2.50	3.25	4.25	6.25	10.75	40.00	

SMALL CENTS

	Quan. Minted	Good	V.G.	Fine	V.F.	E.F.	Unc.	Matte Proof
1914 (1,365)	75,238,432	$ .15	$ .30	$ .75	$ 2.00	$ 4.50	$24.00	$190.00
1914D*......1,193,000		30.00	37.50	47.50	85.00	165.00	560.00	
1914S........4,137,000		3.50	4.25	5.25	8.00	14.00	75.00	
1915 (1,150) 29,092,120		.40	.80	3.25	6.75	14.50	65.00	280.00
1915D......22,050,000		.45	.75	1.20	2.50	6.25	23.50	
1915S........4,833,000		3.00	3.60	4.50	7.00	11.00	42.00	
1916 (1,050)131,833,677		.10	.20	.35	.75	1.50	7.25	320.00
1916D......35,956,000		.20	.35	.70	1.60	3.85	19.00	
1916S......22,510,000		.40	.55	.90	1.75	4.25	26.00	
1917.......196,429,785		.10	.20	.30	.70	1.40	6.75	
1917D......55,120,000		.15	.25	.55	1.65	4.50	24.00	
1917S......32,620,000		.20	.30	.55	1.65	4.50	25.00	

Designer's
Initials
Restored

	Quan. Minted	Good	V.G.	Fine	V.F.	E.F.	Unc.
1918.......288,104,634		.10	.15	.30	.65	1.50	8.25
1918D......47,830,000		.15	.25	.55	1.60	4.25	26.00
1918S......34,680,000		.15	.25	.55	1.60	4.40	28.00
1919.......392,021,000		.10	.15	.25	.55	1.40	7.00
1919D......57,154,000		.10	.20	.40	1.25	3.00	18.00
1919S......139,760,000		.10	.20	.40	1.10	3.15	17.50
1920.......310,165,000		.10	.15	.25	.55	1.20	6.50
1920D......49,280,000		.15	.20	.45	1.25	4.25	30.00
1920S......46,220,000		.15	.20	.45	1.40	4.50	30.00
1921.......39,157,000		.15	.25	.50	1.10	3.80	21.00
1921S......15,274,000		.55	.90	1.60	4.25	12.00	155.00
1922D...... }7,160,000		2.50	3.00	4.25	7.00	11.25	47.50
1922 Plain **		30.00	40.00	60.00	95.00	165.00	700.00
1923........74,723,000		.10	.15	.30	.70	1.60	7.00
1923S........8,700,000		.90	1.40	2.10	5.50	15.00	225.00
1924........75,178,000		.10	.15	.25	.60	1.60	13.00
1924D......2,520,000		7.75	10.00	13.50	18.75	33.00	180.00
1924S......11,696,000		.50	.65	1.25	3.50	8.00	90.00
1925.......139,949,000		.10	.15	.25	.50	1.25	5.75
1925D......22,580,000		.20	.30	.45	1.00	3.00	25.00
1925S......26,380,000		.20	.30	.50	1.10	3.50	27.50
1926.......157,088,000		.10	.15	.25	.50	1.10	5.50
1926D......28,020,000		.15	.25	.45	.95	2.50	24.00
1926S........4,550,000		2.75	3.75	4.75	6.50	12.50	100.00
1927.......144,440,000		.10	.15	.25	.50	1.10	5.25
1927D......27,170,000		.15	.20	.35	.75	2.25	19.00
1927S......14,276,000		.30	.40	.85	1.10	3.00	38.50
1928.......134,116,000		.10	.15	.25	.50	1.10	4.75
1928D......31,170,000		.15	.25	.35	.60	1.40	15.00
1928S......17,266,000		.25	.35	.60	1.10	2.40	28.00

*Beware of altered date or mint mark. No VDB on shoulder of genuine 1914D cent.

**The 1922 without D is the result of a defective die. Beware of removed mint mark.

SMALL CENTS

	Quan. Minted	Good	V.G.	Fine	V.F.	E.F.	Unc.	Proof
1929	185,262,000	$ .10	$ .15	$ .25	$ .40	$ .90	$4.25	
1929D	41,730,000	.10	.15	.25	.45	1.00	8.00	
1929S	50,148,000	.10	.15	.25	.45	.90	5.25	
1930	157,415,000	.10	.15	.25	.40	.85	3.25	
1930D	40,100,000	.10	.15	.25	.45	.90	7.25	
1930S	24,286,000	.10	.15	.25	.45	.90	5.75	
1931	19,396,000	.25	.35	.45	.85	1.80	16.00	
1931D	4,480,000	2.75	3.25	3.75	4.75	7.25	45.00	
1931S	866,000	20.00	25.00	27.50	30.00	35.00	50.00	
1932	9,062,000	.65	1.00	1.15	1.60	2.25	15.00	
1932D	10,500,000	.55	.75	1.10	1.60	2.25	14.00	
1933	14,360,000	.40	.65	1.00	1.50	2.10	17.00	
1933D	6,200,000	2.00	2.25	2.50	3.25	4.00	20.00	
1934	219,080,000			.10	.15	.30	.45	2.75
1934D	28,446,000		.15	.25	.35	.55	.90	8.75
1935	245,388,000			.10	.15	.20	.40	1.25
1935D	47,000,000			.10	.15	.25	.45	2.50
1935S	38,702,000			.10	.25	.40	.65	3.65
1936..(5,569)	309,637,569				.10	.15	.30	1.00 $70.00
1936D	40,620,000			.10	.20	.30	.45	2.00
1936S	29,130,000			.10	.25	.40	.55	2.50
1937..(9,320)	309,179,320				.10	.15	.30	.85 27.50
1937D	50,430,000			.10	.15	.25	.35	1.50
1937S	34,500,000			.10	.20	.30	.40	1.60
1938.(14,734)	156,696,734			.10	.15	.20	.30	1.50 16.00
1938D	20,010,000		.15	.20	.30	.45	.65	2.50
1938S	15,180,000		.30	.40	.60	.70	.95	3.00
1939.(13,520)	316,479,520				.10	.15	.25	.80 13.00
1939D	15,160,000		.35	.45	.60	.70	1.10	4.00
1939S	52,070,000		.10	.15	.20	.30	.45	1.35
1940.(15,872)	586,825,872					.10	.20	.70 12.00
1940D	81,390,000				.10	.15	.25	1.00
1940S	112,940,000				.10	.15	.25	.75
1941.(21,100)	887,039,100					.10	.20	.65 10.50
1941D	128,700,000					.10	.25	1.25
1941S	92,360,000				.10	.15	.30	1.25
1942.(32,600)	657,828,600					.10	.20	.40 10.00
1942D	206,698,000					.10	.20	.45
1942S	85,590,000	.10	.15	.25	.30	.45	3.50	

WARTIME STEEL CENTS 1943

Owing to a shortage of copper during the critical war year 1943 the Treasury Department resorted to the use of zinc coated steel for our cents. No bronze cents were officially issued in 1943. A few specimens struck on bronze planchets by error are known to exist. Through a similar error, a few of the 1944 cents were struck on steel planchets.

1943	684,628,670	.15	.25	.30	.55
1943D	217,660,000	.15	.25	.30	.75
1943S	191,550,000	.30	.45	.55	1.30

"SHELL CASE" COPPER 1944-1945

Shell cases were salvaged for coinage in 1944. Although the color is a little different, the coin has proved satisfactory in every respect.

1944	1,435,400,000	.10	.20	.35

SMALL CENTS

	Quan. Minted	V.F.	E.F.	Unc.	Proof
1944D	430,578,000	$ .10	$ .20	$ .35	
1944S	282,760,000	.10	.20	.40	
1945	1,040,515,000	.10	.15	.30	
1945D	226,268,000	.10	.20	.45	
1945S	181,770,000	.10	.20	.45	

BRONZE PREWAR COMPOSITION RESUMED

	Quan. Minted	V.F.	E.F.	Unc.	Proof
1946	991,655,000	.10	.15	.30	
1946D	315,690,000	.10	.20	.40	
1946S	198,100,000	.10	.20	.45	
1947	190,555,000	.10	.20	.55	
1947D	194,750,000	.10	.20	.40	
1947S	99,000,000	.15	.25	.70	
1948	317,570,000	.10	.20	.40	
1948D	172,637,500	.10	.20	.40	
1948S	81,735,000	.15	.30	1.00	
1949	217,775,000	.10	.20	.55	
1949D	153,132,500	.10	.20	.55	
1949S	64,290,000	.20	.30	1.50	
1950 (51,386)	272,686,386	.10	.20	.40	$21.00
1950D	334,950,000	.10	.20	.30	
1950S	118,505,000	.10	.25	.75	
1951 (57,500)	284,633,500	.10	.15	.60	9.50
1951D	625,355,000	.10	.15	.30	
1951S	136,010,000	.20	.30	.90	
1952 (81,980)	186,856,980	....	.15	.60	7.00
1952D	746,130,000	....	.15	.25	
1952S	137,800,004	....	.20	.60	
1953 (128,800)	256,883,800	....	.10	.30	5.75
1953D	700,515,000	....	.10	.25	
1953S	181,835,000	....	.15	.50	
1954 (233,300)	71,873,350	.25	.35	.70	5.00
1954D	251,552,500	....	.15	.25	
1954S	96,190,000	....	.20	.45	

	Quan. Minted	V.F.	E.F.	Unc.	Proof
1955 (378,200)	330,958,200	....	.10	.25	3.75
1955 Double die obv.		175.00	225.00	400.00	
1955D	563,257,500	....		.25	
1955S	44,610,000	.40	.60	.75	
1956 (669,384)	421,414,384	....		.20	2.25
1956D	1,098,201,100	....		.10	
1957 (1,247,952)	283,787,952	....		.20	2.00

SMALL CENTS

	Quan. Minted		Unc.	Proof
1957D	1,051,342,000		$ .10	
1958	(875,652) 253,400,652		.20	$2.35
1958D	800,953,300		.10	

LINCOLN TYPE, MEMORIAL REVERSE 1959 TO DATE

Frank Gasparro designed the Lincoln Memorial reverse which was introduced in 1959 on the 150th anniversary of Lincoln's birth.

		Unc.	Proof
1959	(1,149,291) 610,864,291	.10	1.85
1959D	1,279,760,000	.10	

Small Date   Large Date

			Unc.	Proof
1960 Large date	} (1,691,602) 588,096,602		.10	2.15
1960 Sm. date			4.50	20.00
1960D Large date	} 1,580,884,000		.10	
1960D Small date			.30	
1961	(3,028,244) 756,373,244		.10	1.10
1961D	1,753,266,700		.10	

Composition Changed to 95% Copper, 5% Zinc

	Unc.	Proof		Unc.	Proof
1962 (3,218,019)			1968......1,707,880,970	$.05	
......609,263,019	$.10	$1.10	1968D.....2,886,269,600	.05	
1962D.....1,793,148,400	.10		1968S (3,041,509)		
1963 (3,075,645)			261,311,510	.10	$ .75
......757,185,645	.10	1.10	1969......1,136,910,000	.05	
1963D.....1,774,020,400	.10		1969D.....4,002,832,200	.05	
1964 (3,950,762)			1969S (2,934,631)		
......2,652,525,762	.05	1.25	547,309,631	.10	.75
1964D.....3,799,071,500	.05		1970..................	.05	
1965......1,497,224,900	.05		1970D.................	.05	
1966......2,188,147,783	.05		1970S.................	.10	.75
1967......3,048,667,100	.05				

TWO-CENT PIECES
Issued 1864-1873

The Act of April 22, 1864, which changed the weight and composition of the cent, included a provision for the bronze two-cent piece. The weight was specified as 96 grains, the alloy being the same as for the cent.

The two-cent piece is one of the short-lived issues of United States coinage. The motto "In God We Trust" appeared for the first time. Its presence on the new coin was due largely to the increased religious sentiment during the Civil War crisis.

There are two varieties for the first year of issue, 1864: the small motto and

[88]

TWO-CENT PIECES

the large motto. The differences are explained in the illustrations below. The small motto variety of 1864 is scarce.

| 1864 Small Motto | 1864 Large Motto |

Details explain the differences in these two well-known varieties. On the obverse the D in God is narrow on the large motto. The stem to the leaf shows plainly on the small motto variety. There is no stem on the large motto coin.

The first T in TRUST touches ribbon crease at left on the small motto variety; there is a $\frac{1}{32}''$ gap on the large motto variety.

It will be noted that the shield device is very similar to the nickel five-cent piece introduced in 1866.

Select uncirculated and proof coins command higher prices.

GOOD—At least IN GOD visible.
VERY GOOD—WE weakly visible.
FINE—Complete motto visible. WE weak.
EXTRA FINE—WE is bold.

	Quan. Minted	Good	V.G.	Fine	E.F.	Unc.	Proof
1864 Sm. motto. }	19,847,500	$36.00	$45.00	$62.50	$100.00	$275.00	
1864 Lg. motto . }		2.25	3.00	4.50	10.50	27.50	$200.00
1865	13,640,000	2.35	3.25	4.75	11.00	27.50	130.00
1866	3,177,000	2.50	4.00	6.00	12.50	35.00	115.00
1867	2,938,750	2.50	4.00	6.00	12.50	35.00	115.00
1868	2,803,750	2.50	4.00	6.00	12.50	35.00	120.00
1869	1,546,500	3.00	4.50	8.00	15.00	37.50	130.00
1870	861,250	4.75	6.50	10.00	18.00	47.50	142.50
1871	721,250	5.75	8.00	12.50	25.00	62.50	150.00
1872	65,000	35.00	45.00	57.50	75.00	132.50	250.00
1873 Closed 3. Proofs only (600)							625.00
1873 Open 3. Restrike (Est. 500)							700.00

(See illustration on page 83.)

THREE-CENT PIECES (NICKEL)
Issued 1865-1889

This series, which was issued uninterruptedly from 1865 until 1889, offers no type variations. The edge is plain. The composition is 75% copper and 25% nickel. Weight is 30 grains.

GOOD—Date and legends complete though worn. III smooth.
VERY GOOD—III is half worn. Rims complete.
FINE—Hair curls well defined.
EXTRA FINE—Slight, even wear.

THREE-CENT PIECES (NICKEL)

	Quan. Minted	Good	V.G.	Fine	E.F.	Unc.	Proof
1865	11,382,000	$1.75	$2.25	$2.75	$ 5.75	$17.50	$500.00
1866	4,801,000	2.00	2.25	3.00	6.00	17.50	150.00
1867	3,915,000	2.00	2.25	3.00	6.00	17.50	70.00
1868	3,252,000	2.00	2.25	3.00	6.00	17.50	75.00
1869	1,604,000	2.25	3.00	4.00	7.50	20.00	75.00
1870	1,335,000	2.50	3.25	4.25	7.50	21.00	75.00
1871	604,000	3.00	4.50	6.00	10.00	27.50	75.00
1872	862,000	2.75	4.00	5.75	8.75	25.00	75.00
1873 All kinds	1,173,000						
1873 Closed 3 (1,100)		2.75	3.50	5.25	9.50	25.00	52.50
1873 Open 3		2.25	3.00	4.00	7.00	22.50	
1874	790,000	3.00	4.50	6.00	12.50	30.00	75.00
1875	228,000	5.50	7.50	11.00	18.00	42.50	77.50
1876	162,000	5.50	7.25	10.50	17.00	42.50	75.00
1877 (Proofs Only)							650.00
1878 (2,350)	2,350						195.00
1879 (3,200)	41,200	6.50	8.50	11.00	14.50	37.50	60.00
1880 (3,955)	24,955	6.50	8.50	11.00	14.50	37.50	60.00
1881 (3,575)	1,080,575	2.50	3.25	4.25	7.50	20.00	50.00
1882 (3,100)	25,300	6.75	8.75	11.50	15.00	37.50	50.00
1883 (6,609)	10,609	6.75	8.75	11.50	15.00	37.50	52.00
1884 (3,942)	5,642	8.50	11.00	13.50	18.50	47.50	60.00
1885 (3,790)	4,790	8.50	11.00	13.50	18.50	47.50	65.00
1886 (4,290)	4,290						75.00
1887 7 over 6							215.00
1887 All K(2,960)	7,961	16.50	22.50	30.00	37.50	100.00	150.00
1888 (4,582)	41,083	7.50	9.50	12.00	16.00	35.00	57.50
1889 (3,436)	21,561	7.50	9.50	12.00	16.00	35.00	57.50

NICKEL FIVE-CENT PIECES
SHIELD TYPE 1866-1883

The shield type nickel was made possible by the act of May 16, 1866. Its weight was set at 77-16/100 grains with the same composition as the nickel three-cent piece which was authorized in 1865. In 1866 the coin was designed with rays between the stars on the reverse. Some of the pieces minted in 1867 have the same details, but later the rays were eliminated creating two varieties for that year. There was no further change in the type until it was replaced by the Liberty head device in 1883.

Proofs only were struck in 1877 and 1878.

GOOD—All letters in motto readable.

VERY GOOD—Motto stands out clearly. Rims worn slightly but even. Part of shield lines visible.

FINE—Half of each olive leaf is smooth.

EXTRA FINE—Leaf tips show slight wear. Cross over shield slightly worn.

Rays Between Stars 1866-1867

1866	14,742,500	6.00	8.50	15.00	37.50	120.00	1200.00
1867 Rays. Both varieties	30,909,500	7.50	12.00	20.00	55.00	160.00	3500.00

NICKEL FIVE-CENT PIECES

Without Rays 1867-1883

	Quan. Minted	Good	V.G.	Fine	E.F.	Unc.	Proof
1867 No rays..............		$ 2.50	$ 3.25	$ 4.75	$11.00	$ 32.00	$ 75.00
1868...........28,817,000		2.50	3.25	4.75	11.00	32.00	75.00
1869...........16,395,000		3.00	4.00	6.00	15.00	37.50	80.00
1870............4,806,000		4.00	6.00	8.00	17.50	40.00	80.00
1871..............561,000		32.50	40.00	50.00	90.00	200.00	300.00
1872............6,036,000		4.00	6.00	8.00	17.50	40.00	77.50
1873 All kinds....4,550,000							
1873 Closed 3 (1,100)......		4.25	6.25	8.50	19.00	42.50	67.50
1873 Open 3..............		4.25	6.25	8.50	19.00	42.50	
1874............3,538,000		6.25	8.75	11.50	20.00	45.00	90.00
1875............2,097,000		12.00	16.00	22.00	45.00	100.00	152.50
1876............2,530,000		7.50	9.00	12.00	22.50	45.00	70.00
1877 Est. Issued							
.....(500)	500						900.00
1878.....(2,350)	2,350						260.00
1879.....(3,200)	29,100	14.00	17.50	23.00	37.00	64.00	90.00
1880.....(3,955)	19,955	18.00	21.00	25.00	40.00	75.00	90.00
1881.....(3,575)	72,375	13.00	15.00	20.00	35.00	60.00	90.00
1882.....(3,100) 11,476,600		2.25	3.00	4.50	10.00	30.00	70.00
1883 .....(5,419)		3.00	4.00	5.00	11.00	32.50	65.00
1883 3 over 2... } 1,456,919			24.00	35.00	75.00	160.00	

1883
3 over 2

LIBERTY HEAD TYPE 1883-1913

In 1883 the type was changed to the familiar "Liberty head." This type first appeared without the word CENTS on the coin, merely a large letter "V." These "centless" coins were goldplated and passed for five dollars. Later in that year the word CENTS was added.

It has been reported that five 1913 Liberty head nickels were originally owned by Col. Green (the deceased son of the famous Hetty Green). These have since been dispersed and are now held in the collections of several individuals. These were not a regular issue and never placed in circulation.

GOOD—No details in head. LIBERTY obliterated.
VERY GOOD—At least 3 letters in LIBERTY readable.
FINE—All letters in LIBERTY show.
EXTRA FINE—LIBERTY sharp. Corn grains at bottom of wreath show, on reverse.

NICKEL FIVE-CENT PIECES

Without CENTS 1883

	Quan. Minted	Good	V.G.	Fine	E.F.	Unc.	Proof
1883 Without CENTS							
.....(5,219)	5,479,519	$1.10	$1.50	$2.25	$4.25	$10.50	$46.00

With CENTS 1883-1913

		Good	V.G.	Fine	E.F.	Unc.	Proof
1883 With CENTS							
.....(6,783)	16,032,983	4.50	6.00	8.50	15.00	40.00	65.00
1884.....(3,942)	11,273,942	4.50	6.25	10.00	17.50	42.50	62.50
1885.....(3,790)	1,476,490	55.00	70.00	95.00	150.00	275.00	350.00
1886.....(4,290)	3,330,290	27.50	37.50	50.00	77.50	130.00	175.00
1887.....(2,960)	15,263,652	2.75	3.75	6.00	12.00	35.00	55.00
1888.....(4,582)	10,720,483	4.50	7.25	11.00	20.00	35.00	60.00
1889.....(3,336)	15,881,361	2.75	3.75	5.50	11.00	35.00	55.00
1890.....(2,740)	16,259,272	3.75	4.75	7.00	15.00	35.00	55.00
1891.....(2,350)	16,834,350	2.75	3.75	6.00	11.00	35.00	55.00
1892.....(2,745)	11,699,642	3.00	4.00	6.25	12.00	35.00	57.50
1893.....(2,195)	13,370,195	2.50	3.75	5.50	11.00	35.00	57.50
1894.....(2,632)	5,413,132	4.50	6.50	11.00	17.50	50.00	70.00
1895.....(2,062)	9,979,884	1.75	3.00	5.25	10.00	37.50	65.00
1896.....(1,862)	8,842,920	2.25	4.25	8.50	18.50	50.00	120.00
1897.....(1,938)	20,428,735	1.25	2.00	3.50	8.00	30.00	60.00
1898.....(1,795)	12,532,087	1.25	2.00	3.50	8.00	30.00	60.00
1899.....(2,031)	26,029,031	1.00	1.50	2.75	7.25	30.00	55.00
1900.....(2,262)	27,255,995	.60	1.25	2.25	5.75	26.00	55.00
1901.....(1,985)	26,480,213	.50	1.00	2.00	5.00	25.00	55.00
1902.....(2,018)	31,489,579	.50	1.00	2.00	5.00	25.00	55.00
1903.....(1,790)	28,006,725	.50	1.00	2.00	5.00	25.00	55.00
1904.....(1,817)	21,404,984	.50	1.00	2.00	5.00	25.00	55.00
1905.....(2,152)	29,827,276	.50	1.00	2.00	5.00	25.00	55.00
1906.....(1,725)	38,613,725	.50	1.00	2.00	5.00	25.00	55.00
1907.....(1,475)	39,214,800	.50	1.00	2.00	5.00	25.00	80.00
1908.....(1,620)	22,686,177	.50	1.00	2.00	5.00	25.00	55.00
1909.....(4,763)	11,590,526	.75	1.25	2.50	6.00	27.50	52.50
1910.....(2,405)	30,169,353	.50	1.00	2.00	5.00	25.00	55.00
1911.....(1,733)	39,559,372	.50	1.00	2.00	5.00	25.00	55.00
1912.....(2,145)	26,236,714	.50	1.00	2.00	5.00	25.00	60.00
1912D............8,474,000		1.50	2.50	6.25	45.00	220.00	
1912S.............238,000		27.50	35.00	47.50	110.00	385.00	
1913 Liberty Hd. (5 Known)				A.N.A. Sale 1967	46,000		

NICKEL FIVE-CENT PIECES

INDIAN HEAD or BUFFALO TYPE 1913-1938

These pieces are known as Buffalo, Bison or Indian Head nickels. In the first year of issue, 1913, there were two distinct varieties, the first showing the bison on a mound, and the second with the base redesigned to a thinner straight line.

James E. Fraser designed this nickel employing three different Indians as models. His initial F is beneath the date. The bison was modeled after "Black Diamond" in the New York Zoological Gardens.

Variety 1
FIVE CENTS
on raised
ground

GOOD—*Legends and date readable. Horn worn off.*

VERY GOOD—*Half horn shows.*

FINE—*Two-thirds horn shows. Obv. rim intact.*

VERY FINE—*Full horn shows. Indian's cheekbone worn.*

EXTRA FINE—*Full horn. Slight wear on Indian's hair ribbon.*

	Quan. Minted	Good	V.G.	Fine	V.F.	E.F.	Unc.	Matte Proof
1913 Var. 1								
(*3,034)	30,993,520	$1.15	$1.50	$2.00	$3.00	$ 4.50	$11.00	$215.00
1913D Var. 1	5,337,000	3.25	4.50	6.00	8.00	10.00	24.00	
1913S Var. 1	2,105,000	4.75	6.75	8.50	11.00	15.00	37.50	

*Both Varieties.

Variety 2
FIVE CENTS
recessed

1918D
8 Over 7 Variety

		Good	V.G.	Fine	V.F.	E.F.	Unc.	Matte Proof
1913 Var. 2	29,858,700	1.50	2.25	3.25	4.00	5.25	12.50	265.00
1913D Var. 2	4,156,000	17.50	21.00	27.50	32.50	42.00	76.50	
1913S Var. 2	1,209,000	29.00	36.00	46.00	55.00	70.00	120.00	
1914 (1,275)	20,665,738	1.50	2.25	3.25	5.00	8.75	23.00	240.00
1914D	3,912,000	16.00	21.00	27.50	35.00	50.00	115.00	
1914S	3,470,000	3.50	5.25	9.00	13.50	22.50	67.50	
1915 (1,050)	20,987,270	1.10	1.75	3.00	5.50	10.00	22.50	265.00
1915D	7,569,500	4.25	6.25	10.50	15.00	24.00	65.00	
1915S	1,505,000	7.25	10.25	16.00	25.00	44.00	130.00	
1916 (600)	63,498,066	.50	.75	1.50	2.50	4.50	16.50	395.00
1916D	13,333,000	2.85	4.25	6.50	11.00	18.50	60.00	
1916S	11,860,000	2.25	3.00	6.00	11.00	20.00	65.00	
1917	51,424,029	.45	.70	1.30	2.25	5.00	18.00	
1917D	9,910,800	2.80	5.00	9.50	20.00	40.00	80.00	
1917S	4,193,000	3.25	5.50	10.50	22.50	42.50	120.00	
1918	32,086,314	.50	.75	1.85	5.00	10.75	47.50	
1918D, 8 over 7	8,362,000	150.00	235.00	400.00	675.00	1,175	5,300	
1918D		3.00	5.00	9.00	21.00	47.50	165.00	
1918S	4,882,000	2.75	5.00	9.00	21.00	47.50	175.00	
1919	60,868,000	.40	.65	1.25	2.75	5.50	24.00	
1919D	8,006,000	3.00	5.25	11.50	22.50	70.00	205.00	
1919S	7,521,000	2.75	5.25	11.50	22.50	67.50	200.00	

NICKEL FIVE-CENT PIECES

	Quan. Minted	Good	V.G.	Fine	V.F.	E.F.	Unc.
1920	63,093,000	$ .40	$ .55	$1.15	$2.75	$5.75	$22.50
1920D	9,418,000	2.50	4.25	9.00	25.00	55.00	195.00
1920S	9,689,000	2.00	3.50	8.00	22.50	48.50	195.00
1921	10,663,000	.75	1.15	2.60	5.75	11.50	59.00
1921S	1,557,000	9.00	15.00	25.00	60.00	95.00	335.00
1923	35,715,000	.40	.55	1.10	2.50	4.85	21.00
1923S	6,142,000	1.50	2.50	6.00	18.00	42.50	165.00
1924	21,620,000	.40	.60	1.20	2.50	4.80	22.50
1924D	5,258,000	2.00	3.00	8.00	22.00	48.00	175.00
1924S	1,437,000	5.25	8.50	16.50	50.00	115.00	675.00
1925	35,565,100	.40	.60	1.15	2.35	4.75	22.50
1925D	4,450,000	4.00	7.00	12.00	25.00	50.00	210.00
1925S	6,256,000	2.50	5.25	8.50	22.50	48.00	230.00
1926	44,693,000	.35	.45	.95	2.25	4.75	18.00
1926D	5,638,000	2.40	4.35	10.00	22.50	50.00	315.00
1926S	970,000	4.75	8.25	16.50	50.00	115.00	440.00
1927	37,981,000	.35	.50	.85	2.00	4.00	15.50
1927D	5,730,000	1.00	1.75	3.75	7.50	15.00	45.00
1927S	3,430,000	1.30	2.80	6.50	15.00	45.00	250.00
1928	23,411,000	.35	.50	.80	1.75	3.75	16.00
1928D	6,436,000	.40	.60	1.40	2.50	4.75	17.50
1928S	6,936,000	.60	1.00	2.00	4.25	8.75	52.50
1929	36,446,000	.35	.45	.75	1.40	2.50	11.75
1929D	8,370,000	.35	.60	.90	1.75	3.50	16.50
1929S	7,754,000	.35	.60	.90	1.75	3.50	16.50
1930	22,849,000	.35	.50	.65	1.10	2.00	14.00
1930S	5,435,000	.60	.85	1.60	3.00	5.50	40.00
1931S	1,200,000	4.25	5.00	6.00	9.00	15.00	60.00
1934	20,213,003	.25	.40	.65	1.10	2.00	11.00
1934D	7,480,000	.30	.45	.70	1.25	2.50	13.50
1935	58,264,000	......	.20	.35	.60	1.10	5.50
1935D	12,092,000	......	.25	.50	1.00	2.00	10.50
1935S	10,300,000	......	.25	.50	1.00	1.90	9.75
1936	119,001,420	......	.15	.30	.45	.65	4.50
1936 Proof	(4,420)	......	......	......	......	......	165.00
1936D	24,814,000	......	.25	.40	.65	1.15	4.75
1936S	14,930,000	......	.25	.40	.65	1.20	5.50
1937	79,485,769	......	.20	.30	.45	.70	4.25
1937 Proof	(5,769)	......	......	......	......	......	140.00
1937D All Kds	17,826,000	......	.25	.40	.60	1.00	5.00
1937D 3-Legged Var.*		35.00	40.00	48.00	60.00	80.00	220.00
1937S	5,635,000	......	.25	.50	.75	1.30	6.25
1938D	⎰7,020,000	......	.20	.45	.70	1.25	4.75
1938D over S	⎱7,020,000	......	......	5.50	8.00	12.75	33.50

*Beware of removed leg.

1937D "3-Legged" Variety

1938D over S Variety

NICKEL FIVE-CENT PIECES

JEFFERSON TYPE 1938 to Date

This nickel was designed by Felix Schlag. He won an award of $1000 in a competition with some 390 artists. It established the definite public approval of portrait and pictorial rather than symbolic devices on our coinage. The designer's initials FS were added below the bust starting in 1966.

VERY GOOD—*Second porch pillar from right nearly gone, other three still visible but weak.*

FINE—*Cheekbone worn flat. Hairlines and eyebrow faint. Second pillar weak, especially at bottom.*

VERY FINE—*Second pillar plain and complete on both sides.*

EXTRA FINE—*Cheekbone, hairlines, eyebrow slightly worn but well defined. Base of triangle above pillars visible but weak.*

	Quan. Minted	V.G.	Fine	V.F.	E.F.	Unc.	Proof
1938 . . . . (19,365)	19,515,365	$ .15	$ .25	$ .40	$ .55	$2.00	$17.00
1938D	5,376,000	1.25	1.75	2.25	2.80	6.00	
1938S	4,105,000	2.15	2.75	3.25	4.10	6.50	
1939 . . . . (12,535)	120,627,535	.15	.25	.35	.50	1.35	15.00
1939D	3,514,000	4.25	5.00	7.50	10.50	38.00	
1939S	6,630,000	1.10	1.50	2.25	3.25	11.50	
1940 . . . . (14,158)	176,499,158					.35	.90	15.00
1940D	43,540,000					.40	1.25	
1940S	39,690,000			.30		.60	1.60	
1941 . . . . (18,720)	203,283,720					.30	.75	13.50
1941D	53,432,000					.35	1.10	
1941S	43,445,000					.45	1.35	
1942 . . . . (29,600)	49,818,600					.40	1.60	13.50
1942D	13,938,000	.40	.85	1.25	2.00	10.50	

Wartime Alloy Variety 1942-1945

On October 8, 1942, the wartime five-cent piece composed of copper (56%), silver (35%) and manganese (9%) made its first appearance. The mint mark was made larger and placed above the dome of Monticello. The letter P for the Philadelphia Mint was used for the first time on this piece to indicate the change of alloy. Nickel, a critical war material, was entirely eliminated.

1942P . . . . . . (27,600)	57,900,600	.25	.40	.80	1.65	7.50	22.50
1942S	32,900,000	.25	.35	.65	1.00	4.25	
1943P	271,165,000	.25	.35	.50	.65	2.00	
1943D	15,294,000	.75	1.15	1.75	2.30	4.50	
1943S	104,060,000	.30	.40	.50	.65	1.75	
1944P*	119,150,000	.25	.35	.45	.70	2.50	
1944D	32,309,000	.25	.40	.60	.90	3.25	
1944S	21,640,000	.35	.50	.80	1.10	3.25	
1945P	119,408,100	.25	.45	.65	.90	2.75	
1945D	37,158,000	.35	.50	.70	.90	2.00	
1945S	58,939,000	.30	.50	.70	.90	1.65	

*1944 nickels without mint marks are counterfeits.

NICKEL FIVE-CENT PIECES

Prewar Composition Resumed
(Small mint mark at right of building 1946-1964)

	Quan. Minted	V.F.	E.F.	Unc.	Proof
1946	161,116,000		$ .25	$ .40	
1946D	45,292,200		.30	.80	
1946S	13,560,000		.65	1.20	
1947	95,000,000		.25	.50	
1947D	37,822,000		.25	1.00	
1947S	24,720,000		.55	1.20	
1948	89,348,000		.25	.50	
1948D	44,734,000		.50	1.35	
1948S	11,300,000	$ .60	.90	1.70	
1949	60,652,000		.30	.90	
1949D	36,498,000		.45	1.10	
1949S	9,716,000	.85	1.25	2.50	
1950 (51,386)	9,847,386	.75	1.00	2.50	$22.00
1950D	2,630,030	9.50	13.00	13.50	
1951 (57,500)	28,609,500		.30	.90	14.00
1951D	20,460,000		.40	1.30	
1951S	7,776,000	.75	1.50	5.25	
1952 (81,980)	64,069,980		.25	.50	8.50
1952D	30,638,000		.50	2.60	
1952S	20,572,000		.40	.95	
1953 (128,800)	46,772,800		.25	.45	5.50
1953D	59,878,600		.25	.40	
1953S	19,210,900		.50	.85	
1954 (233,300)	47,917,350		.20	.30	4.00
1954D	117,183,060		.20	.30	
1954S	29,384,000		.35	.50	
1955 (378,200)	8,266,200	.90	1.50	2.10	4.75
1955D	74,464,100		.25	.35	
1956 (669,384)	35,885,384		.20	.30	2.00
1956D	67,222,940		.20	.25	
1957 (1,247,952)	39,655,952		.20	.30	1.35
1957D	136,828,900		.15	.25	
1958 (875,652)	17,963,652		.40	.50	2.75
1958D	168,249,120		.15	.25	
1959 (1,149,291)	28,397,291		.20	.40	1.45
1959D	160,738,240			.20	
1960 (1,691,602)	57,107,602			.20	1.25
1960D	192,582,180			.20	
1961 (3,028,144)	76,668,244			.20	.90
1961D	229,342,760			.20	
1962 (3,218,019)	100,602,019			.20	1.10
1962D	280,195,720			.20	
1963 (3,075,645)	178,851,645			.15	.85
1963D	276,829,460			.15	
1964 (3,950,762)	1,028,622,762			.15	.85
1964D	1,787,297,160			.15	
1965	136,131,380			.15	
1966	156,208,283			.15	
1967	107,325,800			.15	

NICKEL FIVE-CENT PIECES

Mint mark position
moved to obverse
starting 1968

	Quan. Minted	Unc.	Proof
1968D..	91,227,880	$ .15	
1968S........................(3,041,509)	103,437,510	.15	$ .70
1969D..	202,807,500	.15	
1969S........................(2,934,631)	123,099,631	.15	.70
1970D..		.15	
1970S..		.15	.70

SILVER THREE-CENT PIECES 1851-1873

This smallest of United States silver coins was authorized by Congress March 3, 1851. The first three-cent silver pieces had no lines bordering the six-pointed star. From 1854 through 1858 there were three lines, while issues of the last fifteen years show only two lines. Issues from 1854 through 1873 have an olive sprig over the III and a bundle of three arrows beneath.

The original weight of this piece was 12⅜ grains, .750 fine, which was changed by the law of March 3, 1853, to 11.52 grains, .900 fine.

 Type 1

mint mark
o

GOOD—*Star worn smooth. Legend and date readable.*

VERY GOOD—*Outline of shield defined. Legend and date clear.*

FINE—*Only star points worn smooth.*

VERY FINE—*Only partial wear on star ridges.*

	Quan. Minted	Good	V.G.	Fine	V.F.	Unc.	Proof
1851 Type 1........	5,447,400	$ 5.00	$ 7.00	$10.00	$16.50	$ 60.00	
1851O..............	720,000	10.00	15.00	25.00	40.00	120.00	
1852..............	18,663,500	3.50	4.50	7.50	12.50	50.00	
1853..............	11,400,000	3.50	4.50	7.50	12.50	50.00	

 Type 2
Three
Outlines
to Star   Type 3
Two
Outlines
to Star

		Good	V.G.	Fine	V.F.	Unc.	Proof
1854 Type 2........	671,000	8.00	10.00	14.00	20.00	65.00	
1855..............	139,000	14.00	20.00	32.50	47.50	165.00	1050.00
1856..............	1,458,000	7.50	9.00	13.50	22.50	85.00	1050.00
1857..............	1,042,000	7.50	9.00	13.50	22.50	85.00	950.00
1858..............	1,604,000	7.50	9.00	13.50	22.50	80.00	535.00
1859 Type 3........	365,000	10.00	12.00	15.00	25.00	55.00	140.00
1860.......(1,000)	287,000	10.00	12.00	15.00	25.00	55.00	140.00
1861.......(1,000)	498,000	8.00	10.00	14.00	20.00	52.50	130.00
1862.........(550)	343,550	9.00	11.00	14.50	21.00	52.50	140.00
1863.........(460)	21,460					185.00	250.00
1864.........(470)	12,470					235.00	275.00

SILVER THREE-CENT PIECES

		Quan. Minted			Proof
1865	(500)	8,500			$265.00
1866	(725)	22,725		....	165.00
1867	(625)	4,625	Circulated coins	....	165.00
1868	(600)	4,100	1863 to 1872 are	....	155.00
1869	(600)	5,100	rarely encountered.	....	150.00
1870	(1,000)	4,000	They were melted	....	145.00
1871	(960)	4,360	or exported.	....	145.00
1872	(950)	1,950		....	150.00
1873	(600)	600 (Closed 3 Only)			255.00

HALF DIMES 1794-1873

The half dime types present the same general characteristics as larger United States silver coins. Authorized by the Act of April 2, 1792, they were not coined until February, 1795, although dated 1794. At first the weight was 20.8 grains, and fineness 892.4. By the Act of January 18, 1837 the weight was slightly reduced to 20⅝ grains and the fineness changed to 900. Finally the weight was reduced to 19.2 grains by the Act of February 21, 1853. Both half dimes and dimes offer many varieties in the early dates. Until 1829 there was no indication of value on the half dimes.

Proofs of some dates prior to 1855 are known to exist and all are rare.

Note: Some early half dimes, while strictly uncirculated, bear file or adjustment marks.

FLOWING HAIR TYPE 1794-1795

FAIR—*Details clear enough to identify.*

GOOD—*Eagle, wreath, bust outlined but lack details.*

VERY GOOD—*Some details remain on face. All lettering readable.*

FINE—*Hair ends show. Hair at top smooth.*

VERY FINE—*Hairlines at top show. Hair about ear defined.*

	Quan. Minted	Fair	Good	V.G.	Fine	V.F.	Unc.
1794	}86,416	$110.00	$200.00	$290.00	$450.00	$675.00	$1675.00
1795		82.50	155.00	220.00	325.00	525.00	950.00

DRAPED BUST TYPE, SMALL EAGLE REVERSE 1796-1797

1796

1796-1805

FAIR—*Details clear enough to identify.*

GOOD—*Date, stars, LIBERTY readable. Bust outlined but no details.*

VERY GOOD—*Some details show.*

FINE—*Hair and drapery lines worn, but visible.*

VERY FINE—*Only left of drapery indistinct.*

1796 over 5						
All kinds....10,230	180.00	325.00	500.00	600.00	875.00	1750.00
1796 Normal date....	95.00	175.00	285.00	375.00	525.00	1400.00
1796 LIKERTY.....		225.00	325.00	465.00	750.00	
1797 15 stars.	87.50	160.00	225.00	325.00	485.00	1325.00
1797 16 stars. }44,527	87.50	160.00	225.00	325.00	485.00	1325.00
1797 13 stars.	90.00	170.00	250.00	375.00	525.00	1325.00

HALF DIMES

DRAPED BUST TYPE, HERALDIC EAGLE REVERSE 1800-1805

1800

1800 LIBEKTY

	Quan. Minted	Fair	Good	V.G.	Fine	V.F.	Unc.
1800 All kinds..	24,000	$ 80.00	$130.00	$200.00	$300.00	$415.00	$1150.00
1800 LIBEKTY	....	80.00	130.00	200.00	300.00	415.00	1200.00
1801	33,910	85.00	135.00	210.00	325.00	450.00	1250.00
1802 ...(Rare)	13,010	600.00	1200.00	2000.00	3000.00	4500.00	————
1803	37,850	70.00	130.00	180.00	250.00	400.00	1025.00
1805	15,600	110.00	200.00	300.00	450.00	750.00	————

CAPPED BUST TYPE 1829-1837

GOOD—*Bust outlined, no detail. Date and legend readable.*
VERY GOOD—*Complete legend and date plain. At least 3 letters of LIBERTY show clearly.*
FINE—*All letters in LIBERTY show.*
VERY FINE—*Full rim, both sides. Clasp on shoulder and ear well defined.*

1829..............1,230,000	7.50	10.00	13.00	22.50	92.50
1830..............1,240,000	6.00	7.50	12.00	20.00	82.50
1831..............1,242,700	6.00	7.50	12.00	20.00	82.50
1832................965,000	6.00	7.50	12.00	20.00	82.50
1833..............1,370,000	6.00	7.50	12.00	20.00	82.50
1834..............1,480,000	6.00	7.50	12.00	20.00	82.50
1835 Lg. date & 5c..	6.00	7.50	12.00	20.00	82.50
1835 Lg. dt., sm. 5c.	6.00	7.50	12.00	20.00	82.50
1835 Sm. dt., lg. 5c.. ⎱2,760,000	6.00	7.50	12.00	20.00	82.50
1835 Sm. dt. and 5c.	6.00	7.50	12.00	20.00	82.50
1836 Small 5c.......	6.00	7.50	12.00	20.00	82.50
1836 Large 5c..... ⎱1,900,000	6.00	7.50	12.00	20.00	82.50
1837 Small 5c.......	11.00	17.50	27.50	60.00	200.00
1837 Large 5c.... ⎱2,276,000	6.00	7.50	12.00	20.00	82.50

LIBERTY SEATED TYPE
No Stars On Obverse 1837-1838

GOOD—*LIBERTY on shield smooth. Date and letters readable.*
VERY GOOD—*At least 3 letters in LIBERTY are visible.*
FINE—*Entire LIBERTY visible, weak spots.*
VERY FINE—*Entire LIBERTY strong and even.*

1837 Small date.... ⎱inc. above	40.00	55.00	70.00	95.00	275.00
1837 Large date....	40.00	55.00	70.00	95.00	275.00
1838O No stars.........70,000	45.00	60.00	90.00	140.00	485.00

HALF DIMES

No Drapery from Elbow (Enlarged)   Drapery from Elbow (Enlarged)

	Quan. Minted	Good	V.G.	Fine	V.F.	Unc.
1838 No drapery	2,255,000	$3.00	$4.00	$6.00	$12.00	$52.50
1839 No drapery	1,069,150	3.00	4.00	6.00	12.00	52.50
1839O No drapery	1,034,039	5.00	6.00	10.00	17.50	57.50
1840 No drpy. All K.	1,344,085	2.75	4.00	5.50	10.00	45.00
1840O No drpy. All K.	935,000	5.00	7.50	12.50	25.00	115.00
1840 drapery		2.50	4.00	6.00	12.00	55.00
1840O drapery		6.00	9.00	14.00	27.50	115.00
1841	1,150,000	2.50	3.50	5.50	10.00	40.00
1841O	815,000	3.50	5.50	9.00	16.00	105.00
1842	815,000	3.25	4.00	5.00	9.00	40.00
1842O	350,000	5.50	10.00	17.00	30.00	150.00
1843	1,165,000	2.50	3.50	5.50	9.00	40.00
1844	430,000	3.50	5.50	8.50	12.00	42.50
1844O	220,000	6.50	11.00	19.00	35.00	125.00
1845	1,564,000	2.50	3.50	5.50	9.00	40.00
1846	27,000	50.00	70.00	92.50	125.00	300.00
1847	1,274,000	2.50	3.50	5.50	9.00	40.00
1848 Medium date	} 668,000	2.50	3.50	5.50	9.00	40.00
1848 Large date		2.50	4.00	6.00	10.00	42.00
1848O	600,000	5.00	7.50	12.50	25.00	100.00
1849 9 over 6	} 1,309,000	3.50	5.75	8.00	14.00	52.50
1849 9 over 8		3.50	5.75	8.00	14.00	52.50
1849 Normal date		2.50	3.50	5.50	9.00	40.00
1849O	140,000	25.00	40.00	60.00	90.00	250.00
1850	955,000	2.50	3.50	5.50	9.00	40.00
1850O	690,000	3.50	5.50	8.50	20.00	90.00
1851	781,000	2.50	3.50	5.50	9.00	40.00
1851O	860,000	3.00	5.00	8.00	18.50	95.00
1852	1,000,500	2.50	3.50	5.50	9.00	40.00
1852O	260,000	5.00	8.50	15.00	30.00	130.00
1853 No arrows	135,000	8.50	12.50	20.00	30.00	100.00
1853O No arrows	160,000	60.00	80.00	120.00	170.00	600.00

As on the dimes, quarters and halves, arrows were placed at the sides of the date for a short period starting in 1853. They were placed there to denote the reduction of weight under the terms of the Act of February 21, 1853.

1853 With arrows	13,210,020	3.50	4.50	6.00	11.00	60.00

HALF DIMES

	Quan. Minted	Good	V.G.	Fine	V.F.	Unc.	Proof
1853O	2,200,000	$3.50	$4.50	$6.50	$13.00	$65.00	
1854	5,740,000	2.50	3.25	4.00	7.00	50.00	
1854O	1,560,000	2.75	3.75	5.75	9.50	55.00	
1855	1,750,000	2.50	3.25	4.00	7.00	50.00	$475.00
1855O	600,000	4.00	6.00	9.00	19.00	100.00	

Arrows At Date Removed

	Quan. Minted	Good	V.G.	Fine	V.F.	Unc.	Proof
1856	4,880,000	2.25	2.50	2.75	5.25	40.00	425.00
1856O	1,100,000	2.50	3.25	4.75	9.00	42.50	
1857	7,280,000	2.25	2.50	2.75	5.25	40.00	400.00
1857O	1,380,000	2.50	3.25	4.75	9.00	42.50	
1858	} 3,500,000	2.25	2.50	2.75	5.25	40.00	325.00
1858 over inverted date				30.00	50.00	200.00	
1858O	1,660,000	2.50	3.25	4.75	9.00	42.50	

New die 1859 Philadelphia Mint. Stars hollow in center. Arms slimmer.

	Quan. Minted	Good	V.G.	Fine	V.F.	Unc.	Proof
1859	340,000	3.75	5.25	8.00	12.75	45.00	150.00
1859O	560,000	3.50	4.75	7.00	11.00	52.50	

In the years 1859 and 1860 a half dime type was struck which does not bear our nation's identity. These coins are known as transitional patterns, and were struck at the time the inscription UNITED STATES OF AMERICA was being transferred from the reverse to the obverse side of the coin.

1858 over inverted date

1859 Obv. of 59, rev. of 60............................ 2000.00
1860 Obv. of 59, rev. of 60
    (With stars)100................................ 900.00

Legend on Obverse

	Quan. Minted	Good	V.G.	Fine	V.F.	Unc.	Proof
1860 Legend (1,000)	799,000	2.25	2.50	2.75	5.25	40.00	90.00
1860O	1,060,000	3.00	4.50	6.00	9.50	42.50	
1861.(1,000)	3,361,000	2.25	2.50	2.75	5.25	40.00	90.00
1862.(550)	1,492,550	2.25	2.50	2.75	5.25	40.00	90.00
1863.(460)	18,460	10.00	12.50	17.50	27.50	100.00	175.00
1863S	100,000	10.00	12.50	17.50	30.00	85.00	
1864.(470)	48,470						325.00
1864S	90,000	10.00	15.00	25.00	40.00	120.00	
1865.(500)	13,500	10.00	15.00	18.50	30.00	100.00	200.00
1865S	120,000	7.00	10.00	15.00	25.00	85.00	
1866.(725)	10,725	7.00	10.00	15.00	25.00	85.00	160.00
1866S	120,000	5.50	8.00	13.00	21.50	85.00	
1867.(625)	8,625	7.50	10.00	15.00	25.00	90.00	160.00

HALF DIMES

	Quan. Minted	Good	V.G.	Fine	V.F.	Unc.	Proof
1867S	120,000	$5.00	$7.00	$10.00	$22.00	$80.00	
1868	(600)....89,200	3.50	5.00	7.50	12.00	45.00	$100.00
1868S	280,000	3.25	4.50	7.00	12.00	45.00	
1869	(600)...208,600	3.25	4.50	6.00	9.00	40.00	100.00
1869S	230,000	3.25	4.50	7.00	12.00	45.00	
1870	(1,000)...536,600	2.50	3.50	4.50	5.50	40.00	77.50
1871	(960).1,873,960	2.50	3.50	4.50	5.50	40.00	77.50
1871S	161,000	9.50	14.00	20.00	32.50	85.00	
1872	(950).2,947,950	2.50	3.50	4.50	5.50	40.00	80.00

Mint Mark Within Wreath

Mint Mark Below Wreath

		Good	V.G.	Fine	V.F.	Unc.	Proof
1872S Mint mark within wreath							
All kinds	837,000	2.25	3.25	5.00	9.00	50.00	
1872S Mmk. below wreath..		2.50	3.50	5.50	10.00	45.00	
1873 (Closed 3 only)	(600)...712,600	2.25	2.50	2.75	5.25	40.00	135.00
1873S (Closed 3 only) 324,000		2.50	3.50	5.50	10.00	45.00	

BIBLIOGRAPHY

Newlin, H. P., Early Half Dimes. 1883.
Valentine, D. W., U. S. Half Dimes. 1931.
Breen, W., U. S. Half Dimes; A Supplement. 1958.

DIMES — 1796 To Date

The designs of the dimes, first coined in 1796, follow closely those of the half dimes up through the liberty seated type. The dimes in each instance weigh twice as much as the half dimes. *Bibliography,* U. S. Dimes; A. Kosoff, 1945.

Note: File or adjustment marks as on half dimes.

DRAPED BUST TYPE, SMALL EAGLE REVERSE 1796-1797

FAIR—*Details clear enough to identify.*

GOOD—*Date readable. Bust outlined, but no detail.*

VERY GOOD—*All but deepest drapery folds worn smooth. Hairlines nearly gone and curls lack detail.*

FINE—*All drapery lines visible. Hair partly worn.*

VERY FINE—*Only left side of drapery is indistinct.*

1796	1797-16 Stars	1797-13 Stars

	Quan. Minted	Fair	Good	V.G.	Fine	V.F.	Unc.
1796	22,135	$200.00	$300.00	$400.00	$710.00	$1100.00	$2450.00
1797 16 stars	} 25,261	150.00	260.00	385.00	625.00	825.00	1900.00
1797 13 stars		140.00	245.00	360.00	575.00	775.00	1900.00

DIMES
DRAPED BUST TYPE, HERALDIC EAGLE REVERSE 1798-1807

Proofs of some dates prior to 1855
are known to exist, and all are rare.

Quan. Minted	Fair	Good	V.G.	Fine	V.F.	Unc.
1798 over 97, 13 stars on rev.						
All kinds..27,550				$475.00	$1250.00	
1798 over 97,						
16 stars on rev ..	$82.50	$130.00	$190.00	300.00	485.00	$1025.00
1798...............	82.50	130.00	190.00	300.00	485.00	1025.00
1798 Small 8.........	100.00	175.00	275.00	500.00	850.00	
1800.........21,760	72.50	115.00	170.00	235.00	360.00	800.00
1801.........34,640	82.50	130.00	190.00	300.00	500.00	875.00
1802.........10,975	90.00	145.00	225.00	350.00	575.00	1000.00
1803.........33,040	82.50	130.00	190.00	300.00	500.00	875.00
1804 13 stars on rev.						
All kinds...8,265	115.00	175.00	235.00	350.00	585.00	1400.00
1804 14 stars on rev ..	115.00	175.00	235.00	350.00	585.00	1400.00
1805 4 berries }120,780	57.50	110.00	125.00	165.00	285.00	650.00
1805 5 berries	57.50	110.00	125.00	165.00	285.00	650.00
1807.........165,000	52.50	90.00	110.00	135.00	240.00	700.00

CAPPED BUST TYPE 1809-1837

FAIR—Details clear enough to identify.
GOOD—Date, letters and stars discernible. Bust outlined, no details.
VERY GOOD—Legends and date plain. Minimum of 3 letters in LIBERTY.
FINE—Full LIBERTY. Ear and shoulder clasp visible. Part of rim shows both sides.
VERY FINE—LIBERTY distinct. Full rim. Ear and clasp plain and distinct.

1809

1811
Over
9

1809.........44,710	37.50	52.50	80.00	107.50	190.00	465.00
1811 over 9....65,180	25.00	37.50	45.00	67.50	95.00	275.00

1814
Small
Date

1814
Large
Date

1820
Large
0

1814 Sm. date........ }421,500	16.00	21.00	28.00	50.00	170.00
1814 Large date......	16.00	21.00	28.00	50.00	170.00
1820 Large 0......... }942,587	10.00	13.50	19.00	36.00	165.00
1820 Small 0........	10.00	13.50	19.00	36.00	165.00

DIMES

1821 Small Date | 1821 Large Date | 1822

1823 Over 22

Small E's | Large E's

1824 Over 22 | 1828 Small Date | 1828 Large Date

	Quan. Minted	Good	V.G.	Fine	V.F.	Unc.
1821 Small date.....	} 1,186,512	$9.50	$13.00	$19.00	$35.00	$180.00
1821 Large date.....		9.50	13.00	19.00	35.00	180.00
1822................100,000		50.00	65.00	100.00	200.00	650.00
1823 3 over 2, sm. E's.	} 440,000	12.00	16.50	27.50	55.00	180.00
1823 3 over 2, lg. E's..		12.00	16.50	27.50	55.00	180.00
1824 4 over 2........ ———		16.50	22.50	35.00	55.00	250.00
1825................510,000		11.00	14.00	22.50	35.00	180.00
1827................1,215,000		9.50	13.00	19.00	35.00	180.00
1828 Large date......	} 125,000	24.00	37.50	60.00	100.00	245.00
1828 Small date......		16.00	22.50	30.00	57.50	210.00

New mint equipment was used to make the small date 1828 dimes and subsequent issues. Unlike earlier coinage, these have beaded borders and a uniform diameter.

1829 Small 10c | Large 10c

		Good	V.G.	Fine	V.F.	Unc.
1829 Small 10¢.......		6.75	8.50	16.00	30.00	140.00
1829 Medium 10¢.....	} 770,000	6.75	8.50	16.00	30.00	150.00
1829 Large 10¢.......		11.50	16.50	32.00	47.50	165.00
1830 Small 10¢.......	} 510,000	5.75	8.00	10.50	18.50	150.00
1830 Large 10¢.......		5.75	8.00	10.50	18.50	150.00
1831................771,350		5.25	7.50	10.00	18.50	145.00
1832................522,500		5.25	7.50	10.00	18.50	145.00
1833................	} 485,000	5.25	7.50	10.00	18.50	145.00
1833 Last 3 high......		5.25	7.50	10.00	18.50	145.00
1834 Small 4.........	} 635,000	5.25	7.50	10.00	18.50	145.00
1834 Large 4.........		5.25	7.50	10.00	18.50	145.00

DIMES

	Quan. Minted	Good	V.G.	Fine	V.F.	Unc.
1835	1,410,000	$4.75	$7.00	$9.50	$18.50	$140.00
1836	1,190,000	4.75	7.00	9.50	18.50	140.00
1837 All kinds	1,042,000	5.25	7.50	10.00	18.50	150.00

LIBERTY SEATED TYPE

GOOD—LIBERTY on shield smooth. Date and letters readable.
VERY GOOD—At least 3 letters in LIBERTY are visible.
FINE—Entire LIBERTY visible, weak spots.
VERY FINE—Entire LIBERTY strong and even.

No Drapery From Elbow No Stars On Obverse

		Good	V.G.	Fine	V.F.	Unc.
1837 Small date		45.00	60.00	95.00	160.00	350.00
1837 Large date		45.00	60.00	95.00	160.00	350.00
1838O	406,034	55.00	80.00	127.50	240.00	525.00

No Drapery From Elbow With Stars On Obverse

1838 Small Stars   **1838 Large Stars**

		Good	V.G.	Fine	V.F.	Unc.
1838 Small stars		10.00	14.50	22.00	35.00	100.00
1838 Large stars	1,992,500	5.00	6.00	8.00	14.00	80.00
1838 Partial drapery		14.00	20.00	30.00	47.50	120.00
1839	1,053,115	3.50	4.50	7.00	12.50	60.00
1839O	1,323,000	5.00	8.00	12.00	18.50	60.00
1840 All kinds	1,358,580	3.50	5.25	8.50	13.00	55.00
1840O	1,175,000	5.00	8.00	11.00	16.50	55.00
1841 All kinds	1,622,500					

Drapery From Elbow

		Good	V.G.	Fine	V.F.	Unc.
1840		5.50	8.50	12.00	18.00	60.00
1841		2.25	3.25	4.50	9.00	47.50
1841O	2,007,500	2.25	3.50	6.00	12.00	65.00
1842	1,887,500	2.25	3.25	4.50	9.00	45.00
1842O	2,020,000	4.00	6.00	8.50	16.00	60.00
1843	1,370,000	2.25	3.25	4.50	9.00	45.00
1843O	150,000	13.00	18.50	30.00	50.00	220.00
1844	72,500	20.00	32.50	55.00	80.00	275.00
1845	1,755,000	2.25	3.25	4.50	9.00	45.00

DIMES

	Quan. Minted	Good	V.G.	Fine	V.F.	Unc.	Proof
1845O	230,000	$7.00	$10.00	$14.00	$24.00	———	
1846	31,300	13.00	17.50	27.50	42.50	$185.00	
1847	245,000	4.50	6.00	9.00	17.50	55.00	
1848	451,500	3.50	5.00	7.00	12.00	45.00	
1849	839,000	2.25	3.25	4.50	9.00	45.00	
1849O	300,000	6.00	8.50	15.00	27.50	120.00	
1850	1,931,500	2.25	3.25	4.50	9.00	45.00	
1850O	510,000	5.00	8.00	12.00	22.00	65.00	
1851	1,026,500	2.25	3.25	4.50	9.00	45.00	
1851O	400,000	5.00	6.00	8.50	17.00	65.00	
1852	1,535,500	2.25	3.25	4.50	9.00	45.00	
1852O	430,000	5.00	6.50	10.00	20.00	77.50	
1853 No arrows	95,000	17.50	21.00	27.50	42.50	130.00	

Arrows At Date   Small Date Arrows Removed

	Quan. Minted	Good	V.G.	Fine	V.F.	Unc.	Proof
1853 With arrows	12,078,010	2.75	3.75	5.00	10.00	60.00	
1853O	1,100,000	4.00	5.50	7.50	12.00	60.00	
1854	4,470,000	2.50	3.50	4.75	8.50	47.50	
1854O	1,770,000	2.75	3.75	5.00	10.00	50.00	
1855	2,075,000	2.50	3.50	4.75	8.50	47.50	$500.00
1856 Sm. date	5,780,000	2.75	3.75	5.00	10.00	45.00	475.00
1856 Lg. date		2.75	3.75	5.00	10.00	45.00	
1856O	1,180,000	3.00	4.00	6.00	10.00	47.50	
1856S	70,000	25.00	40.00	60.00	100.00	290.00	
1857	5,580,000	2.00	3.00	4.50	7.00	45.00	400.00
1857O	1,540,000	2.50	3.50	5.00	10.00	47.50	
1858	1,540,000	1.50	2.50	4.00	7.00	45.00	350.00
1858O	290,000	4.00	6.00	8.00	15.00	47.50	
1858S	60,000	16.50	25.00	37.50	75.00	240.00	
1859	430,000	2.00	3.25	4.50	7.50	45.00	200.00
1859O	480,000	2.00	3.25	4.50	10.00	50.00	
1859S	60,000	16.50	22.50	32.50	55.00	150.00	
1860S	140,000	8.00	13.00	22.50	40.00	120.00	

TRANSITIONAL PATTERN—Same as Half Dimes 1859, 1860

Obverse of 1859   Reverse of 1860

1859...3,500.00

DIMES

Legend Replaces
Stars on Obverse

	Quan. Minted	Good	V.G.	Fine	V.F.	Unc.	Proof
1860..(1,000)	607,000	$2.00	$3.00	$5.00	$8.00	$ ·40.00	$105.00
1860O	40,000	65.00	100.00	150.00	250.00	1000.00	
1861..(1,000)	1,884,000	1.50	2.25	3.00	6.00	40.00	105.00
1861S	172,500	12.00	18.50	30.00	50.00	135.00	
1862....(550)	847,550	2.50	3.00	5.00	8.00	40.00	105.00
1862S	180,750	8.50	13.50	22.50	45.00	125.00	
1863....(460)	14,460	12.00	17.50	25.00	35.00	90.00	120.00
1863S	157,500	8.50	13.50	22.50	45.00	135.00	
1864....(470)	11,470	12.00	17.50	25.00	35.00	90.00	145.00
1864S	230,000	8.50	12.00	16.00	20.00	60.00	
1865....(500)	10,500	14.00	20.00	27.50	40.00	100.00	130.00
1865S	175,000	8.50	14.00	20.00	35.00	110.00	
1866....(725)	8,725	14.00	20.00	27.50	40.00	95.00	110.00
1866S	135,000	8.50	14.00	20.00	35.00	120.00	
1867....(625)	6,625	15.00	21.00	30.00	45.00	115.00	130.00
1867S	140,000	8.50	14.00	20.00	35.00	95.00	
1868...(600)	464,600	2.00	3.00	4.00	6.50	40.00	110.00
1868S	260,000	6.00	8.50	12.50	20.00	72.50	
1869....(600)	256,600	2.00	3.00	4.00	6.50	40.00	110.00
1869S	450,000	5.50	8.00	12.00	19.00	62.50	
1870..(1,000)	471,500	2.00	3.00	4.00	6.50	40.00	90.00
1870S	50,000	40.00	55.00	80.00	100.00	300.00	
1871....(960)	907,710	2.00	3.00	4.50	7.00	40.00	90.00
1871CC	20,100	125.00	185.00	275.00	475.00	1600.00	
1871S	320,000	8.50	12.00	20.00	35.00	130.00	
1872....(950)	2,396,450	1.75	2.50	4.50	7.00	40.00	90.00
1872CC	24,000	85.00	120.00	175.00	325.00	825.00	
1872S	190,000	10.00	14.00	22.00	35.00	92.50	
1873 All kinds..1,568,600							
1873 Closed 3 (600).....		1.75	2.75	5.00	8.00	40.00	95.00
1873 Open 3.............		4.00	7.00	12.00	16.00	45.00	
1873CC (Unique).12,400							

Arrows
At
Date

In 1873 the dime was increased in weight to 38.58 grains. Arrows at date in 1873 and 1874 indicate this change.

1873....(800)	2,378,500	10.00	14.00	20.00	37.50	175.00	325.00
1873CC	18,791	300.00	425.00	600.00	800.00	1500.00	
1873S	455,000	15.00	20.00	30.00	45.00	165.00	
1874....(700)	2,940,700	9.50	13.50	19.00	37.50	155.00	300.00
1874CC	10,817	85.00	130.00	200.00	400.00	1700.00	
1874S	240,000	16.00	21.00	32.50	55.00	185.00	

DIMES

	Quan. Minted	Good	V.G.	Fine	V.F.	Unc.	Proof
Arrows at Date Removed.							
1875....(700)	10,350,700	$1.25	$2.00	$3.00	$4.50	$35.00	$85.00
1875CC Under wreath							
All kinds..	4,645,000	3.50	5.00	7.50	13.00	50.00	
1875CC In wreath.......		2.00	3.00	4.50	9.00	45.00	
1875S Under wreath							
All kinds..	9,070,000	1.75	2.75	4.00	7.50	35.00	
1875S In wreath........		1.75	2.75	4.00	7.50	35.00	
1876..(1,150)	11,461,150	1.25	2.00	3.00	4.50	35.00	80.00
1876CC.......	8,270,000	2.00	3.00	4.50	9.00	40.00	
1876S........	10,420,000	1.75	2.75	4.00	7.50	35.00	
1877....(510)	7,310,510	1.25	2.00	3.00	5.00	35.00	160.00
1877CC.......	7,700,000	1.75	2.75	4.00	7.50	35.00	
1877S........	2,340,000	1.75	2.75	4.00	7.50	35.00	
1878....(800)	1,678,800	1.75	2.75	4.00	7.50	35.00	85.00
1878CC.......	200,000	12.00	16.00	25.00	35.00	100.00	
1879..(1,100)	15,100	11.00	15.00	22.50	30.00	70.00	92.50
1880..(1,355)	37,355	10.00	14.00	16.00	20.00	70.00	85.00
1881....(975)	24,975	10.00	14.00	16.00	20.00	70.00	85.00
1882..(1,100)	3,911,100	1.25	2.00	3.00	4.50	35.00	75.00
1883..(1,039)	7,675,712	1.25	2.00	3.00	4.50	35.00	75.00
1884....(875)	3,366,380	1.25	2.00	3.00	4.50	35.00	75.00
1884S..........	564,969	7.50	10.00	14.00	27.50	77.50	
1885....(930)	2,533,427	1.25	2.00	3.00	4.50	35.00	75.00
1885S..........	43,690	60.00	80.00	110.00	185.00	500.00	
1886....(886)	6,377,570	1.25	2.00	3.00	4.50	35.00	75.00
1886S..........	206,524	8.00	10.00	15.00	25.00	65.00	
1887....(710)	11,283,939	1.25	2.00	3.00	4.50	35.00	75.00
1887S..........	4,454,450	2.00	3.00	4.50	8.00	35.00	
1888....(832)	5,496,487	1.25	2.00	3.00	4.50	35.00	75.00
1888S........	1,720,000	3.00	4.00	6.00	9.00	40.00	
1889....(711)	7,380,711	1.25	2.00	3.00	4.50	35.00	75.00
1889S..........	972,678	8.00	12.00	16.00	45.00	135.00	
1890....(590)	9,911,541	1.25	2.00	3.00	4.50	35.00	80.00
1890S........	1,423,076	3.00	4.00	6.00	9.00	45.00	
1891....(600)	15,310,600	1.25	2.00	3.00	4.50	35.00	80.00
1891O.........	4,540,000	2.25	3.25	5.50	14.00	50.00	
1891S........	3,196,116	2.00	3.00	4.00	8.00	42.50	

BARBER OR LIBERTY HEAD TYPE 1892-1916

GOOD—Date and letters plain. LIBERTY over brow is obliterated.

VERY GOOD—At least 3 letters visible in LIBERTY.

FINE—All letters in LIBERTY visible, though some are weak.

VERY FINE—All letters of LIBERTY evenly plain.

EXTRA FINE—All letters in LIBERTY are sharp, distinct. Headband edges are distinct.

Designed by Charles E. Barber, Chief Engraver of the Mint. He also designed the 25 and 50-cent pieces. His initial B is at the truncation of the neck.

	Quan. Minted	Good	V.G.	Fine	V.F.	E.F.	Unc.	Proof
1892 (1,245)	12,121,245	$1.00	$2.00	$3.00	$4.00	$6.50	$25.00	$77.50
1892O.......	3,841,700	2.25	3.50	4.50	7.50	12.50	35.00	
1892S..........	990,710	15.00	20.00	27.50	37.50	50.00	100.00	

DIMES

	Quan. Minted	Good	V.G.	Fine	V.F.	E.F.	Unc.	Proof
1893 (792)	3,340,792	$2.25	$3.25	$ 3.75	$ 5.00	$ 8.00	$25.00	$80.00
1893O	1,760,000	4.00	5.50	9.00	13.00	20.00	55.00	
1893S	2,491,401	4.00	5.50	9.00	14.00	25.00	50.00	
1894 (972)	1,330,972	4.25	6.00	7.50	9.00	12.50	27.50	80.00
1894O	720,000	24.00	37.50	65.00	85.00	125.00	280.00	
1894S	24			Century Sale 1965				$12,250.00
1895 (880)	690,880	23.50	30.00	40.00	60.00	75.00	160.00	260.00
1895O	440,000	45.00	72.50	120.00	155.00	275.00	650.00	
1895S	1,120,000	6.50	10.00	14.00	27.50	45.00	120.00	
1896 (762)	2,000,762	3.50	5.00	6.50	8.00	13.00	27.50	100.00
1896O	610,000	20.00	27.50	45.00	65.00	95.00	200.00	
1896S	575,056	25.00	35.00	50.00	75.00	130.00	250.00	
1897 (731)	10,869,264	.75	1.25	2.35	4.00	6.00	24.00	100.00
1897O	666,000	18.00	27.50	40.00	57.50	90.00	195.00	
1897S	1,342,844	5.50	9.00	15.00	25.00	40.00	115.00	
1898 (735)	16,320,735	.55	1.00	1.65	2.75	5.00	22.50	100.00
1898O	2,130,000	3.00	5.00	8.50	20.00	42.50	100.00	
1898S	1,702,507	3.00	5.50	9.00	18.00	32.50	82.50	
1899 (846)	19,580,846	.50	1.00	1.65	2.50	4.00	22.50	95.00
1899O	2,650,000	3.00	5.50	9.00	18.00	35.00	95.00	
1899S	1,867,493	3.50	5.75	8.50	15.00	24.00	72.50	
1900 (912)	17,600,912	.50	1.00	1.50	2.25	4.00	22.50	90.00
1900O	2,010,000	2.75	4.75	8.50	15.00	35.00	100.00	
1900S	5,168,270	1.75	3.00	6.00	8.00	15.00	50.00	
1901 (813)	18,860,478	.50	.85	1.50	2.25	4.00	22.50	95.00
1901O	5,620,000	1.50	2.75	6.50	13.00	32.50	97.50	
1901S	593,022	17.50	40.00	75.00	135.00	185.00	475.00	
1902 (777)	21,380,777	.45	.75	1.25	2.00	3.75	22.50	95.00
1902O	4,500,000	1.00	2.25	5.00	10.00	22.50	65.00	
1902S	2,070,000	3.00	5.00	8.50	15.00	30.00	85.00	
1903 (755)	19,500,755	.45	.75	1.25	2.25	4.00	22.50	95.00
1903O	8,180,000	.75	2.00	5.00	7.50	17.50	50.00	
1903S	613,300	12.00	18.00	22.50	37.50	60.00	160.00	
1904 (670)	14,601,027	.40	.75	1.25	2.25	3.50	22.50	100.00
1904S	800,000	10.00	14.00	20.00	30.00	45.00	125.00	
1905 (727)	14,552,350	.40	.75	1.25	2.25	3.50	22.50	100.00
1905O	3,400,000	1.25	2.50	4.50	7.50	18.00	65.00	
1905S	6,855,199	.80	1.75	3.50	6.00	11.00	30.00	
1906 (675)	19,958,406	.40	.75	1.25	2.25	4.00	22.50	95.00
1906D	4,060,000	1.15	2.00	3.00	4.00	5.00	24.00	
1906O	2,610,000	1.50	3.00	5.00	7.00	11.00	34.00	
1906S	3,136,640	1.25	2.25	3.50	5.00	10.00	30.00	
1907 (575)	22,220,575	.40	.75	1.25	2.25	4.50	23.50	100.00
1907D	4,080,000	1.00	1.75	3.50	5.50	12.00	33.00	
1907O	5,058,000	.90	1.50	3.00	5.00	10.00	30.00	
1907S	3,178,470	1.25	1.75	3.50	5.00	11.00	30.00	
1908 (545)	10,600,545	.35	.70	1.00	2.00	3.75	24.00	100.00
1908D	7,490,000	.45	.80	1.50	2.50	5.00	24.00	
1908O	1,789,000	2.25	4.00	5.50	7.00	10.00	47.50	
1908S	3,220,000	1.15	2.00	3.50	6.00	9.00	35.00	
1909 (650)	10,240,650	.35	.65	1.25	2.25	3.75	24.00	95.00
1909D	954,000	2.50	4.50	8.00	12.50	22.50	50.00	
1909O	2,287,000	1.75	3.75	7.50	10.00	20.00	55.00	
1909S	1,000,000	2.50	4.50	9.00	13.00	22.50	55.00	

DIMES

	Quan. Minted	Good	V.G.	Fine	V.F.	E.F.	Unc.	Proof
1910 (551)	11,520,551	$ .30	$ .55	$ 1.00	$ 2.00	$ 3.50	$24.00	$100.00
1910D	3,490,000	.80	1.35	2.00	3.00	5.00	25.00	
1910S	1,240,000	2.00	3.00	4.50	7.00	12.00	42.50	
1911 (543)	18,870,543	.30	.50	1.00	2.00	3.50	23.50	100.00
1911D	11,209,000	.45	.85	1.50	2.50	4.50	22.50	
1911S	3,520,000	.80	1.65	2.75	5.50	10.00	32.50	
1912 (700)	19,350,700	.30	.50	1.00	2.00	3.50	24.00	105.00
1912D	11,760,000	.40	.75	1.50	2.25	4.00	24.00	
1912S	3,420,000	1.00	1.75	4.00	7.00	11.00	35.00	
1913 (622)	19,760,622	.30	.50	1.00	2.00	3.50	24.00	160.00
1913S	510,000	7.50	12.50	25.00	35.00	75.00	185.00	
1914 (425)	17,360,655	.30	.50	1.00	2.00	3.50	24.00	260.00
1914D	11,908,000	.40	.75	1.25	2.25	4.00	22.50	
1914S	2,100,000	1.25	2.00	3.50	6.50	13.00	35.00	
1915 (450)	5,620,450	.40	.75	1.25	2.25	3.75	24.00	260.00
1915S	960,000	2.00	3.00	4.50	7.00	12.00	37.50	
1916	18,490,000	.30	.50	1.00	2.00	3.50	24.00	
1916S	5,820,000	.40	.75	1.50	2.50	3.75	24.00	

WINGED LIBERTY HEAD or "MERCURY" TYPE 1916-1945

This dime was designed by A. A. Weinman. Although it is commonly called the "Mercury Dime," the main device is in fact a representation of Liberty. The wings crowning her cap are intended to symbolize liberty of thought. The designer's initials AW are found back of the neck.

GOOD— Letters and dates clear. Lines and diagonal bands in fasces are obliterated.

VERY GOOD—One-third of sticks discernible in fasces.

FINE—All sticks in fasces are defined. Diagonal bands worn at center high points only.

EXTRA FINE—Diagonal bands complete, with only slight wear. Hair braids and hair before ear show clearly.

	Quan. Minted	Good	V.G.	Fine	V.F.	E.F.	Unc.	Proof
1916	22,180,080	$ .35	$ .50	$1.00	$1.35	$2.50	$10.00	
1916D	264,000	95.00	125.00	185.00	235.00	310.00	675.00	
1916S	10,450,000	1.40	2.00	3.65	4.85	7.50	19.00	
1917	55,230,000	.25	.35	.65	1.00	2.25	9.00	
1917D	9,402,000	1.35	2.25	4.75	8.75	19.00	62.50	
1917S	27,330,000	.35	.60	1.35	2.75	5.00	24.00	
1918	26,680,000	.40	.65	1.65	3.75	7.50	27.00	
1918D	22,674,800	.40	.70	2.50	4.50	14.00	40.00	
1918S	19,300,000	.50	.90	2.00	3.50	11.50	33.00	
1919	35,740,000	.30	.50	1.25	2.50	6.50	28.00	
1919D	9,939,000	1.10	2.00	5.00	12.50	30.00	110.00	
1919S	8,850,000	1.10	2.00	5.00	12.50	30.00	110.00	
1920	59,030,000	.25	.35	.65	1.35	2.75	14.00	
1920D	19,171,000	.40	.70	2.00	3.50	10.00	40.00	
1920S	13,820,000	.40	.70	2.00	3.50	10.00	40.00	
1921	1,230,000	12.00	20.00	40.00	57.50	125.00	375.00	
1921D	1,080,000	17.50	26.50	47.50	75.00	125.00	325.00	
1923*	50,130,000	.25	.50	.90	1.25	2.00	14.00	

*Dimes dated 1923D are counterfeit.

DIMES

Quan. Minted	Good	V.G.	Fine	V.F.	E.F.	Unc.	Proof
1923S......6,440,000	$ .75	$1.25	$3.25	$6.00	$20.00	$85.00	
1924......24,010,000	.25	.35	.75	1.25	3.50	22.50	
1924D.....6,810,000	.65	1.25	2.25	4.00	12.00	92.50	
1924S......7,120,000	.65	1.25	2.25	4.00	12.00	85.00	
1925......25,610,000	.25	.35	.75	1.25	3.50	22.50	
1925D.....5,117,000	1.50	2.50	4.50	17.50	60.00	265.00	
1925S......5,850,000	.65	1.25	2.25	6.00	17.50	90.00	
1926......32,160,000	.25	.35	.75	1.25	3.50	15.00	
1926D.....6,828,000	.60	.90	1.60	3.50	12.00	50.00	
1926S......1,520,000	5.00	7.00	11.50	19.00	60.00	275.00	
1927......28,080,000	.25	.35	.75	1.00	2.25	13.00	
1927D.....4,812,000	.75	1.50	4.00	9.50	35.00	185.00	
1927S......4,770,000	.50	.90	2.25	6.00	20.00	105.00	
1928......19,480,000	.25	.35	.65	1.00	2.25	13.00	
1928D.....4,161,000	.75	1.25	3.50	10.00	25.00	95.00	
1928S......7,400,000	.40	.75	1.50	3.50	12.00	50.00	
1929......25,970,000	.25	.35	.50	.80	1.75	8.00	
1929D.....5,034,000	.45	.75	1.50	2.50	4.50	13.00	
1929S......4,730,000	.45	.75	1.50	2.50	4.50	16.00	
1930......6,770,000	.45	.60	1.00	2.00	4.00	14.50	
1930S......1,843,000	2.50	3.50	4.50	8.00	15.00	40.00	
1931......3,150,000	.75	1.25	2.00	3.00	5.25	27.50	
1931D.....1,260,000	4.50	6.00	8.00	12.50	20.00	55.00	
1931S......1,800,000	2.50	3.50	4.50	8.00	15.00	50.00	
1934......24,080,000	.25	.35	.50	.75	1.50	8.00	
1934D.....6,772,000	.50	.75	1.00	1.50	3.00	16.00	
1935......58,830,000	.20	.30	.40	.60	1.00	3.50	
1935D....10,477,000	.25	.35	.60	1.00	2.75	22.50	
1935S.....15,840,000	.25	.35	.55	.85	1.50	7.00	
1936 (4,130)							
.....87,504,130	.12	.15	.18	.20	.40	2.50	120.00
1936D....16,132,000	.20	.25	.40	.60	2.00	14.50	
1936S......9,210,000	.20	.25	.50	.75	2.00	7.00	
1937 (5,756)							
.....56,865,756	.12	.15	.18	.20	.40	2.50	62.50
1937D....14,146,000	.20	.25	.40	.65	1.00	5.00	
1937S......9,740,000	.20	.25	.50	.70	1.15	5.00	
1938 (8,728)							
.....22,198,728	.12	.15	.18	.20	.30	3.00	31.00
1938D.....5,537,000	.20	.30	.50	.75	1.50	9.00	
1938S......8,090,000	.20	.25	.50	.75	1.50	7.50	
1939 (9,321)							
.....67,749,321	.12	.15	.18	.20	.30	2.50	24.00
1939D....24,394,000	.15	.20	.30	.45	.60	2.50	
1939S.....10,540,000	.20	.25	.50	.90	1.60	10.00	
1940 (11,827)							
.....65,361,827		.15	.18	.20	.30	2.00	22.50
1940D....21,198,000		.15	.20	.25	.50	2.00	
1940S.....21,560,000		.15	.20	.25	.50	2.25	
1941 (16,557)							
....175,106,557		.15	.18	.20	.30	1.50	22.50
1941D....45,634,000		.15	.20	.30	.50	2.25	
1941S.....43,090,000		.15	.20	.25	.50	1.75	

DIMES

Enlarged Detail of 1942
2 over 1 Dime

	Quan. Minted	V.G.	Fine	V.F.	E.F.	Unc.	Proof
1942 2 over 1.. }	205,432,329	$100.00	$125.00	$150.00	$180.00	$500.00	
1942....(22,329) }						.35	1.25	$20.00
1942D..........60,740,000						.35	1.25
1942S..........49,300,000						.35	1.75
1943..........191,710,000						.35	1.25
1943D..........71,949,000						.35	1.25
1943S..........60,400,000						.35	1.50
1944..........231,410,000						.35	1.25
1944D..........62,224,000						.35	1.25
1944S..........49,490,000						.35	1.25
1945..........159,130,000						.35	1.25
1945D..........40,245,000						.35	1.25
1945S Normal S. }	41,920,000					.35	1.25
1945S Micro S... }			.25	.50	1.00	2.00	7.50

ROOSEVELT TYPE 1946 to Date

John R. Sinnock (whose initials JS are at the truncation of the neck) designed this dime showing a portrait of Franklin D. Roosevelt. The design has heavier lettering and a more modernistic character than preceding types. The reverse displays the torch of liberty between sprays of laurel and oak.

FINE—Flame worn smooth. Horizontal lines on torch do not show. All vertical lines will show.

VERY FINE—Hair above ear slightly worn. All vertical lines on torch plain.

EXTRA FINE—All lines of torch, flame and hair very plain.

	Quan. Minted	Fine	V.F.	E.F.	Unc.	Proof
1946..............255,250,000		$ .15	$ .20	$ .30	$ .45	
1946D.............61,043,500		.15	.20	.30	.55	
1946S.............27,900,000		.15	.25	.40	1.20	
1947..............121,520,000		.15	.25	.40	1.40	
1947D.............46,835,000		.20	.30	.40	1.25	
1947S.............34,840,000		.15	.25	.40	1.00	
1948..............74,950,000		.20	.35	.60	2.00	
1948D.............52,841,000		.20	.30	.40	1.25	
1948S.............35,520,000		.15	.25	.40	1.20	
1949..............30,940,000		.30	.50	1.00	7.50	
1949D.............26,034,000		.20	.35	.60	2.50	
1949S.............13,510,000		.65	1.00	1.75	12.50	
1950.......(51,386) 50,181,500		.20	.30	.40	1.50	20.00
1950D.............46,803,000		.20	.30	.50	1.50	
1950S.............20,440,000		.40	.70	1.25	8.00	
1951......(57,500) 103,937,602		.15	.25	.35	.90	11.50
1951D.............56,529,000		.15	.25	.35	.90	
1951S.............31,630,000		.30	.50	1.00	6.00	

DIMES

	Quan. Minted	Fine	V.F.	E.F.	Unc.	Proof
1952......(81,980)	99,122,073	$ .15	$ .25	$ .35	$ .70	$7.50
1952D	122,100,000	.15	.20	.30	.60	
1952S	44,419,500	.20	.30	.50	2.25	
1953.....(128,800)	53,618,920	.15	.20	.30	.65	4.75
1953D	136,433,000	.15	.20	.30	.50	
1953S	39,180,000	.15	.20	.35	.75	
1954.....(233,300)	114,243,503	.15	.20	.25	.40	3.50
1954D	106,397,000	.15	.20	.25	.40	
1954S	22,860,000	.15	.20	.35	.90	
1955.....(378,200)	12,828,381	.30	.45	.85	1.50	4.25
1955D	13,959,000	.25	.40	.70	1.10	
1955S	18,510,000	.20	.30	.50	.80	
1956.....(669,384)	109,309,384				.35	1.65
1956D	108,015,100				.45	
1957...(1,247,952)	161,407,952				.30	1.50
1957D	113,354,330			.20	.50	
1958.....(875,652)	32,785,652			.30	.75	3.00
1958D	136,564,600				.40	
1959...(1,149,291)	86,929,291				.35	1.50
1959D	164,919,790				.35	
1960...(1,691,602)	72,081,602				.35	1.25
1960D	200,160,400				.35	
1961...(3,028,244)	96,758,244				.35	.90
1961D	209,146,550				.35	
1962...(3,218,019)	75,668,019				.35	.90
1962D	334,948,380				.35	
1963...(3,075,645)	126,725,645				.25	.90
1963D	421,476,530				.25	
1964...(3,950,762)	933,310,762				.25	.90
1964D	1,357,517,180				.25	

CLAD COINAGE

	Quan. Minted	Fine	V.F.	E.F.	Unc.	Proof
1965	1,652,140,570				.20	
1966	1,382,734,540				.20	
1967	2,244,007,320				.20	
1968	424,470,400				.20	
1968D	480,748,280				.20	
1968S Proof only	3,041,509					3.50
1969	145,790,000				.20	
1969D	563,323,870				.20	
1969S Proof only	2,934,631					3.10
1970					.20	
1970D					.20	
1970S Proof only						3.00

TWENTY-CENT PIECES — 1875-1878

This short-lived coin was authorized by the Act of March 3, 1875. Soon after

the appearance of the first twenty-cent pieces, the people complained about the similarity in design and size to the quarter-dollar. The eagle is very similar to that used on the Trade Dollar. The edge of the coin is plain. Most of the 1876CC coins were melted at the mint and never released. Weight: 77.16 grains.

TWENTY-CENT PIECES

	Quan. Minted	Good	V.G.	Fine	V.F.	E.F.	Unc.	Proof
1875..	(1,200) 39,700	$22.50	$28.50	$42.50	$54.00	$80.00	$185.00	$260.00
1875CC....	.133,290	26.00	32.00	45.00	60.00	85.00	210.00	
1875S......	1,155,000	22.50	25.00	40.00	50.00	67.50	175.00	
1876..	(1,150) 15,900	28.00	34.50	47.50	62.50	87.50	195.00	275.00
1876CC......	10,000				Waldorf Sale 1966 $12,750.00			
1877....	(510) 510							650.00
1878....	(600) 600							550.00

QUARTER DOLLARS 1796 To Date

Authorized in 1792, this denomination was not issued until four years later. The first coinage, dated 1796, follows the pattern of the early half-dimes and dimes by the absence of a mark of value. In 1804 the value "25c" was added to the reverse. Figures were used until 1838 when the term "QUAR. DOL." appeared. It was not until 1892 that the value was spelled out entirely.

The first type weighed 104 grains which remained standard until modified to 103⅛ grains by the Act of January 18, 1837. As with the dime and half dime, the weight was reduced and arrows placed at the date in 1853, and rays were placed in the field of the reverse during that year only.

The law of 1873 also affected the quarter, for the weight was slightly increased and arrows again placed at the date.

Proofs of some dates prior to 1855 are known to exist, and all are rare.

DRAPED BUST TYPE, SMALL EAGLE REVERSE 1796

	Quan. Minted	Fair	Good	V.G.	Fine	V.F.	Unc.
1796...........	6,146	$525.00	$725.00	$1350.00	$2150.00	$3000.00	$5750.00

DRAPED BUST TYPE, HERALDIC EAGLE REVERSE 1804-1807

1804..........	6,738	85.00	140.00	190.00	360.00	650.00	———
1805........	121,394	50.00	70.00	85.00	150.00	275.00	900.00

[114]

QUARTER DOLLARS

1806 Over 5

1806 Normal Date

	Quan. Minted	Fair	Good	V.G.	Fine	V.F.	Unc.
1806 6 over 5	206,124	$40.00	$60.00	$87.50	$140.00	$275.00	$950.00
1806 Normal date....							
		37.50	55.00	82.50	125.00	235.00	850.00
1807.........220,643		40.00	57.50	85.00	130.00	270.00	900.00

CAPPED BUST TYPE 1815-1828

FAIR—Details clear enough to identify.

GOOD—Date, letters and stars readable. Hair under headband smooth. Cap lines worn smooth.

VERY GOOD—Rim well defined. Main details visible. Full LIBERTY on cap. Hair above eye nearly smooth.

FINE—All hairlines show but drapery has only part details. Shoulder clasp distinct.

VERY FINE—All details show, but some wear. Clasp and ear sharp.

EXTRA FINE—All details show distinctly. Hair well outlined.

1818
8 over 5

	Quan. Minted	Fair	Good	V.G.	Fine	V.F.	E.F.	Unc.
1815.........89,235		16.00	20.00	32.50	50.00	150.00	250.00	550.00
1818 8 over 5	361,174	16.00	20.00	32.50	50.00	150.00	250.00	525.00
1818 Normal date....								
		15.00	17.50	30.00	45.00	85.00	150.00	450.00
1819 Small 9.	144,000	15.00	19.00	31.00	47.50	87.50	150.00	450.00
1819 Large 9.		15.00	19.00	31.00	47.50	87.50	150.00	450.00

1820 Small 0

1820 Large 0

1822, 25 Over 50c

1820 Small 0.	127,444	14.50	19.00	25.00	35.00	75.00	125.00	450.00
1820 Large 0.		14.50	19.00	25.00	35.00	75.00	125.00	450.00
1821.........216,851		14.50	19.00	25.00	35.00	75.00	125.00	450.00
1822 All kinds..64,080		15.00	20.00	28.50	47.50	110.00	185.00	475.00
1822 25 over 50c.....		130.00	160.00	225.00	335.00	600.00	900.00	1700.00

QUARTER DOLLARS

Quan. Minted	Fair	Good	V.G.	Fine	V.F.	E.F.	Unc.
1823 3 over 2..17,800	$465.00	$675.00	$900.00	$1,250	$2,250		
1824..........——	24.00	35.00	47.50	70.00	115.00	190.00	485.00

1825 Over 22 (wide date)   1825 Over 23 (close date)

	Fair	Good	V.G.	Fine	V.F.	E.F.	Unc.
1825 over 22	16.00	22.50	32.00	40.00	75.00	125.00	425.00
1825 over 23 }168,000	16.00	22.50	32.00	40.00	75.00	125.00	425.00
1825 over 24	16.00	22.50	32.00	40.00	75.00	125.00	425.00
1827 Original (Curled base 2 in 25c) 4,000 Minted..........(6 or 7 known)							
1827 Restrike (Square base 2 in 25c)............................——							
1828 All kds..102,000	16.00	22.50	32.00	40.00	75.00	125.00	425.00
1828 25 over 50c	40.00	65.00	90.00	130.00	200.00	300.00	700.00

REDUCED SIZE — NO MOTTO ON REVERSE 1831-1838

GOOD—*Bust is well defined. Hair under headband is smooth. Date, letters, stars readable. Scant rims.*

VERY GOOD—*Details apparent but worn on high spots. Rims strong. Full LIBERTY.*

FINE—*All hairlines visible. Drapery partly worn. Shoulder clasp distinct.*

VERY FINE—*Only top spots worn. Clasp sharp. Ear distinct.*

1831   Small Letters   Large Letters

	Fair	Good	V.G.	Fine	V.F.	E.F.
1831 Small letters...} 398,000	12.00	16.00	25.00	45.00	75.00	300.00
1831 Large letters...| 398,000	12.00	16.00	25.00	45.00	75.00	300.00
1832...............320,000	12.00	16.00	25.00	45.00	75.00	300.00
1833...............156,000	16.00	22.50	32.50	55.00	100.00	700.00
1834...............286,000	12.00	16.00	25.00	45.00	75.00	300.00
1835.............1,952,000	12.00	16.00	25.00	45.00	75.00	300.00
1836...............472,000	12.00	16.00	25.00	45.00	75.00	300.00
1837...............252,400	12.00	16.00	25.00	45.00	75.00	300.00
1838.....Both types 832,000	12.00	16.00	25.00	45.00	75.00	300.00

QUARTER DOLLARS

LIBERTY SEATED TYPE 1838-1891

GOOD—*Scant rim. LIBERTY on shield worn off. Date and letters readable.*
VERY GOOD—*Rim fairly defined, at least 3 letters in LIBERTY evident.*
FINE—*LIBERTY complete, but partly weak.*
VERY FINE—*LIBERTY strong.*

No
Drapery
From
Elbow

Drapery
From
Elbow

	Quan. Minted	Good	V.G.	Fine	V.F.	Unc.
1838 No drapery.............		$7.00	$11.00	$16.00	$28.00	$125.00
1839 No drapery......491,146		5.50	10.00	14.00	25.00	110.00
1840O No drapery						
All kinds.........425,200		5.50	10.00	14.00	25.00	110.00
1840 Drapery.........188,127		5.50	10.00	14.00	25.00	110.00
1840O Drapery.............		5.50	9.00	13.00	22.50	110.00
1841................120,000		13.00	17.50	24.00	39.00	130.00
1841O...............452,000		5.00	7.50	11.00	20.00	100.00

Small
Date

Large
Date

	Quan. Minted	Good	V.G.	Fine	V.F.	Unc.
1842 Small date......⎫	88,000			Proofs Only ———		
1842 Large date......⎭		5.00	7.50	10.00	18.00	70.00
1842O Small date.....⎫	769,000	13.00	18.00	22.50	32.00	120.00
1842O Large date.....⎭		5.50	8.50	12.00	22.50	85.00
1843................645,600		4.00	6.00	9.00	15.00	57.50
1843O...............968,000		4.00	6.00	9.00	15.00	70.00
1844................421,200		4.00	6.00	9.00	15.00	70.00
1844O...............740,000		4.00	6.00	9.00	15.00	70.00
1845................922,000		4.00	6.00	9.00	15.00	65.00
1846................510,000		4.00	6.00	9.00	15.00	60.00
1847................734,000		4.00	6.00	9.00	15.00	60.00
1847O...............368,000		4.50	6.50	10.00	16.00	65.00
1848................146,000		5.00	7.50	11.00	17.50	70.00
1849................340,000		4.00	6.00	9.00	15.00	67.50
1849O ....———		65.00	85.00	125.00	190.00	525.00
1850................190,800		5.00	7.50	11.00	17.50	67.50
1850O...............412,000		4.00	6.00	9.00	16.00	70.00
1851................160,000		4.00	6.00	9.00	16.00	70.00
1851O................88,000		4.50	7.50	12.00	22.50	100.00
1852................177,060		4.25	6.50	10.00	17.50	75.00
1852O................96,000		7.00	10.00	15.00	27.50	95.00
1853* Recut date, no						
arrows or rays....44,200		50.00	70.00	110.00	160.00	500.00

*Beware of altered 1858.

QUARTER DOLLARS

Arrows at Date, Rays Around Eagle

The reduction in weight is indicated by the arrows at the date. Rays were added on the reverse side in the field around the eagle. The arrows were retained until 1856, but the rays were omitted after 1853.

	Quan. Minted	Good	V.G.	Fine	V.F.	Unc.	Proof
1853	15,210,020	$6.00	$7.50	$12.00	$27.50	$350.00	
1853O	1,332,000	8.50	12.00	17.50	35.00	375.00	

Arrows At Date — Rays Removed From Reverse

1854	12,380,000	4.00	5.00	7.00	12.50	85.00	
1854O	1,484,000	4.25	5.50	8.00	14.00	85.00	
1855	2,857,000	4.00	5.00	7.00	12.50	85.00	$700.00
1855O	176,000	40.00	55.00	80.00	140.00	400.00	
1855S	396,400	40.00	55.00	80.00	140.00	425.00	

Arrows At Date Removed

1856	7,264,000	3.00	4.00	5.50	8.50	50.00	600.00
1856O	968,000	3.50	5.00	7.00	10.00	45.00	
1856S	286,000	18.00	27.50	40.00	80.00	240.00	
1857	9,644,000	2.75	3.50	5.00	7.50	47.50	600.00
1857O	1,180,000	3.50	4.50	6.00	10.00	47.50	
1857S	82,000	19.00	30.00	45.00	80.00	250.00	
1858	7,368,000	3.00	4.00	5.50	8.50	47.50	450.00
1858O	520,000	4.50	6.50	8.00	12.00	50.00	
1858S	121,000	25.00	30.00	40.00	75.00	250.00	
1859	1,344,000	3.25	4.25	5.50	8.00	50.00	175.00
1859O	260,000	4.50	6.50	8.00	12.00	55.00	
1859S	80,000	25.00	30.00	40.00	80.00	250.00	
1860 .....(1,000)	805,400	3.00	4.00	5.50	8.00	47.50	140.00
1860O	388,000	4.00	6.00	7.50	11.00	47.50	
1860S	56,000	17.50	22.50	32.50	65.00	250.00	
1861 .....(1,000)	4,854,600	2.75	3.75	5.00	8.00	47.50	140.00
1861S	96,000	16.50	20.00	30.00	60.00	200.00	
1862 ......(550)	932,550	3.00	4.00	5.00	8.00	50.00	140.00
1862S	67,000	15.00	17.50	27.50	60.00	200.00	
1863 ......(460)	192,060	4.00	5.00	7.00	12.00	47.50	140.00
1864 ......(470)	94,070	5.00	6.00	9.00	16.00	55.00	140.00
1864S	20,000	20.00	30.00	50.00	100.00	300.00	
1865 ......(500)	59,300	5.00	7.00	9.00	13.00	57.50	140.00
1865S	41,000	10.00	14.00	20.00	43.00	175.00	

1866 No motto (1 known) Hydeman Sale 1961............Proof $24,500.00

QUARTER DOLLARS

MOTTO ABOVE EAGLE

The motto IN GOD WE TRUST was added to the reverse side in 1866. As on the half dollar and silver dollar the motto has been retained since that time.

	Quan. Minted	Good	V.G.	Fine	V.F.	Unc.	Proof
1866 . . . . . . (725)	17,525	$ 5.00	$ 6.50	$ 8.50	$14.00	$ 65.00	$130.00
1866S	28,000	12.50	16.00	22.00	50.00	250.00	
1867 . . . . . . (625)	20,625	4.00	5.00	8.00	12.00	65.00	120.00
1867S	48,000	11.00	15.00	20.00	40.00	175.00	
1868 . . . . . . (600)	30,000	4.00	5.50	7.50	11.00	65.00	120.00
1868S	96,000	10.00	12.50	15.00	35.00	175.00	
1869 . . . . . . (600)	16,600	5.00	6.50	10.00	15.00	72.50	120.00
1869S	76,000	10.00	13.00	16.00	35.00	130.00	
1870 . . . . . . (1,000)	87,400	3.50	4.50	6.00	8.50	55.00	110.00
1870CC	8,340	125.00	150.00	200.00	425.00	950.00	
1871 . . . . . . (960)	119,160	3.00	4.00	5.00	6.50	55.00	110.00
1871CC	10,890	110.00	130.00	165.00	285.00	850.00	
1871S	30,900	8.50	12.50	20.00	40.00	150.00	
1872 . . . . . . (950)	182,950	3.00	4.00	5.00	6.50	55.00	110.00
1872CC	9,100	165.00	200.00	275.00	500.00	1200.00	
1872S	83,000	15.00	20.00	30.00	50.00	130.00	
1873 Closed 3 (600). }	212,600	7.50	11.00	16.00	20.00	80.00	115.00
1873 Open 3 . . . . }		6.50	9.50	13.00	17.50	70.00	
1873CC	4,000	450.00	550.00	700.00	1400.00	———	

Arrows were placed at the date in the years 1873 and 1874 to denote the change of weight from 96 to 96.45 grains.

Arrows at Date 1873-1874

1873 . . . . . . (540)	1,271,700	19.00	23.00	28.00	50.00	200.00	375.00
1873CC	12,462	325.00	425.00	600.00	850.00	1800.00	
1873S	156,000	25.00	30.00	40.00	60.00	215.00	
1874 . . . . . . (700)	471,900	20.00	23.00	28.00	45.00	200.00	325.00
1874S	392,000	25.00	30.00	40.00	60.00	225.00	

QUARTER DOLLARS

Arrows Removed Starting 1875

	Quan. Minted	Good	V.G.	Fine	V.F.	Unc.	Proof
1875 . . . . (700)	4,293,500	$ 3.00	$ 3.75	$ 5.00	$ 8.00	$50.00	$95.00
1875CC	140,000	9.00	11.00	16.50	35.00	140.00	
1875S	680,000	9.00	11.00	16.50	35.00	100.00	
1876 . . . . . . (1,150)	17,817,150	3.00	3.75	5.00	8.00	50.00	80.00
1876CC	4,944,000	3.50	4.50	6.00	10.00	52.50	
1876S	8,596,000	3.00	3.75	5.00	8.00	47.50	
1877 . . . . (510)	10,911,710	2.50	3.25	4.50	7.00	45.00	125.00
1877CC	4,192,000	3.50	4.50	6.00	10.00	52.50	
1877S All kinds	8,996,000	3.00	3.75	5.00	8.00	47.50	
1877S over horizontal S				90.00	115.00	235.00	
1878 . . . . (800)	2,260,800	3.00	3.75	5.00	8.00	47.50	80.00
1878CC	996,000	6.00	8.00	10.00	16.00	75.00	
1878S	140,000	135.00	185.00	250.00	375.00	1000.00	
1879 . . . . . . (250)	14,700	20.00	22.50	27.50	35.00	85.00	145.00
1880 . . . . . . (1,355)	14,955	20.00	22.50	27.50	35.00	85.00	100.00
1881 . . . . (975)	12,975	20.00	22.50	27.50	35.00	85.00	100.00
1882 . . . . . . (1,100)	16,300	20.00	22.50	27.50	35.00	85.00	100.00
1883 . . . . . . (1,039)	15,439	20.00	22.50	27.50	35.00	85.00	100.00
1884 . . . . (875)	8,875	25.00	27.50	30.00	37.50	90.00	110.00
1885 . . . . (930)	14,530	20.00	22.50	27.50	35.00	85.00	110.00
1886 . . . . (886)	5,886	30.00	35.00	40.00	55.00	130.00	170.00
1887 . . . . (710)	10,710	22.50	25.00	32.50	40.00	85.00	110.00
1888 . . . . (832)	10,833	22.50	25.00	32.50	40.00	85.00	100.00
1888S	1,216,000	3.00	3.75	5.00	9.00	50.00	
1889 . . . . (711)	12,711	20.00	22.50	27.50	35.00	80.00	110.00
1890 . . . . . . (590)	80,590	5.00	7.00	10.00	12.50	50.00	110.00
1891 . . . . (600)	3,920,600	2.75	3.50	4.75	7.00	50.00	110.00
1891O	68,000	80.00	95.00	125.00	200.00	550.00	
1891S	2,216,000	3.00	4.25	5.75	10.00	50.00	

BARBER or LIBERTY HEAD TYPE 1892-1916

Like other silver coins of this type the quarter dollars minted from 1892 to 1916 were designed by Charles E. Barber. His initial B is found at the base of the neck of Liberty.

GOOD—Date and legends readable. LIBERTY worn off headband.

VERY GOOD—Minimum of 3 letters in LIBERTY readable.

FINE—LIBERTY completely readable but not sharp.

VERY FINE—All letters in LIBERTY evenly plain.

EXTRA FINE—LIBERTY bold, and its ribbon distinct.

QUARTER DOLLARS

	Quan. Minted	Good	V.G.	Fine	V.F.	E.F.	Unc.	Proof
1892 (1,245)	8,237,245	$ .90	$1.35	$2.25	$6.00	$12.50	$40.00	$115.00
1892O	2,640,000	3.00	4.00	6.50	9.50	15.00	47.50	
1892S	964,079	9.00	14.00	22.50	35.00	55.00	150.00	
1893 (792)	5,444,815	1.00	1.35	2.00	5.00	12.00	40.00	110.00
1893O	3,396,000	1.75	3.00	5.00	9.00	15.00	45.00	
1893S	1,454,535	3.25	4.50	7.00	10.00	16.00	60.00	
1894 (972)	3,432,972	1.25	2.00	2.75	6.00	12.00	45.00	100.00
1894O	2,852,000	1.75	3.50	6.00	9.50	15.00	60.00	
1894S	2,648,821	1.75	3.25	5.50	9.00	15.00	57.50	
1895 (880)	4,440,880	.85	1.50	2.25	5.00	12.00	42.50	100.00
1895O	2,816,000	1.75	3.50	6.50	15.00	30.00	100.00	
1895S	1,764,681	3.00	4.50	7.50	12.50	17.50	75.00	
1896 (762)	3,874,762	1.00	2.00	3.00	6.00	12.50	42.50	105.00
1896O	1,484,000	4.00	7.50	12.50	25.00	55.00	220.00	
1896S	188,039	77.50	130.00	185.00	275.00	460.00	1275.00	
1897 (731)	8,140,731	.80	1.25	2.25	5.00	11.25	42.50	105.00
1897O	1,414,800	6.25	9.00	15.00	25.00	45.00	125.00	
1897S	542,229	7.50	10.00	17.50	27.50	47.50	175.00	
1898 (735)	11,100,735	.75	1.25	2.25	5.00	11.00	42.50	105.00
1898O	1,868,000	1.75	3.00	5.75	12.50	27.50	100.00	
1898S	1,020,592	2.25	3.75	7.00	12.50	27.50	115.00	
1899 (846)	12,624,846	.75	1.25	2.25	5.00	11.00	42.50	100.00
1899O	2,644,000	1.75	3.00	5.50	10.00	22.50	80.00	
1899S	708,000	6.00	8.00	10.00	15.00	25.00	95.00	
1900 (912)	10,016,912	.75	1.15	2.25	5.00	11.00	42.50	100.00
1900O	3,416,000	2.00	3.75	7.00	12.50	20.00	85.00	
1900S	1,858,585	1.35	3.25	7.50	14.00	32.00	95.00	
1901 (813)	8,892,813	.75	1.10	2.00	4.00	11.00	42.50	100.00
1901O	1,612,000	7.50	13.50	27.50	50.00	97.50	325.00	
1901S	72,664	185.00	275.00	395.00	560.00	750.00	1850.00	
1902 (777)	12,197,744	.75	1.10	2.00	4.00	11.00	42.50	105.00
1902O	4,748,000	1.75	3.25	7.50	14.00	24.00	75.00	
1902S	1,524,612	3.00	5.00	10.00	17.50	35.00	115.00	
1903 (755)	9,670,064	.75	1.10	2.00	4.00	11.00	42.50	105.00
1903O	3,500,000	2.00	4.25	9.00	20.00	55.00	160.00	
1903S	1,036,000	3.50	5.50	10.00	22.50	55.00	170.00	
1904 (670)	9,588,813	.75	1.10	2.00	4.00	11.00	42.50	110.00
1904O	2,456,000	4.50	7.50	14.00	27.50	60.00	265.00	
1905 (727)	4,968,250	1.00	1.65	2.50	5.00	11.00	47.50	105.00
1905O	1,230,000	4.50	7.50	12.50	22.50	40.00	160.00	
1905S	1,884,000	3.00	5.00	8.00	13.00	25.00	90.00	
1906 (675)	3,656,435	1.00	1.65	2.50	5.00	11.00	45.00	110.00
1906D	3,280,000	1.25	2.00	4.00	6.00	12.50	45.00	
1906O	2,056,000	1.60	2.25	4.00	6.50	15.00	50.00	
1907 (575)	7,192,575	.75	1.10	2.00	4.00	11.00	42.50	120.00
1907D	2,484,000	1.25	2.00	3.50	5.25	12.00	42.50	
1907O	4,560,000	1.00	1.85	3.00	5.50	12.00	42.50	
1907S	1,360,000	1.85	3.00	6.00	11.00	21.00	65.00	
1908 (545)	4,232,545	.75	1.25	2.25	4.50	11.50	42.50	120.00
1908D	5,788,000	.75	1.25	2.50	4.75	12.00	42.50	
1908O	6,244,000	.65	1.25	2.50	4.75	11.00	42.50	
1908S	784,000	4.25	6.75	12.00	17.50	25.00	85.00	
1909 (650)	9,268,650	.65	1.10	2.00	4.00	11.00	42.50	120.00

QUARTER DOLLARS

	Quan. Minted	Good	V.G.	Fine	V.F.	E.F.	Unc.	Proof
1909D	5,114,000	$ .75	$ 1.25	$ 2.50	$ 4.75	$ 12.00	$ 42.50	
1909O	712,000	9.00	14.50	29.00	45.00	85.00	325.00	
1909S	1,348,000	1.75	3.00	5.00	9.75	16.00	65.00	
1910 (551)	2,244,551	.80	1.50	3.00	5.00	12.00	45.00	$120.00
1910D	1,500,000	1.50	2.50	4.00	6.00	13.00	47.50	
1911 (543)	3,720,543	.75	1.10	2.00	4.00	11.00	45.00	120.00
1911D	933,600	2.25	3.25	6.00	10.00	16.00	57.50	
1911S	988,000	1.75	3.00	6.50	11.00	17.00	65.00	
1912 (700)	4,400,700	.65	1.10	2.00	4.00	11.00	42.50	120.00
1912S	708,000	2.50	4.50	8.50	17.50	32.50	125.00	
1913 (613)	484,613	4.00	6.25	8.50	14.00	25.00	100.00	175.00
1913D	1,450,800	1.60	2.75	4.50	6.50	14.00	57.50	
1913S	40,000	87.50	130.00	185.00	250.00	475.00	1100.00	
1914 (380)	6,244,610	.65	1.00	2.00	4.00	11.00	42.50	300.00
1914D	3,046,000	.65	1.00	2.00	4.00	11.00	45.00	
1914S	264,000	8.25	12.50	17.50	40.00	80.00	300.00	
1915 (450)	3,480,450	.70	1.00	2.00	4.00	11.00	42.50	300.00
1915D	3,694,000	.70	1.00	2.00	4.00	11.00	45.00	
1915S	704,000	2.50	3.75	5.00	9.00	15.00	55.00	
1916	1,788,000	.85	1.50	2.75	4.50	12.00	45.00	
1916D	6,540,800	.65	1.00	2.00	4.00	11.00	42.50	

STANDING LIBERTY TYPE 1916-1930

This type quarter was designed by Hermon A. MacNeil. The left arm of Liberty is upraised bearing a shield in the attitude of protection, from which the cover is being drawn. The right hand bears the olive branch of peace. The designer's initial M is located above and to the right of the date.

There was a modification in 1917. The reverse has a new arrangement of the stars and the eagle is higher.

In 1925 a depression was made in the pedestal on which Liberty stands, and which bears the date. On the first issues the dates wore off easily because they were too high and were not protected by other features of the coin. The new "recessed" dates proved more durable as a result of this change.

GOOD—*Date and lettering readable. Top of date worn. Liberty's right leg and toes worn off. Left leg and drapery lines show much wear.*

VERY GOOD—*Distinct date. Toes show faintly. Drapery lines visible above her left leg.*

FINE—*High curve of right leg flat from thigh to ankle. Left leg shows only slight wear. Drapery lines over right thigh seen only at sides of leg.*

VERY FINE—*Garment line across right leg will be worn but show at sides.*

EXTRA FINE—*Flattened only at high spots. Her toes are sharp. Drapery lines across right leg are evident. (Some modifications must be made for grading variety 2.)*

Variety 1

Uncirculated pieces with fully struck head of Liberty are worth more than prices listed below.

	Quan. Minted	Good	V.G.	Fine	V.F.	E.F.	Unc.
1916	52,000	230.00	325.00	410.00	490.00	575.00	875.00
1917 Variety 1	8,792,000	3.25	4.25	6.00	9.50	16.00	47.50
1917D Variety 1	1,509,200	5.50	7.50	11.00	16.00	22.50	60.00
1917S Variety 1	1,952,000	5.50	7.50	11.00	16.00	22.50	70.00

QUARTER DOLLARS

Variety 2

1918S 8 over 7

	Quan. Minted	Good	V.G.	Fine	V.F.	E.F.	Unc.
1917 Variety 2	13,880,000	$ 3.50	$ 5.00	$ 7.50	$11.00	$17.50	$40.00
1917D Variety 2	6,224,400	7.50	12.00	16.50	21.00	30.00	70.00
1917S Variety 2	5,552,000	10.00	14.00	18.00	25.00	35.00	72.50
1918	14,240,000	4.00	6.00	10.00	15.00	25.00	57.50
1918D	7,380,000	7.50	10.50	15.00	22.50	30.00	75.00
1918S Norm. date	} 11,072,000	4.00	6.00	10.00	15.00	25.00	65.00
1918S 8 over 7			300.00	475.00	625.00	900.00	3,250
1919	11,324,000	5.00	6.75	10.00	15.00	25.00	55.00
1919D	1,944,000	25.00	32.50	47.50	65.00	115.00	290.00
1919S	1,836,000	27.50	37.50	50.00	70.00	125.00	325.00
1920	27,860,000	3.50	4.50	6.00	8.50	12.00	37.50
1920D	3,586,400	10.00	15.00	22.50	30.00	55.00	130.00
1920S	6,380,000	7.00	9.50	13.00	18.50	28.00	75.00
1921	1,916,000	22.50	30.00	45.00	62.50	90.00	250.00
1923	9,716,000	2.50	4.00	6.00	8.50	12.00	35.00
1923S	1,360,000	37.50	50.00	65.00	85.00	110.00	260.00
1924	10,920,000	2.50	4.00	6.00	8.50	12.00	37.50
1924D	3,112,000	8.50	12.00	14.00	19.00	25.00	52.50
1924S	2,860,000	9.50	12.50	18.00	25.00	35.00	97.50
1925	12,280,000	.65	1.00	2.75	4.00	7.50	32.50
1926	11,316,000	.65	1.00	2.75	4.00	7.50	32.50
1926D	1,716,000	.85	1.25	3.50	5.00	8.50	35.00
1926S	2,700,000	2.25	3.50	6.50	18.50	45.00	160.00
1927	11,912,000	.65	1.00	2.50	3.75	7.00	35.00
1927D	976,400	2.25	3.50	6.00	9.50	17.50	80.00
1927S	396,000	5.00	7.50	15.00	75.00	140.00	700.00
1928	6,336,000	.65	1.00	2.25	3.50	6.75	34.00
1928D	1,627,600	.65	1.00	2.75	3.75	7.50	35.00
1928S	2,644,000	.65	1.00	2.75	3.75	7.50	35.00
1929	11,140,000	.60	.90	1.75	3.00	7.00	35.00
1929D	1,358,000	.60	1.00	2.25	3.50	7.50	45.00
1929S	1,764,000	.60	1.00	2.25	3.50	7.50	40.00
1930	5,632,000	.60	1.00	2.25	3.50	7.00	32.50
1930S	1,556,000	.60	1.00	2.25	3.50	7.50	40.00

WASHINGTON TYPE 1932 to Date

GOOD—Letters and date flat, but separated from rim. No hairlines near face.

VERY GOOD—Wing tips outlined. Rims on both sides are fine and even. Tops of letters at rim are flattened.

FINE—Hairlines about ear are visible. Tiny feathers on eagle's breast are faintly visible.

EXTRA FINE—Hairlines sharp. Wear spots confined to top of eagle's legs and center of breast.

[123]

QUARTER DOLLARS

This type was intended to be a commemorative issue marking the two-hundredth anniversary of Washington's birth. John Flanagan, a New York sculptor, was the designer. The initials JF are found at the base of the neck.

	Quan. Minted	Good	V.G.	Fine	E.F.	Unc.	Proof
1932	5,404,000	$ .75	$ 1.10	$ 1.55	$ 3.50	$15.00	
1932D	436,800	32.50	40.00	48.00	75.00	250.00	
1932S	408,000	32.50	37.50	45.00	60.00	115.00	
1934 Light motto	} 31,912,052	.40	.75	2.00	5.00	18.00	
1934 Hvy. motto		.40	.60	1.25	3.00	10.00	
1934D	3,527,200	1.25	1.75	4.00	13.00	65.00	
1935	32,484,000	.40	.50	1.00	2.75	7.50	
1935D	5,780,000	.50	1.00	2.00	9.50	65.00	
1935S	5,660,000	.50	.90	1.75	8.50	32.50	
1936 (3,837)	41,303,837	.35	.40	.75	1.50	7.00	$300.00
1936D	5,374,000	1.00	1.50	4.00	45.00	245.00	
1936S	3,828,000	.75	1.00	1.50	7.00	30.00	
1937 (5,542)	19,701,542	.35	.50	.75	2.00	7.00	70.00
1937D	7,189,600	.40	.85	1.25	4.00	10.00	
1937S	1,652,000	4.50	5.50	7.50	20.00	57.50	
1938 (8,045)	9,480,045	.50	1.00	1.75	12.00	40.00	50.00
1938S	2,832,000	1.75	2.10	3.00	9.00	27.50	
1939 (8,795)	33,548,795	.40	.75	1.00	2.50	6.50	37.50
1939D	7,092,000	.40	.75	1.00	2.75	8.00	
1939S	2,628,000	2.00	2.50	3.00	8.50	30.00	
1940 (11,246)	35,715,246	.40	.75	1.00	2.50	7.50	27.50
1940D	2,797,600	1.50	1.85	2.85	11.00	42.50	
1940S	8,244,000	.40	.80	1.00	2.00	6.00	
1941 (15,287)	79,047,287		.40	.75	1.25	1.75	25.00
1941D	16,714,800		.40	.90	1.60	5.50	
1941S	16,080,000		.35	.50	1.50	6.00	
1942 (21,123)	102,117,123		.35	.50	1.10	2.00	25.00
1942D	17,487,200		.35	.50	1.15	3.00	
1942S	19,384,000		.35	.60	2.00	17.50	
1943	99,700,000		.35	.50	1.10	2.00	
1943D	16,095,600		.35	.50	1.10	2.75	
1943S	21,700,000		.35	.50	1.50	5.25	
1944	104,956,000		.35	.50	.90	1.25	
1944D	14,600,800		.35	.50	1.10	2.75	
1944S	12,560,000		.35	.50	1.25	2.50	
1945	74,372,000		.35	.50	.90	1.25	
1945D	12,341,600		.35	.50	1.10	2.75	
1945S	17,004,001		.35	.50	1.00	2.25	
1946	53,436,000		.35	.50	.75	1.25	
1946D	9,072,800		.35	.50	1.10	3.00	
1946S	4,204,000		.35	.50	1.75	4.00	
1947	22,556,000		.35	.50	.75	1.60	
1947D	15,338,400		.35	.50	.75	1.60	
1947S	5,532,000		.35	.50	1.50	3.50	

QUARTER DOLLARS

	Quan. Minted	Fine	E.F.	Unc.	Proof
1948	35,196,000	$ .50	$ .75	$1.10	
1948D	16,766,800	.75	1.00	2.25	
1948S	15,960,000	.50	.75	1.75	
1949	9,312,000	.75	2.25	9.50	
1949D	10,068,400	.80	1.10	4.25	
1950	(51,386) 24,971,512	.55	.85	1.50	$19.00
1950D	21,075,600	.60	.90	1.75	
1950S	10,284,004	.75	1.10	3.00	
1951	(57,500) 43,505,602	.50	.60	1.00	11.00
1951D	35,354,800	.50	.75	1.00	
1951S	8,948,000	.90	1.50	6.00	
1952	(81,980) 38,862,073	.50	.60	1.00	7.50
1952D	49,795,200	.50	.60	1.00	
1952S	13,707,800	.75	1.00	2.75	
1953	(128,800) 18,664,920	.50	.75	1.50	5.00
1953D	56,112,400	.40	.60	.85	
1953S	14,016,000	.40	.60	1.75	
1954	(233,300) 54,645,503	.40	.50	.75	3.50
1954D	46,305,500	.40	.50	.75	
1954S	11,834,722	.40	.60	1.25	
1955	(378,200) 18,558,381	.40	.60	2.00	4.00
1955D	3,182,400	2.75	3.50	4.25	
1956	(669,384) 44,813,384	....		.85	2.00
1956D	32,334,500	....		.85	
1957	(1,247,952) 47,779,952	....		.85	1.50
1957D	77,924,160	....		.85	
1958	(875,652) 7,235,652		.90	1.75	3.25
1958D	78,124,900	....		.75	
1959	(1,149,291) 25,533,291	....		.75	1.90
1959D	62,054,232	....		.70	
1960	(1,691,602) 30,855,602	....		.70	1.75
1960D	63,000,324	....		.70	
1961	(3,028,244) 40,064,244	....		.70	1.10
1961D	83,656,928	....		.70	
1962	(3,218,019) 39,374,019	....		.70	1.10
1962D	127,554,756	....		.70	
1963	(3,075,645) 77,391,645	....		.70	1.10
1963D	135,288,184	....		.70	
1964	(3,950,762) *564,341,347	....		.70	1.10
1964D	704,135,528	....		.70	

*19,870,585 of these were minted at San Francisco without mint mark.

CLAD COINAGE

	Quan. Minted	Unc.	Proof		Quan. Minted	Unc.	Proof
1965	1,819,717,540	$ .50		1969	176,212,000	$ .50	
1966	821,101,500	.50		1969D	114,372,000	.50	
1967	1,524,031,848	.50		1969S Proof only			
1968	220,731,500	.50			2,934,631		$2.75
1968D	101,534,000	.50		1970	....		
1968S Proof only				1970D	....		
	3,041,509		$3.00	1970S Proof only	.....		2.50

BIBLIOGRAPHY

Browning, A. W., Early Quarter Dollars of the U. S. (1796-1838). 1925.
Haseltine, J. W., Type Table of U. S. Dollars, Halves, Quarters. Reprint 1927.

HALF DOLLARS 1794 To Date

The half dollar, authorized by the Act of April 2, 1792, was not minted until December, 1794. The early types of this series have been extensively collected by die varieties, of which many exist for most dates. Valuations given below are in each case for the most common variety, and scarcer ones as listed by Beistle and Overton (See page 141, Bibliography) generally command higher prices.

The weight of the half-dollar was 208 grains and its fineness 892.4 when first issued. This standard was not changed until 1837 when the law of January 18, 1837 specified 206¼ grains, .900 fine.

Arrows at the date in 1853 indicate the reduction of weight to 192 grains, in conformity with the Act of February 21, 1853. During that year only, rays were added to the field on the reverse side. Arrows remained in 1854 and 1855.

In 1873 the weight was raised by law to 192.9 grains and arrows were again placed at the date, to be removed in 1875.

The half dollars had FIFTY CENTS OR HALF A DOLLAR lettered on the edge until 1836, after which the edge of the coins was reeded.

Proofs prior to 1855 are known to exist of some dates, and all are rare.

FAIR—Clear enough to identify.
GOOD—Date and letters sufficient to be readable. Main devices outlined, but lack details.
VERY GOOD—Major details discernible. Letters well formed but worn.
FINE—Hair ends distinguishable. Top hairlines show, but otherwise worn smooth.
VERY FINE—Hair in center shows some detail. Other details more bold.

1794

→ 3 Leaves Under Wings

Quan. Minted	Fair	Good	V.G.	Fine	V.F.
1794.................5,300	$150.00	$265.00	$375.00	$550.00	$975.00
1795 All kinds........317,844	100.00	135.00	185.00	275.00	525.00
1795 Recut date............	140.00	225.00	350.00	500.00	725.00
1795 3 leaves under each wing.	165.00	335.00	500.00	700.00	1000.00

Grading same as above for Fair to Fine.

VERY FINE—*Right side of drapery slightly worn. Left side to curls is smooth.*

1796, 15 Stars

		Fair	Good	V.G.	Fine	V.F.
1796 15 stars........(Quantity included in 1797 report)		750.00	1475.00	2350.00	3650.00	4400.00

HALF DOLLARS

1796, 16 Stars

1797

Quan. Minted	Fair	Good	V.G.	Fine	V.F.
1796 16 stars................	$800.00	$1600.00	$2550.00	$3800.00	$4650.00
1797.................3,918	800.00	1600.00	2550.00	3800.00	4650.00

1801

1803 Large 3

GOOD—*Letters and date readable. E PLURIBUS UNUM obliterated.*

VERY GOOD—*Motto partially readable. Only deepest drapery details visible. All other lines smooth.*

FINE—*All drapery lines distinguishable. Hairlines near cheek and neck show some detail.*

VERY FINE—*Left side of drapery worn smooth.*

	Quan. Minted	Good	V.G.	Fine	V.F.	Unc.
1801.................	30,289	$80.00	$135.00	$225.00	$375.00	$1200.00
1802.................	29,890	75.00	125.00	190.00	325.00	975.00
1803 Small 3........	⎱ 188,234	70.00	100.00	150.00	200.00	750.00
1803 Large 3........	⎰	50.00	60.00	85.00	150.00	600.00

1805 Over 4

1806 Over 5

1805 5 over 4					
All kinds.........211,722	65.00	85.00	140.00	225.00	650.00

HALF DOLLARS

	Quan. Minted	Good	V.G.	Fine	V.F.	Unc.
1805...................		$30.00	$45.00	$65.00	$115.00	$475.00
1806 6 over 5						
All kinds........839,576		40.00	55.00	75.00	140.00	525.00
1806 6 over inverted 6........		65.00	92.50	145.00	275.00	700.00

Knobbed Top 6 Large Stars

Branch Stem Through Claw

Pointed Top 6

Branch Stem Not Through Claw

1806 Knobbed 6, large stars					
(traces of overdate)......	30.00	45.00	65.00	100.00	425.00
1806 Knobbed 6, small stars...	30.00	45.00	65.00	100.00	425.00
1806 Knobbed 6, stem not					
through claw............	Rare				
1806 Pointed 6, stem through					
claw..................	30.00	45.00	65.00	100.00	425.00
1806 Pointed 6, stem not					
through claw............	30.00	45.00	65.00	100.00	425.00
1807................301,076	30.00	45.00	65.00	100.00	425.00

CAPPED BUST TYPE, Lettered edge 1807-1836

John Reich designed the first Turban Head concept of Liberty. The head of Liberty facing left was used on all U.S. coin denominations for the next thirty years. Reich was the first artist to consistently include the denomination on our gold and silver coins. He was from Germany and a bondman freed from servitude by a mint official.

GOOD—*Date and letters readable. Bust worn smooth with outline distinct.*

VERY GOOD—*LIBERTY visible but faint. Legends distinguishable. Clasp at shoulder visible. Curl above it nearly smooth.*

FINE—*Clasp and adjacent curl clearly outlined with slight details.*

VERY FINE—*Clasp at shoulder clear. Curl has wear only on highest point. Hair over brow distinguishable.*

EXTRA FINE—*Clasp and adjacent curl fairly sharp. Brow and hair above distinct. Curls well defined.*

HALF DOLLARS

Small Stars   Large Stars   50 Over 20c

	Quan. Minted	Good	V.G.	Fine	V.F.	E.F.	Unc.
1807 Small stars........	} 750,500	$20.00	$27.50	$40.00	$85.00	$150.00	$425.00
1807 Large stars........		17.50	25.00	37.50	70.00	110.00	350.00
1807 50 over 20........		16.50	22.50	35.00	65.00	100.00	325.00

1808
Over
7

		Good	V.G.	Fine	V.F.	E.F.	Unc.
1808 8 over 7........	} 1,368,600	12.50	19.00	30.00	42.50	65.00	160.00
1808.................		10.00	12.50	17.50	27.50	45.00	140.00
1809.................	1,405,810	10.00	12.50	16.00	26.00	40.00	130.00
1810.................	1,276,276	10.00	12.50	16.00	26.00	40.00	125.00

1811 Small 8   Punctuated Date 18.11   1814 Over 13

		Good	V.G.	Fine	V.F.	E.F.	Unc.
1811 Sm. 8. All kinds...	1,203,644	7.50	10.00	14.00	22.50	35.00	125.00
1811 Large 8		9.00	12.50	17.50	27.50	50.00	150.00
1811 Date 18.11 (11 over 10)....		15.00	25.00	50.00	80.00	100.00	185.00
1812 2 over 1	} 1,628,059	15.00	22.50	35.00	60.00	90.00	210.00
1812.................		8.00	12.00	16.50	25.00	37.50	125.00
1813.................	1,241,903	8.00	12.00	16.50	25.00	37.50	125.00

HALF DOLLARS

	Quan. Minted	Good	V.G.	Fine	V.F.	E.F.	Unc.
1814 4 over 3 . . . . }	1,039,075	$15.00	$20.00	$30.00	$45.00	$70.00	$200.00
1814 . . . . }		10.00	12.00	15.00	22.50	35.00	125.00

1815
(Mint Report for
1816 — 47,150.)

All have 1815 over 12.
Good . . . . $ 95.00
V. Good 130.00
Fine 185.00
V. Fine 245.00
Ex. Fine 350.00
Unc 875.00

1817
Over
13

1819
Over
18
Small
9

		Good	V.G.	Fine	V.F.	E.F.	Unc.
1817 7 over 3 . . . . }		16.00	27.50	40.00	60.00	85.00	210.00
1817 7 over 4 . . . . }	1,215,567						
1817 Dated 181.7 . . . . . }		15.00	25.00	35.00	50.00	75.00	200.00
1817 Normal date . . . . . }		7.50	11.00	15.00	24.00	35.00	100.00
1818 8 over 7 . . . . }	1,960,322	7.50	11.00	15.00	24.00	35.00	110.00
1818 . . . . }		7.50	10.00	14.00	22.50	34.00	80.00
1819 9 over 8. Sm. 9 . . . }		9.00	12.50	16.00	25.00	37.50	95.00
1819 9 over 8. Lg. 9 . . . . }	2,208,000	9.00	12.50	16.00	25.00	37.50	95.00
1819 Normal date . . . . . }		7.00	9.50	14.00	22.50	34.00	85.00
1820 20 over 19 . . . . . . }		13.00	20.00	27.50	37.50	55.00	140.00
1820 Small date . . . . . . }	751,122	15.00	22.50	30.00	42.50	70.00	150.00
1820 Large date . . . . . . }		14.00	20.00	27.50	40.00	60.00	135.00
1821 1,305,797		7.50	10.00	14.00	20.00	32.50	85.00
1822 . . . . }	1,559,573	7.50	10.00	14.00	20.00	32.50	85.00
1822 2 over 1 . . . . }		35.00	50.00	75.00	100.00	130.00	280.00
1823* 1,694,200		8.00	10.00	14.00	20.00	30.00	75.00
1824 over 21 . . . . }		10.00	15.00	20.00	30.00	42.50	100.00
1824 4 over 4 . . . . }	3,504,954	9.00	12.00	16.00	22.50	35.00	90.00
1824 over various dates }		8.50	11.00	15.00	20.00	30.00	85.00
1824 Normal . . . . }		8.00	10.00	14.00	18.00	25.00	70.00
1825 2,943,166		8.00	10.00	14.00	18.00	25.00	70.00
1826 4,004,180		8.00	10.00	14.00	18.00	25.00	70.00

*There are interesting varieties of this date in which the 3 appears to be
broken, patched, or deformed.

HALF DOLLARS

1827
Over
6

1828
Small
8's
Square-
base
2

	Quan. Minted	Good	V.G.	Fine	V.F.	E.F.	Unc.
1827 7 over 6		$12.50	$17.00	$25.00	$38.00	$60.00	$135.00
1827 Square-base 2	5,493,400	6.00	7.00	10.00	15.00	20.00	65.00
1827 Curled-base 2		12.50	18.00	26.50	40.00	60.00	135.00
1828 Curled-base w/out knobbed 2							
All kinds 3,075,200		8.00	11.00	15.00	22.00	30.00	75.00
1828 Curled-base knobbed 2		35.00	45.00	60.00	85.00	100.00	225.00
1828 Lg. 8's, square-base 2		10.00	12.00	17.00	22.50	30.00	80.00
1828 Sm. 8's, sq-base 2, lg. let . . .		7.50	10.00	13.00	16.00	26.00	70.00
1828 Sm. 8's, sq-base 2, sm. let. . .		20.00	35.00	40.00	75.00	125.00	250.00
1829 over 27	3,712,156	9.00	12.00	15.00	22.00	30.00	80.00
1829 Normal date		7.50	10.00	13.00	16.00	26.00	70.00
1830 Small 0 in date . .	4,764,800	6.50	9.00	12.00	14.00	22.50	62.50
1830 Large 0 in date . .		7.50	10.00	13.00	16.00	25.00	65.00
1831 5,873,660		6.50	9.00	12.00	14.00	22.50	65.00
1832 Small letters	4,797,000	6.50	9.00	12.00	14.00	22.50	65.00
1832 Large letters		7.50	10.00	13.00	16.00	25.00	70.00
1833 5,206,000		6.50	9.00	12.00	14.00	22.50	65.00

1828
Large 8
Curled-
base
Knobbed
2

1834
Small
Date
Small
Stars

	Good	V.G.	Fine	V.F.	E.F.	Unc.
1834 Small date, lg. stars, sm. let.						
All kinds 6,412,004	6.00	8.00	10.00	13.00	22.50	60.00
1834 Small date-stars-letters	9.00	13.00	18.00	27.50	45.00	70.00
1834 Large date, small letters	6.00	8.00	10.00	13.00	22.50	60.00
1834 Large date, large letters	8.00	10.50	13.00	16.00	27.50	65.00
1835 5,352,006	6.50	7.50	9.00	12.50	22.00	60.00
1836 (Lettered edge)						
All kinds 6,546,200	6.50	7.50	9.00	12.50	22.00	65.00
1836 (Ltd. edge) 50 over 00	30.00	40.00	50.00	70.00	95.00	225.00

HALF DOLLARS

Reeded Edge 1836-1839

GOOD—*LIBERTY discernible on headband.*

VERY GOOD—*Minimum of 3 letters in LIBERTY must be clear.*

FINE—*LIBERTY complete.*

VERY FINE—*LIBERTY is sharp. Shoulder clasp is clear.*

EXTRA FINE—*LIBERTY sharp and strong. Hair details show.*

50 CENTS On Reverse 1836-1837

	Quan. Minted	Good	V.G.	Fine	V.F.	E.F.	Unc.
1836 Reeded edge		$50.00	$65.00	$80.00	$140.00	$185.00	$325.00
1837	3,629,820	12.50	18.00	30.00	45.00	65.00	190.00

1838-O

HALF DOL. on Reverse 1838-1839

1838	3,546,000	12.50	18.00	30.00	45.00	65.00	175.00
1838O . . . . (20)	Charles Jay Sale 1967						14,000.00

1838O Not mentioned in Director's report. (Rufus Tyler, coiner of New Orleans Mint, stated that only 20 were coined.)

First branch mint half-dollar. This and following year mint mark appears on Obverse.

1839 All kinds . .	3,334,560	12.50	18.00	30.00	45.00	65.00	175.00
1839O	178,976	55.00	75.00	120.00	160.00	200.00	375.00

LIBERTY SEATED TYPE, no motto above eagle 1839-1866

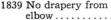

GOOD—*Scant rim. LIBERTY on shield worn off. Date and letters readable.*

VERY GOOD—*Rim fairly defined. At least 3 letters in LIBERTY are evident.*

FINE—*LIBERTY complete, but weak.*

VERY FINE—*LIBERTY mostly sharp.*

EXTRA FINE—*LIBERTY entirely sharp. Scroll edges and clasp distinct.*

1839 No drapery from elbow	27.50	40.00	60.00	80.00	150.00	375.00

HALF DOLLARS

Drapery From Elbow

Small Letters in Legend

	Quan. Minted	Good	V.G.	Fine	V.F.	Unc.
1839........................		$10.00	$13.00	$17.00	$27.50	$110.00
1840 Small letters.	1,435,008	6.00	7.50	12.00	19.00	80.00
1840 Large letters.		25.00	37.50	60.00	100.00	250.00

Letters on Reverse Larger Than Previous Variety

1840O............855,100		6.00	7.50	12.00	19.00	80.00
1841.............310,000		9.00	13.00	18.00	30.00	100.00
1841O............401,000		7.50	9.50	14.00	22.00	80.00

Small Date

Large Date

Larger Letters Than on 1840 Reverse

1842 Small date...	2,012,764	4.50	6.00	10.00	17.50	70.00
1842 Large date...		4.50	6.00	10.00	17.50	70.00
1842O Small date and letters						
All kinds.....957,000		55.00	75.00	100.00	150.00	300.00
1842O Large date and letters		4.50	6.00	10.00	17.50	70.00
1843.............3,844,000		4.50	6.00	10.00	17.50	70.00
1843O............2,268,000		4.50	6.00	10.00	17.50	70.00
1844.............1,766,000		4.50	6.00	10.00	17.50	70.00
1844O............2,005,000		4.50	6.00	10.00	17.50	70.00

HALF DOLLARS

	Quan. Minted	Good	V.G.	Fine	V.F.	Unc.	Proof
1845	589,000	$5.00	$7.00	$10.00	$17.50	$70.00	
1845O	} 2,094,000	5.00	7.00	10.00	17.50	70.00	
1845O No drapery		18.00	27.50	40.00	65.00	135.00	

In 1846 date size was again enlarged. The 1846 small date is approximately the size of the 1842 large date shown on page 133.

	Quan. Minted	Good	V.G.	Fine	V.F.	Unc.	Proof
1846 Sm. date All	2,210,000	4.50	6.00	10.00	17.50	67.50	
1846 Tall date		5.00	7.00	10.00	17.50	67.50	
1846 over horizontal 6 (error)		40.00	60.00	85.00	135.00	310.00	
1846O Small date	} 2,304,000	5.00	7.00	10.00	17.50	67.50	
1846O Tall date		27.50	40.00	65.00	120.00	225.00	
1847 7 over 6	} 1,156,000	———					
1847 Normal date		5.00	7.00	10.00	17.50	70.00	
1847O	2,584,000	5.00	7.00	10.00	17.50	70.00	
1848	580,000	5.00	7.00	10.00	17.50	70.00	
1848O	3,180,000	5.00	7.00	10.00	17.50	70.00	
1849	1,252,000	5.00	7.00	10.00	17.50	70.00	
1849O	2,310,000	5.00	7.00	10.00	17.50	70.00	
1850	227,000	27.50	35.00	50.00	80.00	175.00	
1850O	2,456,000	6.50	8.50	12.00	18.50	75.00	
1851	200,750	27.50	35.00	50.00	80.00	175.00	
1851O	402,000	6.50	8.50	12.00	18.50	75.00	
1852	77,130	30.00	37.50	65.00	140.00	285.00	
1852O	144,000	22.50	30.00	40.00	75.00	170.00	
1853O	(Ex. Rare)	———	———	———	———		

Arrows at Date

Rays Around Eagle

	Quan. Minted	Good	V.G.	Fine	V.F.	Unc.	Proof
1853	3,532,708	10.00	14.00	25.00	40.00	450.00	
1853O All kinds	1,328,000	11.00	16.00	27.50	47.50	475.00	

Arrows At Date — No Rays on Reverse

	Quan. Minted	Good	V.G.	Fine	V.F.	Unc.	Proof
1854	2,982,000	4.50	6.00	8.50	15.00	100.00	
1854O	5,240,000	4.50	6.00	8.50	15.00	90.00	
1855	759,500	5.00	7.00	10.00	17.50	110.00	1200.00
1855O	3,688,000	4.00	6.00	8.50	15.00	90.00	
1855S	129,950	35.00	55.00	100.00	195.00	525.00	

No Arrows At Date

	Quan. Minted	Good	V.G.	Fine	V.F.	Unc.	Proof
1856	938,000	3.50	5.00	7.00	12.00	55.00	900.00
1856O	2,658,000	3.50	5.00	7.00	12.00	55.00	
1856S	211,000	13.00	18.00	27.00	75.00	200.00	
1857	1,988,000	3.50	5.00	7.00	12.00	55.00	900.00
1857O	818,000	4.50	6.00	8.50	14.00	65.00	
1857S	158,000	16.00	23.00	35.00	77.50	225.00	
1858	4,226,000	3.50	5.00	7.00	12.00	55.00	475.00

HALF DOLLARS

	Quan. Minted	Good	V.G.	Fine	V.F.	Unc.	Proof
1858O	7,294,000	$3.50	$5.00	$7.00	$12.00	$60.00	
1858S	476,000	7.00	12.50	20.00	31.00	150.00	
1859	748,000	3.50	5.00	7.00	12.00	60.00	$260.00
1859O	2,834,000	3.50	5.00	7.00	12.00	60.00	
1859S	566,000	7.00	12.50	20.00	31.00	120.00	
1860 (1,000)	303,700	3.50	5.00	7.00	12.00	60.00	165.00
1860O	1,290,000	3.50	5.00	7.00	12.00	60.00	
1860S	472,000	6.00	9.00	13.00	22.00	85.00	
1861 (1,000)	2,888,400	3.50	5.00	7.00	12.00	60.00	165.00
1861O*		3.50	5.00	8.50	14.00	70.00	
1861S	939,500	5.00	7.00	10.00	18.00	75.00	
1862 (550)	253,550	3.50	5.00	9.00	14.00	65.00	170.00
1862S	1,352,000	5.00	7.00	9.50	17.00	65.00	
1863 (460)	503,660	5.00	7.00	9.50	16.00	65.00	165.00
1863S	916,000	5.00	7.00	9.50	16.00	65.00	
1864 (470)	379,570	5.00	7.00	9.50	16.00	65.00	175.00
1864S	658,000	5.00	7.00	9.50	16.00	65.00	
1865 (500)	511,900	5.00	7.00	9.50	16.00	65.00	175.00
1865S	675,000	5.00	7.00	9.50	16.00	65.00	
1866 Unique		Hydeman Sale 1961........Proof $15,500.00					
1866S No motto		40.00	65.00	100.00	190.00	425.00	

1861O* Struck by U.S. Govt	330,000
1861O For Louisiana	1,240,000
1861O For Confed	962,633

Motto Above Eagle

	Quan. Minted	Good	V.G.	Fine	V.F.	Unc.	Proof
1866 (725)	745,625	5.00	7.00	9.50	16.00	60.00	145.00
1866S All Kinds	1,054,000	5.00	7.00	9.50	16.00	60.00	
1867 (625)	449,925	5.00	7.00	9.50	16.00	65.00	150.00
1867S	1,196,000	4.00	6.00	8.00	14.00	60.00	
1868 (600)	418,200	5.00	7.00	9.50	16.00	75.00	160.00
1868S	1,160,000	4.00	6.00	8.00	14.00	65.00	
1869 (600)	795,900	5.00	7.00	9.50	16.00	60.00	160.00
1869S	656,000	4.50	6.50	8.50	14.00	65.00	
1870 (1,000)	634,900	4.50	6.50	8.50	14.00	65.00	125.00
1870CC	54,617	50.00	75.00	110.00	225.00	675.00	
1870S	1,004,000	5.00	7.00	10.00	21.00	75.00	
1871 (960)	1,204,560	4.50	6.50	8.50	12.50	60.00	125.00
1871CC	139,950	42.50	65.00	100.00	200.00	525.00	
1871S	2,178,000	4.50	6.50	8.50	12.50	70.00	
1872 (950)	881,550	4.50	6.50	8.50	12.50	60.00	125.00
1872CC	272,000	30.00	50.00	75.00	125.00	375.00	
1872S	580,000	5.00	8.00	11.00	21.00	75.00	
1873 Closed 3 (600) ⎫ 1873 Open 3 ⎭	801,800	4.50	7.00	9.00	16.50	70.00	200.00
		15.00	25.00	40.00	50.00	135.00	
1873CC	122,500	35.00	60.00	100.00	150.00	450.00	
1873S No arrows	5,000	Unknown in any collection.					

HALF DOLLARS

Arrows
At
Date

	Quan. Minted	Good	V.G.	Fine	V.F.	Unc.	Proof
1873......(550)	1,815,700	$15.00	$25.00	$35.00	$55.00	$250.00	$500.00
1873CC............	214,560	22.50	35.00	60.00	85.00	350.00	
1873S.............	228,000	20.00	30.00	45.00	70.00	275.00	
1874......(700)	2,360,300	15.00	27.50	36.00	60.00	250.00	450.00
1874CC............	59,000	35.00	55.00	100.00	165.00	550.00	
1874S.............	394,000	25.00	35.00	60.00	90.00	285.00	

No Arrows At Date

	Quan. Minted	Good	V.G.	Fine	V.F.	Unc.	Proof
1875......(700)	6,027,500	3.50	5.50	7.50	11.00	57.50	135.00
1875CC..........	1,008,000	7.50	9.00	12.50	30.00	95.00	
1875S............	3,200,000	3.50	5.50	7.50	11.00	57.50	
1876......(1,150)	8,419,150	3.50	5.50	7.50	11.00	57.50	115.00
1876CC..........	1,956,000	6.00	7.00	10.00	19.00	65.00	
1876S............	4,528,000	3.50	5.50	7.50	11.00	57.50	
1877......(510)	8,304,510	3.50	5.50	7.50	11.00	57.50	180.00
1877CC..........	1,420,000	7.00	9.00	12.00	22.50	75.00	
1877S............	5,356,000	3.50	5.50	7.50	11.00	57.50	
1878......(800)	1,378,400	5.00	7.00	10.00	17.50	60.00	130.00
1878CC............	62,000	85.00	110.00	150.00	240.00	675.00	
1878S.............	12,000	300.00	400.00	600.00	1250.00	3500.00	
1879......(1,100)	5,900	45.00	50.00	60.00	65.00	100.00	130.00
1880......(1,355)	9,755	40.00	45.00	55.00	60.00	95.00	120.00
1881......(975)	10,975	40.00	45.00	55.00	60.00	95.00	120.00
1882......(1,100)	5,500	45.00	50.00	60.00	65.00	100.00	130.00
1883......(1,039)	9,039	40.00	45.00	55.00	60.00	95.00	120.00
1884......(875)	5,275	45.00	50.00	60.00	65.00	100.00	140.00
1885......(930)	6,130	45.00	50.00	60.00	65.00	100.00	140.00
1886......(886)	5,886	65.00	70.00	75.00	80.00	115.00	160.00
1887......(710)	5,710	50.00	60.00	70.00	80.00	115.00	160.00
1888......(832)	12,833	40.00	45.00	55.00	60.00	95.00	145.00
1889......(711)	12,711	40.00	45.00	55.00	60.00	95.00	150.00
1890......(590)	12,590	40.00	45.00	55.00	60.00	95.00	175.00
1891......(600)	200,600	6.00	7.50	10.00	17.50	70.00	170.00

BARBER or LIBERTY HEAD TYPE 1892-1915

Like the dime and quarter dollar, this type was designed by Charles E. Barber, whose initial B is at the base of the neck.

GOOD—*Date and legends readable. LIBERTY worn off headband.*

VERY GOOD—*Minimum of 3 letters readable in LIBERTY.*

FINE—*LIBERTY completely readable, but not sharp.*

VERY FINE—*All letters in LIBERTY evenly plain.*

EXTRA FINE—*LIBERTY bold, and its ribbon distinct.*

HALF DOLLARS

	Quan. Minted	Good	V.G.	Fine	V.F.	E.F.	Unc.	Proof
1892 (1,245)	935,245	$4.50	$6.50	$8.00	$12.50	$25.00	$100.00	$140.00
1892O	390,000	24.00	36.00	42.50	52.50	75.00	120.00	
1892S	1,029,028	25.00	35.00	45.00	62.50	90.00	165.00	
1893 (792)	1,826,792	3.25	4.50	7.50	12.00	22.50	100.00	155.00
1893O	1,389,000	8.00	10.00	14.00	25.00	37.50	100.00	
1893S	740,000	24.00	35.00	40.00	52.50	75.00	140.00	
1894 (972)	1,148,972	4.00	6.00	8.00	13.00	27.50	100.00	145.00
1894O	2,138,000	4.50	8.50	14.00	26.00	55.00	125.00	
1894S	4,048,690	3.75	7.00	13.50	25.00	47.50	125.00	
1895 (880)	1,835,218	2.50	4.00	7.00	11.00	22.50	100.00	145.00
1895O	1,766,000	3.00	5.50	11.50	18.00	40.00	125.00	
1895S	1,108,086	6.00	10.00	15.00	25.00	50.00	135.00	
1896 (762)	950,762	4.50	6.50	9.00	17.50	27.50	100.00	150.00
1896O	924,000	7.50	11.50	18.50	40.00	90.00	235.00	
1896S	1,140,948	25.00	35.00	50.00	75.00	125.00	350.00	
1897 (731)	2,480,731	2.00	3.50	6.00	11.00	25.00	100.00	150.00
1897O	632,000	22.50	32.50	47.50	70.00	115.00	300.00	
1897S	933,900	25.00	35.00	47.50	70.00	115.00	335.00	
1898 (735)	2,956,735	2.00	3.50	6.00	12.50	25.00	100.00	155.00
1898O	874,000	4.50	7.50	10.00	15.00	40.00	125.00	
1898S	2,358,550	4.00	6.00	9.50	15.00	40.00	120.00	
1899 (846)	5,538,846	2.00	3.00	5.00	10.00	25.00	100.00	145.00
1899O	1,724,000	3.00	4.50	8.00	15.00	40.00	120.00	
1899S	1,686,411	4.00	5.50	8.00	15.00	40.00	120.00	
1900 (912)	4,762,912	1.75	2.50	5.00	10.00	25.00	95.00	140.00
1900O	2,744,000	2.00	3.50	8.00	20.00	40.00	125.00	
1900S	2,560,322	2.25	3.50	8.00	20.00	35.00	125.00	
1901 (813)	4,268,813	1.75	2.75	5.00	10.00	25.00	95.00	140.00
1901O	1,124,000	3.00	7.50	13.00	45.00	125.00	350.00	
1901S	847,044	9.00	20.00	45.00	95.00	200.00	850.00	
1902 (777)	4,922,777	1.75	2.50	5.00	10.00	25.00	95.00	145.00
1902O	2,526,000	2.00	3.50	7.50	15.00	35.00	115.00	
1902S	1,460,670	2.50	4.50	10.00	30.00	75.00	235.00	
1903 (755)	2,278,755	1.75	2.50	5.00	10.00	25.00	100.00	145.00
1903O	2,100,000	2.00	4.00	8.50	27.50	55.00	190.00	
1903S	1,920,772	2.75	5.00	10.00	30.00	85.00	400.00	
1904 (670)	2,992,670	2.00	3.00	5.00	10.00	25.00	95.00	155.00
1904O	1,117,600	2.50	4.50	8.00	18.00	35.00	150.00	
1904S	553,038	8.50	17.50	25.00	50.00	100.00	435.00	
1905 (727)	662,727	4.50	7.50	9.00	16.00	30.00	100.00	155.00
1905O	505,000	7.50	12.00	17.50	25.00	50.00	195.00	

HALF DOLLARS

	Quan. Minted	Good	V.G.	Fine	V.F.	E.F.	Unc.	Proof
1905S........2,494,000		$2.25	$3.75	$7.50	$15.00	$30.00	$120.00	
1906 (675) 2,638,675		1.75	2.25	5.00	10.00	25.00	95.00	150.00
1906D......4,028,000		1.75	2.25	6.00	12.00	25.00	100.00	
1906O......2,446,000		2.00	3.25	7.00	14.00	27.50	100.00	
1906S........1,740,154		2.25	4.50	8.00	15.00	32.50	120.00	
1907 (575) 2,598,575		1.75	2.50	5.00	10.00	25.00	100.00	170.00
1907D......3,856,000		1.75	2.50	6.00	12.00	25.00	100.00	
1907O......3,946,000		1.75	2.50	6.00	12.00	25.00	100.00	
1907S........1,250,000		2.25	3.75	8.00	16.00	35.00	140.00	
1908 (545) 1,354,545		2.00	3.75	6.50	12.50	25.00	100.00	170.00
1908D......3,280,000		1.75	2.50	6.00	12.00	25.00	100.00	
1908O......5,360,000		1.75	2.50	6.00	12.00	25.00	100.00	
1908S........1,644,828		2.50	4.00	8.00	16.50	27.50	110.00	
1909 (650) 2,368,650		1.75	2.50	5.00	10.00	25.00	100.00	155.00
1909O.........925,400		3.00	4.75	7.50	16.00	35.00	135.00	
1909S........1,764,000		2.00	3.50	6.50	12.50	27.50	120.00	
1910 (551) 418,551		5.00	8.00	11.00	16.00	27.50	110.00	215.00
1910S........1,948,000		1.75	3.25	7.00	11.00	25.00	110.00	
1911 (543) 1,406,543		1.75	3.25	5.00	10.00	25.00	95.00	215.00
1911D.........695,080		3.00	5.00	8.50	13.00	27.50	100.00	
1911S........1,272,000		1.75	3.00	7.00	11.00	27.50	100.00	
1912 (700) 1,550,700		1.75	3.00	5.25	11.00	25.00	100.00	175.00
1912D......2,300,800		1.75	3.00	5.00	10.00	25.00	100.00	
1912S........1,370,000		2.00	3.50	6.50	11.50	27.50	100.00	
1913 (627) 188,627		15.00	19.00	25.00	35.00	60.00	200.00	375.00
1913D.........534,000		3.50	4.50	8.00	16.00	27.50	105.00	
1913S.........604,000		3.50	4.50	9.00	20.00	50.00	175.00	
1914 (380) 124,610		18.00	25.00	42.50	60.00	85.00	275.00	625.00
1914S.........992,000		2.75	4.50	8.00	16.00	32.50	120.00	
1915 (450) 138,450		16.00	21.00	37.50	50.00	90.00	250.00	550.00
1915D......1,170,400		2.00	3.00	5.00	10.00	25.00	100.00	
1915S........1,604,000		2.00	3.00	6.00	11.00	30.00	100.00	

LIBERTY WALKING TYPE 1916-1947

This type was designed by A. A. Weinman. The designer's monogram **AW** appears under the tip of the wing feathers. On the 1916 coins and some of the 1917 coins the mint mark is located on the obverse below the motto.

GOOD—*Rims are defined. Motto IN GOD WE TRUST readable.*

VERY GOOD—*Motto is distinct. About half of skirt lines at left are clear.*

FINE—*All skirt lines evident, but worn in spots. Details in sandal below motto are clear.*

VERY FINE—*Skirt lines sharp including leg area. Little wear on breast and right arm.*

EXTRA FINE—*All skirt lines bold.*

Uncirculated, well-struck
specimens worth
25 % to 50 % above
prices listed.

HALF DOLLARS

	Quan. Minted	Good	V.G.	Fine	V.F.	E.F.	Unc.	Proof
1916	608,000	$9.00	$11.00	$18.50	$25.00	$40.00	$110.00	
1916D on Obv.	1,014,400	6.00	9.00	14.00	20.00	32.50	85.00	
1916S on Obv.	508,000	20.00	27.50	40.00	52.50	77.50	210.00	
1917	12,292,000	1.25	2.00	2.75	6.00	10.00	32.50	
1917D on Obv.	765,400	6.00	9.00	19.00	28.00	52.50	115.00	
1917D on Rev.	1,940,000	2.50	3.75	9.00	22.50	50.00	160.00	
1917S on Obv.	952,000	6.50	11.00	32.50	65.00	110.00	475.00	
1917S on Rev.	5,554,000	2.00	2.75	5.00	11.00	25.00	125.00	
1918	6,634,000	1.50	2.00	4.75	13.00	29.00	125.00	
1918D	3,853,040	1.75	3.00	5.50	15.00	42.50	150.00	
1918S	10,282,000	1.25	2.25	4.00	12.50	34.00	115.00	
1919	962,000	5.00	6.50	12.00	30.00	60.00	385.00	
1919D	1,165,000	4.00	6.50	12.00	60.00	135.00	550.00	
1919S	1,552,000	4.00	6.50	15.00	60.00	160.00	625.00	
1920	6,372,000	1.25	1.75	4.00	7.00	13.50	80.00	
1920D	1,551,000	3.50	5.50	10.00	27.50	75.00	530.00	
1920S	4,624,000	2.00	3.00	8.00	22.50	70.00	400.00	
1921	246,000	30.00	45.00	60.00	95.00	175.00	700.00	
1921D	208,000	60.00	70.00	90.00	125.00	225.00	900.00	
1921S	548,000	9.00	14.00	30.00	60.00	165.00	1100.00	
1923S	2,178,000	2.00	3.00	6.00	30.00	85.00	365.00	
1927S	2,392,000	1.75	2.25	3.50	10.00	27.50	135.00	
1928S	1,940,000	1.75	2.25	3.25	8.00	25.00	165.00	
1929D	1,001,200	2.75	3.50	5.00	9.00	20.00	95.00	
1929S	1,902,000	1.50	2.25	3.25	6.00	19.00	85.00	
1933S	1,786,000	1.50	2.25	3.00	6.00	20.00	110.00	
1934	6,964,000	1.00	1.25	1.50	2.00	3.00	11.50	
1934D	2,361,400	1.25	1.50	2.00	2.50	6.00	35.00	
1934S	3,652,000	1.00	1.25	1.75	4.00	20.00	65.00	
1935	9,162,000	1.00	1.25	1.50	2.00	3.00	10.00	
1935D	3,003,800	1.00	1.25	1.75	2.75	9.00	42.50	
1935S	3,854,000	1.00	1.25	1.50	2.50	15.00	65.00	
1936 (3,901)	12,617,901		1.00	1.25	1.50	3.00	9.00	$265.00
1936D	4,252,400	1.00	1.25	1.50	2.25	3.50	18.00	
1936S	3,884,000	1.00	1.25	1.50	2.50	7.00	40.00	
1937 (5,728)	9,527,728		1.00	1.25	1.50	3.00	11.00	110.00
1937D	1,760,001	2.50	3.00	4.00	6.00	12.00	65.00	
1937S	2,090,000	1.50	2.00	3.00	4.50	12.00	55.00	
1938 (8,152)	4,118,152	1.00	1.25	1.50	2.25	6.00	35.00	85.00
1938D	491,600	24.00	27.50	30.00	35.00	55.00	185.00	
1939 (8,808)	6,820,808		1.00	1.25	2.00	4.00	10.00	75.00
1939D	4,267,800	1.00	1.25	1.50	2.25	4.50	15.00	
1939S	2,552,000	1.25	1.50	2.00	3.00	9.00	30.00	
1940 (11,279)	9,167,279		1.00	1.25	1.50	2.50	8.00	60.00
1940S	4,550,000	1.00	1.25	1.50	2.00	4.00	14.00	
1941 (15,412)	24,207,412		1.00	1.25	1.50	2.25	7.50	*55.00
1941D	11,248,400		1.00	1.25	1.50	2.50	14.00	
1941S	8,098,000		1.00	1.25	1.50	5.00	35.00	
1942 (21,120)	47,839,120		1.00	1.25	1.50	2.00	6.50	55.00
1942D	10,973,800		1.00	1.25	1.50	3.00	15.00	
1942S	12,708,000		1.00	1.25	1.50	4.00	16.00	
1943	53,190,000			1.00	1.50	2.50	6.25	

*Proofs struck with or without designer's initials.

HALF DOLLARS

Quan. Minted	V.F.	E.F.	Unc.
1943D..11,346,000	$1.00	$2.50	$13.50
1943S...13,450,000	1.00	3.00	16.50
1944....28,206,000	1.00	1.50	6.00
1944D...9,769,000	1.00	2.00	7.50
1944S...8,904,000	1.00	2.00	8.00
1945....31,502,000	1.00	1.50	6.75
1945D...9,966,800	1.00	1.75	6.75

Quan. Minted	V.F.	E.F.	Unc.
1945S...10,156,000	$1.00	$1.75	$7.50
1946....12,118,000	1.00	1.75	7.00
1946D...2,151,000	2.00	4.00	12.00
1946S....3,724,000	1.00	2.00	8.50
1947.....4,094,000	1.00	2.00	12.50
1947D...3,900,600	1.00	2.00	9.00

FRANKLIN-LIBERTY BELL TYPE 1948-1963

Select, well-struck uncirculated halves command higher prices.

The designer was John R. Sinnock, and his initials appear under the shoulder.

EXTRA FINE—*Wear spots appear at top of end curls and hair back of ears. On reverse, Liberty Bell will show wear at top.*

Quan. Minted	E.F.	Unc.	Proof
1948.....3,006,814	$5.00	$12.00	
1948D...4,028,600	2.75	7.00	
1949.....5,714,000	4.00	26.50	
1949D...4,120,600	3.25	21.00	
1949S....3,744,000	5.00	24.00	
1950 (51,386)			
......7,793,509	2.75	18.50	$62.50
1950D...8,031,600	2.25	12.00	
1951 (57,500)			
......16,859,602	2.00	5.00	40.00
1951D...9,475,200	3.50	21.50	
1951S...13,696,000	2.50	13.00	
1952 (81,980)			
......21,274,073	1.50	3.75	21.00
1952D..25,395,600	1.50	3.00	
1952S....5,526,000	3.00	12.00	
1953 (128,800)			
......2,796,920	5.00	13.00	17.50
1953D..20,900,400	1.25	2.50	
1953S....4,148,000	2.25	6.25	
1954 (233,300)			
......13,421,503	1.35	2.50	9.00
1954D..25,445,580	1.25	2.00	
1954S....4,993,400	1.80	4.00	

Quan. Minted	E.F.	Unc.	Proof
1955 (378,200)			
......2,876,381	$7.50	$10.00	$15.50
1956 (669,384)			
......4,701,384	2.00	4.25	6.75
1957 (1,247,952)			
......6,361,952	1.50	3.50	3.65
1957D..19,966,850	1.25	2.00	
1958 (875,652)			
......4,917,652	1.75	4.00	7.00
1958D..23,962,412	1.10	1.80	
1959 (1,149,291)			
......7,349,291	1.35	3.00	3.75
1959D..13,053,750	1.10	2.00	
1960 (1,691,602)			
......7,715,602	1.25	2.50	3.75
1960D..18,215,812	1.10	1.85	
1961 (3,028,244)			
......11,318,244	1.10	2.00	2.90
1961D..20,276,442	1.00	2.00	
1962 (3,218,019)			
......12,932,019	1.15	2.00	2.90
1962D..35,473,281	1.00	1.85	
1963 (3,075,645)			
......25,239,645	1.00	1.65	3.00
1963D..67,069,292	1.00	1.60	

HALF DOLLARS
KENNEDY TYPE 1964 to Date

Gilroy Roberts, former Chief Sculptor of the Mint, designed the obverse of this coin. His stylized initials are on the truncation of the forceful bust of President John F. Kennedy. The reverse, which uses the presidential coat of arms for the motif, is the work of Frank Gasparro, now Head Engraver at the Mint.

	Quan. Minted	Unc.	Proof
1964	(3,950,762) 277,254,766	$1.25	$6.25
1964D	156,205,446	1.35	

CLAD COINAGE

1965	65,879,366	1.35	
1966	108,984,932	1.00	
1967	295,046,978	1.00	
1968D	246,951,930	1.00	
1968S Proof only	3,041,509		5.00
1969D	129,881,800	1.00	
1969S Proof only	2,934,631		4.25
1970S Proof only			4.00

BIBLIOGRAPHY

Beistle, M.L., Register of U. S. Half Dollar Die Varieties. 1929.
Haseltine J. W., Type Table of U. S. Dollars, Half and Quarter Dollars, 1881. Mehl reprint 1927. Hewitt reprint 1968.
Overton, Al C., Early Half Dollar Varieties 1794-1836. 1967.

SILVER DOLLARS
Issued 1794-1935

The silver dollar was authorized by Congress April 2, 1792. Weight and fineness were specified at 416 grains and 892.4 fine. The first issues appeared in 1794 and until 1804 all silver dollars had the value stamped on the edge: HUNDRED CENTS, ONE DOLLAR OR UNIT. After a lapse in coinage of the silver dollar covering the period 1804 to 1840, these coins had reeded edges and the value was placed on the reverse side.

There were several interesting pattern dollars produced by Christian Gobrecht from 1836 to 1839. The seated figure of Liberty was the resulting type, becoming a regular coinage issue starting in 1840. Thenceforth the edge was reeded.

The weight was changed by the law of January 18, 1837 to $412\frac{1}{2}$ grains, fineness .900. The coinage was discontinued by the act of February 12, 1873 and reauthorized by the Act of February 28, 1878. The dollar was again discontinued after 1935.

ORIGIN OF THE DOLLAR

The word Dollar evolves from German Taler, the name given to the first large-sized European silver coin. Designed as a substitute for the gold Florin, the coin originated in the Tyrol in 1484. So popular did these large silver coins

SILVER DOLLARS

become during the 16th century that many other countries struck similar pieces, giving them names derived from taler. In the Netherlands the coin was called Rijksdaalder, in Denmark Rigsdaler, in Italy Tallero, in Poland Talar, in France Jocandale, in Russia Jefimok. All these names are abbreviations of "Joachimsthaler." Until the discovery of the great silver deposits in Mexican and South American mines, the mint with the greatest output of large silver coins was that of Joachimsthal in the Bohemian Erzgebirge.

The Spanish Dollar, or piece-of-eight, was widely used and familiar to everyone in the English-American colonies. It was only natural therefore that the word "dollar" was adopted officially as the standard monetary unit of the United States by Congress on July 6, 1785.

FLOWING HAIR TYPE 1794-1795

FAIR—*Clear enough to identify.*
GOOD—*Date and letters readable. Main devices outlined, but lack details.*
VERY GOOD—*Major details discernible. Letters well formed but worn.*
FINE—*Hair ends distinguishable. Top hairlines show, but otherwise worn smooth.*
VERY FINE—*Hair in center shows some detail. Other details more bold.*

Quan. Minted	Fair	Good	V.G.	Fine	V. Fine	Unc.
1794.....1,758	$800.00	$1300.00	$2100.00	$3000.00	$5500.00	$12,500.00

Two Leaves Beneath Each Wing (11 Varieties)			Three Leaves Beneath Each Wing		

	Fair	Good	V.G.	Fine	V. Fine	Unc.
1795 All kinds ...203,033 Two leaves	135.00	210.00	250.00	300.00	475.00	1,600.00
1795 Three leaves....	135.00	210.00	250.00	300.00	475.00	1,600.00

SILVER DOLLARS

DRAPED BUST TYPE, SMALL EAGLE REVERSE 1795-1798

FAIR—Clear enough to identify.
GOOD—Bust outlined, no detail. Date readable, some leaves evident.
VERY GOOD—Drapery worn except deepest folds. Hairlines smooth.
FINE—All drapery lines distinguishable. Hairlines near cheek and neck show some detail.
VERY FINE—Left side of drapery worn smooth.

	Quan. Minted	Fair	Good	V.G.	Fine	V. F.	Unc.
1795 (Two varieties)		$120.00	$160.00	$240.00	$320.00	$500.00	$1,850

Small Date   Large Date

Small Letters   Large Letters

		Fair	Good	V.G.	Fine	V. F.	Unc.
1796 Sm. date, sm. let. (3 var.)							
All kinds	72,920	110.00	145.00	210.00	285.00	425.00	1,600
1796 Sm. date lg. let.		110.00	145.00	210.00	285.00	425.00	1,600
1796 Lg. date sm. let.		110.00	145.00	210.00	285.00	425.00	1,600
1797 9 stars left, 7 right							
Sm. let. All kinds	7,776	250.00	340.00	425.00	550.00	1,100	——
1797 9 stars l., 7 r., lg. let.		120.00	190.00	240.00	360.00	525.00	1,800
1797 10 stars left, 6 right		120.00	190.00	240.00	360.00	525.00	1,800
1798 15 stars (small eagle)		120.00	180.00	235.00	340.00	475.00	1,750
1798 13 stars (small eagle)							
All kinds	327,536	110.00	160.00	210.00	275.00	425.00	1,500

[143]

SILVER DOLLARS

HERALDIC EAGLE REVERSE 1798-1804

GOOD—*Letters and date readable. E PLURIBUS UNUM obliterated.*

VERY GOOD—*Motto partially readable. Only deepest drapery details visible. All other lines smooth.*

FINE—*All drapery lines distinguishable. Hairlines near cheek and neck show some detail.*

VERY FINE—*Left side of drapery worn smooth.*

	Quan. Minted	Good	V.G.	Fine	V. Fine	Unc.
1798 Large heraldic eagle, knob 9 (5 varieties)		$95.00	$120.00	$195.00	$250.00	$950.00
1798 Lg. eagle, 10 arrows (5 var.)		90.00	115.00	175.00	235.00	900.00
1798 Close date, 4 berries in branch		90.00	115.00	175.00	235.00	900.00
1798 Close date, 5 berries, 12 arrows		90.00	115.00	175.00	235.00	900.00
1798 Close date, high 8 (6 var.)		90.00	115.00	175.00	235.00	900.00
1798 Wide date, 13 arrows (11 var.)		90.00	115.00	175.00	235.00	900.00

1799 Over 98, Stars 7 & 6

Stars 8 & 5

	Quan. Minted	Good	V.G.	Fine	V. Fine	Unc.
1799 9 over 8 rev. with 15 stars All kinds	423,515	110.00	145.00	190.00	300.00	925.00
1799 9 over 8 rev. with 13 stars		110.00	145.00	190.00	300.00	925.00
1799 Irregular date, 15-star rev.		100.00	130.00	175.00	250.00	825.00
1799 Irregular date, 13-star rev.		100.00	130.00	175.00	250.00	825.00
1799 Norm. date, no berries in br.		100.00	130.00	175.00	250.00	825.00
1799 Norm. date, small berries		100.00	130.00	175.00	250.00	825.00
1799 Norm. date, medium large berries (15 varieties)		100.00	130.00	175.00	250.00	825.00
1799 Norm. date, ex. lg. berries		100.00	130.00	175.00	250.00	825.00
1799 Stars - 8 left, 5 right		110.00	145.00	190.00	300.00	925.00
1800 LIBERTY with R double cut All kinds	220,920	95.00	115.00	160.00	240.00	775.00
1800 First T in STATES double cut		95.00	115.00	160.00	240.00	775.00
1800 Both R in LIBERTY and first T in STATES double cut		95.00	115.00	160.00	240.00	775.00
1800 Let. T in UNITED double cut		95.00	115.00	160.00	240.00	775.00
1800 Very wide date, low 8		95.00	115.00	160.00	240.00	775.00

SILVER DOLLARS

	Quan. Minted	Good	V.G.	Fine	V. Fine	Unc.
1800 Small berries in branch.......		$95.00	$115.00	$160.00	$240.00	$775.00
1800 "Dotted date" from die breaks.		95.00	115.00	160.00	240.00	775.00
1800 Only 12 arrows...............		95.00	115.00	160.00	240.00	775.00
1800 Only 10 arrows...............		95.00	115.00	160.00	240.00	775.00
1800 AMERICAI (2 varieties)........		110.00	140.00	180.00	260.00	850.00
1801 (4 vars.) 54,454		100.00	130.00	175.00	250.00	825.00
1801 Proof restrike (rev. struck from first die of 1804 dollar).......				(Proof) ———		

1802 Over 1

		Good	V.G.	Fine	V. Fine	Unc.
1802 2 over 1, narrow date...		100.00	130.00	175.00	250.00	800.00
1802 2 over 1, wide date.....	41,650	100.00	130.00	175.00	250.00	800.00
1802 Narrow norm. date.....		100.00	130.00	175.00	250.00	800.00
1802 Wide norm. date.......		100.00	130.00	175.00	250.00	800.00
1802 Proof restrike..............				(Proof) ———		

Small
3

Large
3

		Good	V.G.	Fine	V. Fine	Unc.
1803 Large 3 (1 variety).....	85,634	110.00	140.00	185.00	260.00	800.00
1803 Small 3 (5 varieties)....		110.00	140.00	185.00	260.00	800.00
1803 Proof restrike..............				(Proof) ———		

THE 1804 DOLLAR

This piece is one of the most publicized rarities in the United States series. There are specimens known as originals (type 1), of which eight are known, and restrikes (type 2), of which seven are known.

Opinion has long been divided regarding the origin, date of issue and authenticity of this coin. Those who have stated that these coins were struck in 1804 point to such evidence as the letter written by Robert Patterson, Director of the Mint, to President Thomas Jefferson. This letter stated that no dollars had been minted "during the last two years." Inasmuch as the letter was dated April 2, 1807, they infer that dollars were struck during 1804.

Mint records show that 19,570 silver dollars were coined in 1804 and that these coins were struck before March 28, 1804. Years later a die with the date 1804 was found at the mint among discarded dies. It is a matter of record that Director Boudinot stopped the coinage of silver dollars in 1804 to prevent their exportation because their face value was less than their bullion value.

Numismatists now know that the 1804 "original" dollars were struck at the mint between 1834 and 1835, for use in presentation proof sets. The first known specimen, a proof, was obtained from a mint officer by Mr. Stickney on May 9, 1843, in exchange for an "Immune Columbia" piece of gold. Later, in 1859, the pieces known as restrikes were made at the mint to supply the needs of collectors who wanted specimens of these dollars.

SILVER DOLLARS

Evidence that these pieces were struck during the later period is based on the fact that the 1804 dollars differ from issues of 1803 or earlier and conform more closely to those struck after 1836, their edges or borders having beaded segments and raised rim, not elongated denticles such as are found on the earlier dates.

Although the mint records state that 19,570 dollars were coined in 1804, in no place does it mention that they were dated 1804. It was the practice in those days to use old dies as long as they were serviceable with no regard in the annual reports for the dating of the coins. It is probable that the 1804 total for dollars actually covered coins that were dated 1803.

The 321 silver dollars reported for 1805 were not dated 1805. An entry in Bullion Journal dated June 28, 1805, mentions these 321 pieces as "being found amongst Spanish Dollars brought to the Mint." They were of earlier coinage and instead of being melted they were transferred to the Director.

TYPE 1

Note Position of Words STATES OF With Relation to Clouds

1804 Type 1, Original (Stickney specimen sold for $10,500.00 in 1946.)
(Dexter specimen sold for $10,000.00 in 1950.)

TYPE 2

Compare With Type 1 Above

1804 Type 2, Restrike (Idler specimen sold for $29,000.00 in 1961.)
(Davis-Hale specimen sold for $28,000.00 in 1960.)

BIBLIOGRAPHY

Bolender, M. H., The UNITED STATES EARLY SILVER DOLLARS from 1794 to 1803. 1950.
Newman-Bressett — THE FANTASTIC 1804 DOLLAR. 1962.

SILVER DOLLARS
CHRISTIAN GOBRECHT

Christian Gobrecht was born December 23, 1785. He went to Philadelphia in 1811 and became an engraver of bank notes, seals, calico printers' rolls, bookbinders' dies, etc. He was appointed assistant to Mint Engraver William Kneass in 1836. According to Edgar H. Adams, he prepared a series of dies for pattern dollars, after designs by Sully, exquisite in design and character. The first pattern shows the familiar seated figure of Liberty on the obverse. The name C. Gobrecht F. (F.=Fecit=made it) was placed just under the figure of Liberty and over the date. In the field on the reverse was a large eagle in full flight surrounded by twenty-six stars and the legend UNITED STATES OF AMERICA ONE DOLLAR.

In response to criticism Gobrecht removed his name from the die after a few specimens had been struck, some in silver and some in copper.

Director Patterson ordered the name replaced, this time on the base. Patterns were also made in 1836 with the stars omitted from the field of the reverse.

1836 C. GOBRECHT F. in field between base and date. Rev. Eagle   Proof
     flying left amid stars. Plain edge (Rare.) (18)............... ———
1836 Obv. as above. Rev. Eagle flying in plain field.
     Plain edge (Very rare.) (5)............................... ———

1836 C. GOBRECHT on base. Rev. Eagle flying left in field containing stars.

	V. Fine	Proof
Plain edge. Although scarce, this is the most common variety. (1,000)........................	$900.00	$1900.00
1836 As above, reeded edge. (Very rare.) (3)............	———	

SILVER DOLLARS

In 1838 the engraver's name was omitted altogether from the design and thirteen stars were placed around the seated figure of Liberty on the obverse. Stars were omitted from the reverse on one pattern and retained on another. Similar pieces were struck in 1839.

Proof

1838 As above, reeded edge. Generally considered to be very rare. 25 Struck. Also unknown quantity of restrikes.............. $4000.00

1838 Obv. as above. Rev. Eagle in plain field. Plain edge. (Very rare.) (3).. ———

1838 Seated Liberty. Obv. name of designer is left off and stars added around obverse border. Rev. Eagle flying left surrounded by stars. Plain edge. (Very rare.) (3)........................ ———

1839 Obv. same as 1838. Rev. Eagle in plain field. Plain edge. (Very rare.) (3).. ———

1839 Obv. as above. Rev. Eagle amid stars. Plain edge. (Very rare.) (3).. ———

1839 Obv. as above. Rev. Eagle in plain field. Reeded edge. Most common 1839 variety. (Rare) (300)................ 4000.00

Quantities shown for the above patterns are probably inaccurate as restrikes of many are known to have been made.

When in 1840 silver dollars were again issued for general circulation, the seated figure of Liberty device was adopted for the obverse. For some mysterious reason the flying eagle design was rejected, and the more familiar form with olive branch and arrows was used.

SILVER DOLLARS
LIBERTY SEATED TYPE — REGULAR ISSUES 1840-1873

VERY GOOD—Any 3 letters of LIBERTY at least two-thirds complete.
FINE—All 7 letters of LIBERTY visible though weak.
VERY FINE—LIBERTY is strong but its ribbon shows slight wear.

	Quan. Minted	V.G.	Fine	V.F.	Unc.	Proof
1840	61,005	$35.00	$50.00	$60.00	$200.00	$1,100
1841	173,000	30.00	40.00	50.00	175.00	1,000
1842	184,618	30.00	40.00	50.00	175.00	1,000
1843	165,100	30.00	40.00	50.00	175.00	1,000
1844	20,000	50.00	75.00	100.00	260.00	1,000
1845	24,500	50.00	75.00	100.00	260.00	1,000
1846	110,600	25.00	35.00	45.00	160.00	900.00
1846O	59,000	35.00	45.00	60.00	200.00	
1847	140,750	30.00	40.00	50.00	175.00	900.00
1848	15,000	60.00	75.00	100.00	260.00	1,000
1849	62,600	32.50	42.50	55.00	175.00	950.00
1850	7,500	75.00	110.00	175.00	325.00	1,050
1850O	40,000	40.00	52.50	75.00	190.00	
1851 Orig., high date	1,300	450.00	650.00	850.00	1,800	3,000
1851 Restrike, date centered						2,250
1852 Original	1,100					3,000
1852 Restrike						2,000
1853	46,110	50.00	75.00	110.00	350.00	1,700
1854	33,140	85.00	130.00	185.00	400.00	1,500
1855	26,000	95.00	150.00	200.00	450.00	1,500
1856	63,500	50.00	70.00	100.00	340.00	1,000
1857	94,000	47.50	70.00	100.00	300.00	850.00
1858	Estimated (80)					2,000
1859	256,500	32.50	45.00	65.00	180.00	375.00
1859O	360,000	30.00	37.50	50.00	150.00	
1859S	20,000	55.00	80.00	100.00	350.00	
1860 (1,330)	218,930	32.50	42.50	60.00	150.00	300.00
1860O	515,000	25.00	35.00	42.50	120.00	
1861 (1,000)	78,500	40.00	55.00	77.50	180.00	325.00
1862 (550)	12,090	45.00	65.00	90.00	275.00	425.00
1863 (460)	27,660	45.00	65.00	80.00	245.00	425.00
1864 (470)	31,170	45.00	65.00	80.00	225.00	425.00
1865 (500)	47,000	40.00	55.00	77.50	225.00	425.00
1866 No motto (2 known)	Charles Jay Sale 1967...Proof $15,000.00					

SILVER DOLLARS

Motto "In God We Trust" Added To Reverse

	Quan. Minted	V.G.	Fine	V.F.	Unc.	Proof
1866 . . . . (725)	49,625	$40.00	$55.00	$77.50	$200.00	$375.00
1867 . . . . (625)	47,525	40.00	55.00	77.50	200.00	375.00
1868 . . . . (600)	162,700	32.50	45.00	65.00	145.00	375.00
1869 . . . . (600)	424,300	25.00	32.50	45.00	140.00	375.00
1870 . . . . (1,000)	416,000	25.00	32.50	45.00	125.00	325.00
1870CC 12,462		80.00	120.00	170.00	525.00	
1870S		Wolfson Sale, 1963 . . .$12,000.00				
1871 . . . . (960)	1,074,760	22.50	30.00	35.00	125.00	325.00
1871CC 1,376		475.00	650.00	950.00	2600.00	
1872 . . . . (950)	1,106,450	22.50	30.00	35.00	125.00	325.00
1872CC 3,150		220.00	325.00	425.00	1500.00	
1872S 9,000		65.00	100.00	135.00	400.00	
1873 . . . . (600)	293,600	27.50	35.00	45.00	145.00	375.00
1873CC 2,300		650.00	900.00	1400.00	3000.00	
1873S 700		. . . . .Unknown in any collection.				

LIBERTY HEAD MORGAN TYPE 1878-1921

The mint law of 1873 made no provision for the standard silver dollar. During the lapse in coinage of this piece the gold dollar became the unit coin and the trade dollar was used for our commercial transactions with the Orient.

The legal tender character was restored to the silver dollar by the Act of February 28, 1878 known as the Bland-Allison Act. The weight, $412\frac{1}{2}$ grains and fineness .900 were to conform with the act of January 18, 1837.

George T. Morgan, formerly a pupil of Wyon in the Royal Mint in London, designed the new dollar. His initial M is found at the truncation of the neck, at the last tress. It also appears on the reverse on the left-hand loop of the ribbon. It is very difficult to detect.

Coinage of the silver dollar was again suspended after 1904 when the bullion supply became exhausted. Under provisions of the Pittman Act of 1918 coinage of the silver dollar was resumed in 1921. The Morgan design, with some slight refinements, was employed until the new Peace design was adopted later in that year.

VERY FINE—Two-thirds of hairlines from top of forehead to ear must show. Ear well defined. Feathers on eagle's breast worn at center.

EXTRA FINE—All hairlines strong and ear bold. Eagle's feathers all plain but slight wear on breast and wing tips.

SILVER DOLLARS

Beware of early strike Philadelphia mint uncirculated dollars being offered as proofs.

8 Tail Feathers 1878 Philadelphia Only

1880CC
80 over 79

Most uncirculated silver dollars have scratches or nicks because of handling of mint bags. Perfect coins without blemishes are generally worth 50% more than listed values.

7 Tail Feathers
1878 and Later Dates

	Quan. Minted	V. F.	Ex. F.	Unc.	Proof
1878 8 tail feathers . . . . (700)	750,000	$5.50	$7.00	$15.00	$300.00
1878 7 tail feathers					
All kinds . . . . (300)	9,759,550				
1878 7 feathers, rev. of 1878*		2.50	3.50	6.50	380.00
1878 7 feathers, rev. of 1879*		2.50	5.00	8.00	
1878 7 feathers over 8 feathers		8.00	12.50	17.50	
1878CC 2,212,000		5.50	6.50	16.00	
1878S 9,774,000		2.50	3.25	5.00	
1879 . . . . (1,100) 14,807,100		2.50	2.75	4.50	220.00
1879CC 756,000		30.00	55.00	210.00	
1879O 2,887,000		2.75	3.60	7.50	
1879S Rev. of 1878* . . . . } 9,110,000		3.00	7.00	17.50	
1879S Rev. of 1879*		2.50	3.25	4.00	
1880 . . . . (1,355) } 12,601,355		2.50	3.25	5.00	220.00
1880 8 over 7					
1880CC Rev. of 1878*		30.00	40.00	65.00	
1880CC Rev. of 1879* . . . . } 591,000		25.00	30.00	60.00	
1880CC 80 over 79					
1880O 5,305,000		2.75	3.50	6.00	
1880S 8,900,000		2.50	3.00	3.75	
1881 . . . . (975) 9,163,975		2.50	3.50	5.00	220.00
1881CC 296,000		50.00	60.00	80.00	
1881O 5,708,000		2.50	3.25	4.50	
1881S 12,760,000		2.50	3.25	4.00	

*Reverse of 1878 has parallel feathers on the arrows.
Reverse of 1879 and later dates has slanting feathers.

SILVER DOLLARS

	Quan. Minted	V. Fine	Ex. Fine	Unc.	Proof
1882.............(1,100)	11,101,000	$ 2.50	$ 3.25	$ 4.50	$220.00
1882CC...................	1,133,000	16.00	20.00	35.00	
1882O	6,090,000	2.50	3.25	4.25	
1882O O over S		5.00	7.50	15.00	
1882S...................	9,250,000	2.50	3.25	4.00	
1883.............(1,039)	12,291,039	2.50	3.25	4.00	220.00
1883CC.................	1,204,000	15.00	17.50	30.00	
1883O.................	8,725,000	2.50	3.25	4.00	
1883S.................	6,250,000	3.50	6.00	27.50	
1884.............(875)	14,070,875	2.50	3.25	4.00	230.00
1884CC.................	1,136,000	25.00	30.00	40.00	
1884O.................	9,730,000	2.50	3.25	4.00	
1884S.................	3,200,000	4.00	6.00	65.00	
1885.............(930)	17,787,767	2.50	3.25	4.00	220.00
1885CC...............	228,000	45.00	50.00	65.00	
1885O.................	9,185,000	2.50	3.25	4.00	
1885S.................	1,497,000	4.00	6.00	16.00	
1886.............(886)	19,963,886	2.50	3.25	4.00	230.00
1886O.................	10,710,000	3.25	4.50	15.00	
1886S.................	750,000	17.50	22.50	37.50	
1887.............(710)	20,290,710	2.50	3.25	4.00	230.00
1887O.................	11,550,000	3.00	3.50	6.00	
1887S.................	1,771,000	7.50	9.00	16.00	
1888.............(832)	19,183,833	2.50	3.25	4.00	230.00
1888O.................	12,150,000	2.75	3.50	5.00	
1888S.................	657,000	16.50	21.00	37.50	
1889.............(811)	21,726,811	2.50	3.25	4.00	230.00
1889CC...............	350,000	100.00	200.00	950.00	
1889O.................	11,875,000	3.50	4.50	15.00	
1889S.................	700,000	17.50	20.00	35.00	
1890.............(590)	16,802,590	2.50	3.25	5.00	285.00
1890CC...............	2,309,041	9.50	13.50	30.00	
1890O.................	10,701,000	3.00	4.00	8.50	
1890S.................	8,230,373	3.00	4.00	8.00	
1891.............(650)	8,694,206	3.00	4.00	11.00	260.00
1891CC...............	1,618,000	11.00	15.00	27.50	
1891O.................	7,954,529	3.00	4.00	14.00	
1891S.................	5,296,000	3.00	4.00	12.50	
1892.............(1,245)	1,037,245	4.00	6.00	30.00	230.00
1892CC...............	1,352,000	25.00	35.00	65.00	
1892O.................	2,744,000	3.50	5.50	25.00	
1892S.................	1,200,000	15.00	35.00	1,800.00	
1893.............(792)	378,792	12.50	16.50	60.00	275.00
1893CC...............	677,000	35.00	55.00	225.00	
1893O.................	300,000	25.00	60.00	210.00	
1893S.................	100,000	300.00	550.00	5,250	
1894.............(972)	110,972	65.00	85.00	210.00	700.00
1894O.................	1,723,000	5.00	12.50	75.00	
1894S.................	1,260,000	12.50	20.00	55.00	
1895*.............(880)	12,880				4,750
1895O.................	450,000	25.00	40.00	350.00	
1895S.................	400,000	45.00	85.00	525.00	
1896.............(762)	9,976,762	2.50	3.25	4.00	240.00

*Beware removed mint letter.

SILVER DOLLARS

	Quan. Minted	V. Fine	Ex. Fine	Unc.	Proof
1896O	4,900,000	$ 4.50	$ 7.50	$ 65.00	
1896S	5,000,000	12.50	35.00	225.00	
1897 (731)	2,822,731	3.25	4.00	6.50	$240.00
1897O	4,004,000	4.50	7.50	45.00	
1897S	5,825,000	3.00	4.00	12.50	
1898 (735)	5,884,735	2.50	3.25	4.50	240.00
1898O	4,440,000	2.50	3.25	4.50	
1898S	4,102,000	5.00	9.00	32.50	
1899 (846)	330,846	10.00	15.00	25.00	275.00
1899O	12,290,000	2.50	3.25	4.00	
1899S	2,562,000	7.00	11.00	40.00	
1900 (912)	8,830,912	2.50	3.25	4.00	225.00
1900O	} 12,590,000	2.50	3.25	4.00	
1900O O over CC		6.00	10.00	30.00	
1900S	3,540,000	6.00	10.00	35.00	
1901 (813)	6,962,813	8.00	13.00	90.00	225.00
1901O	13,320,000	2.50	3.25	4.00	
1901S	2,284,000	6.50	11.00	50.00	
1902 (777)	7,994,777	3.25	4.75	9.00	240.00
1902O	8,636,000	2.50	3.25	4.00	
1902S	1,530,000	33.00	42.50	100.00	
1903 (755)	4,652,755	3.00	4.50	7.50	240.00
1903O	4,450,000	27.50	32.50	40.00	
1903S	1,241,000	14.00	40.00	385.00	
1904 (650)	2,788,650	3.50	5.00	17.50	275.00
1904O	3,720,000	2.50	3.25	5.50	
1904S	2,304,000	11.50	27.50	200.00	

270,232,722 silver dollars were melted under the Pittman Act of April, 1918, 259,121,554 for export to India, and 11,111,168 for domestic subsidiary coins.

1921	44,690,000	2.50	3.25	4.00	———
1921D	20,345,000	2.50	3.25	6.00	
1921S	21,695,000	2.50	3.25	6.00	

BIBLIOGRAPHY

Haseltine, J. W., Type Table of U. S. Dollars, Half and Quarter Dollars. 1881. Reprint 1927.

PEACE TYPE 1921-1935

Anthony De Francisci, a medalist, designed this dollar. His monogram is located in the field of the coin under the neck of Liberty.

The new Peace Dollar was placed in circulation January 3, 1922. 1,006,473 pieces were struck in December, 1921.

The high relief of the 1921 design was found impractical for coinage and was slightly modified in 1922. The three known matte proof specimens of 1922 are of the high relief style of 1921.

VERY FINE—*Hair over eye well worn. Some strands over ear well defined. Some eagle feathers on top and outside edge of right wing will show.*

EXTRA FINE—*Hairlines over brow and ear are strong though slightly worn. Outside wing feathers at right and those at top are visible but faint.*

SILVER DOLLARS

Most uncirculated silver dollars have scratches or nicks because of handling of mint bags. Perfect coins without blemishes are generally worth 50% more than listed values.

	Quan. Minted	V. Fine	Ex. Fine	Unc.	Matte Proof
1921	1,006,473	$15.00	$20.00	$40.00	———
1922	51,737,000	2.50	3.00	4.00	———
1922D	15,063,000	2.50	3.00	6.00	
1922S	17,475,000	2.50	3.00	6.00	
1923	30,800,000	2.50	3.00	4.00	
1923D	6,811,000	2.50	3.00	12.00	
1923S	19,020,000	2.50	3.00	6.00	
1924	11,811,000	2.50	3.00	5.00	
1924S	1,728,000	6.00	9.00	42.50	
1925	10,198,000	2.50	3.00	4.00	
1925S	1,610,000	4.00	6.50	16.00	
1926	1,939,000	5.00	7.00	10.00	
1926D	2,348,700	3.75	5.00	15.00	
1926S	6,980,000	2.75	3.50	9.00	
1927	848,000	12.00	15.00	25.00	
1927D	1,268,900	8.50	12.50	40.00	
1927S	866,000	9.00	14.00	47.50	
1928	360,649	65.00	80.00	100.00	
1928S	1,632,000	6.00	8.50	32.50	
1934	954,057	10.00	14.00	22.50	
1934D	1,569,500	7.50	10.00	35.00	
1934S	1,011,000	15.00	45.00	275.00	
1935	1,576,000	6.00	8.00	15.00	
1935S	1,964,000	5.00	12.00	45.00	

EISENHOWER DOLLAR 1970

It is anticipated that dollar size coins with a portrait of President Eisenhower will be minted during 1970. These pieces are not included in this catalog as authorizing legislation has not been passed as of press time.

TRADE DOLLARS 1873 - 1885

This coin was issued for circulation in the Orient to compete with dollar-size coins of other countries. It weighed 420 grains compared to 412½ grains, the weight of the regular silver dollar.

TRADE DOLLARS

At first the coin was legal tender, but in 1876 Congress restricted its use to export demands. After 1878, strikings were specimen proofs only.

The Trade Dollars of 1884 and 1885 were unknown to collectors generally until 1908. None is listed in the Director's report and numismatists believe that they are not a part of the regular mint issue. The law authorizing Trade Dollars was repealed in February, 1887.

VERY GOOD—*About half of mottoes IN GOD WE TRUST and E PLURIBUS UNUM will show. Rim on both sides well defined.*

FINE—*Mottoes and LIBERTY readable but worn.*

EXTRA FINE—*Mottoes and LIBERTY are sharp. Only slight wear on rims.*

	Quan. Minted	V.G.	Fine	E.F.	Unc.	Proof
1873 ....(865) 397,500		$22.50	$35.00	$52.50	$175.00	$450.00
1873CC 124,500		30.00	52.50	115.00	285.00	
1873S 703,000		22.50	35.00	67.50	170.00	
1874 ....(700) 987,800		19.00	27.50	40.00	110.00	340.00
1874CC 1,373,200		30.00	47.50	90.00	185.00	
1874S 2,549,000		22.50	32.50	52.50	137.50	
1875 ....(700) 218,900		27.50	40.00	75.00	175.00	340.00
1875CC 1,573,700		27.50	40.00	75.00	175.00	
1875S .... } 4,487,000		19.00	27.50	40.00	100.00	
1875S S over CC.... }						
1876 ....(1,150) 456,150		22.50	27.50	47.50	110.00	340.00
1876CC 509,000		27.50	42.50	75.00	175.00	
1876S 5,227,000		19.00	25.00	37.50	100.00	
1877 ....(710)3,039,710		19.00	25.00	37.50	100.00	500.00
1877CC 534,000		32.50	52.50	125.00	250.00	
1877S 9,519,000		19.00	25.00	37.50	100.00	
1878 ....(900) 900						460.00
1878CC 97,000		85.00	175.00	275.00	550.00	
1878S 4,162,000		19.00	25.00	37.50	100.00	
1879 ....(1,541) 1,541						375.00
1880 ....(1,987) 1,987						350.00
1881 ....(960) 960						400.00
1882 ....(1,097) 1,097						375.00
1883 ....(979) 979						420.00
1884 ....(10) 10 ....Wolfson Sale 1963						$8,750.00
1885 ....(5) 5						9,000.00

Bibliography: John M. Willem, Jr., *The United States Trade Dollar,* 1965.

GOLD

Gold, the earliest known and most beautiful of all metallic substances, has been and remains of the greatest commercial consequence. Of the precious metals, gold particularly has for ages been the chief material used for coins.

Gold is common to most nations as a standard for measurement of all other values. In our own country paper currency and token coins now serve exclusively as money. Gold continues to serve as the yardstick of money values, although it is no longer used for actual coinage.

Because gold did not circulate as money after 1933, it was stored in bullion form, thus saving the expense of coinage. Being a standard of value its worth is the same whether in the shape of coins or in bars.

As a result of the gold surrender order, United States gold coins have become scarce, and the small remaining supply of these beautiful and respected representatives of our monetary past is being legally and carefully preserved by the numismatic fraternity.

GOLD DOLLARS

1849-1889

Coinage of the gold dollar was authorized by the Act of March 3, 1849. The weight was 25.8 grains, fineness .900. The first type, struck until 1854, is known as the Liberty Head or Small-sized type. Its size is the smallest of all U.S. coins.

In 1854 the piece was made larger in diameter and thinner. The design was changed to a feather headdress on a female, generally referred to as the Indian Head or Large-sized type. In 1856 the type was changed slightly by enlarging the size of the head.

The Type 1 dollars after 1849 all have a closed wreath on the reverse.

LIBERTY HEAD TYPE 1849-1854

 Type 1

FINE—*Full LIBERTY but knobs over coronet partially worn.*

VERY FINE—*LIBERTY on headband complete and readable. Knobs on coronet are defined.*

EXTRA FINE—*Slight wear on Liberty's hair. Knobs on coronet sharp.*

	Quan. Minted	Fine	V. Fine	E. Fine	Unc.
1849 Open wreath - All kinds	688,567	$40.00	$52.50	$65.00	$90.00
1849 Closed wreath (wreath ends closer to Fig. 1)		40.00	52.50	65.00	90.00
1849C Closed wreath	11,634	150.00	200.00	350.00	600.00
1849C Open wreath (2 known)		...1956 A.N.A.	Sale	$6,000.00	
1849D Open wreath	21,588	125.00	235.00	325.00	425.00
1849O Open wreath	215,000	45.00	55.00	65.00	85.00
1850	481,953	45.00	55.00	65.00	75.00
1850C	6,966	170.00	285.00	425.00	650.00
1850D	8,382	150.00	235.00	325.00	450.00
1850O	14,000	57.50	75.00	110.00	160.00
1851	3,317,671	40.00	50.00	60.00	75.00
1851C	41,267	110.00	170.00	240.00	325.00
1851D	9,882	135.00	220.00	325.00	425.00
1851O	290,000	50.00	60.00	70.00	80.00

GOLD DOLLARS

	Quan. Minted	Fine	V. Fine	E. Fine	Unc.	Proof
1852	2,045,351	$45.00	$55.00	$60.00	$75.00	
1852C	9,434	140.00	225.00	350.00	450.00	
1852D	6,360	140.00	225.00	350.00	450.00	
1852O	140,000	50.00	60.00	70.00	85.00	
1853	4,076,051	45.00	55.00	60.00	75.00	
1853C	11,515	110.00	165.00	250.00	375.00	
1853D	6,583	140.00	225.00	350.00	475.00	
1853O	290,000	47.50	57.50	70.00	85.00	
1854	736,709	45.00	55.00	60.00	75.00	
1854D	2,935	265.00	390.00	525.00	800.00	
1854S	14,632	100.00	150.00	260.00	350.00	

INDIAN HEAD TYPE, Small head 1854-1856

Type 2

FINE—Feather curl tips partially worn away.

VERY FINE—Feather curl tips outlined but details worn.

EXTRA FINE—Slight wear on tips of feather curls on headdress.

1854	902,736	120.00	190.00	290.00	450.00
1855	758,269	120.00	190.00	290.00	450.00
1855C	9,803	200.00	300.00	400.00	500.00
1855D	1,811	950.00	1,500	2,400	3,250
1855O	55,000	115.00	185.00	285.00	440.00
1856S	24,600	140.00	210.00	350.00	500.00

INDIAN HEAD TYPE, Large head 1856-1889

Type 3

FINE—Full LIBERTY on headband but beads partially worn. Curled feathers flat—no detail.

VERY FINE—Curled feathers have slight detail. Details worn smooth at eyebrow, hair below headdress and behind ear and bottom curl.

EXTRA FINE—Slight wear above and to right of eye and on top of curled feathers.

		Fine	V. Fine	E. Fine	Unc.	Proof
1856 Upright 5	33,660	50.00	57.50	67.50	82.50	
1856 Slant 5	1,729,276	45.00	55.00	65.00	75.00	$1,100
1856D	1,460	975.00	1,500	2,500	3,400	
1857	774,789	50.00	60.00	75.00	85.00	1,100
1857C	13,280	130.00	190.00	325.00	425.00	
1857D	3,533	275.00	400.00	650.00	850.00	
1857S	10,000	85.00	125.00	185.00	250.00	
1858	117,995	50.00	60.00	75.00	90.00	900.00
1858D	3,477	375.00	700.00	1,100	1,450	
1858S	10,000	95.00	145.00	210.00	275.00	
1859	168,244	50.00	60.00	70.00	85.00	700.00
1859C	5,235	160.00	270.00	400.00	525.00	
1859D	4,952	200.00	300.00	450.00	600.00	
1859S	15,000	85.00	140.00	190.00	240.00	
1860 (154)	36,668	50.00	60.00	75.00	90.00	650.00
1860D	1,566	1,250	2,700	3,500	4,500	
1860S	13,000	85.00	130.00	190.00	250.00	
1861 (349)	527,499	50.00	60.00	70.00	85.00	600.00
1861D		2,750	4,000	5,750	7,500	
1862 (35)	1,361,390	50.00	60.00	70.00	85.00	600.00
1863 (50)	6,250	185.00	275.00	375.00	550.00	1,000

GOLD DOLLARS

	Quan. Minted	Fine	V. Fine	E. Fine	Unc.	Proof
1864................(50)	5,950	$120.00	$175.00	$300.00	$400.00	$1,050
1865................(25)	3,725	160.00	275.00	400.00	500.00	750.00
1866................(30)	7,130	110.00	160.00	225.00	300.00	700.00
1867................(50)	5,250	120.00	160.00	225.00	300.00	700.00
1868................(25)	10,525	90.00	135.00	200.00	275.00	700.00
1869................(25)	5,925	110.00	175.00	225.00	300.00	700.00
1870................(35)	6,335	95.00	140.00	200.00	275.00	650.00
1870S................	3,000	290.00	400.00	750.00	1,050	
1871................(30)	3,930	95.00	140.00	200.00	275.00	650.00
1872................(30)	3,530	95.00	140.00	200.00	275.00	650.00
1873 Closed 3.........(25)	125,125	50.00	60.00	80.00	125.00	650.00
1873 Open 3.............		50.00	60.00	80.00	100.00	
1874................(20)	198,820	50.00	57.50	70.00	85.00	650.00
1875................(20)	420	800.00	1,000	1,550	1,850	3,700
1876................(45)	3,245	95.00	130.00	200.00	260.00	550.00
1877................(20)	3,920	95.00	135.00	210.00	260.00	650.00
1878................(20)	3,020	85.00	125.00	175.00	250.00	650.00
1879................(30)	3,030	85.00	125.00	175.00	250.00	600.00
1880................(36)	1,636	100.00	125.00	150.00	250.00	600.00
1881................(87)	7,707	70.00	100.00	125.00	150.00	425.00
1882................(125)	5,125	75.00	100.00	125.00	160.00	425.00
1883................(207)	11,007	.75.00	100.00	125.00	150.00	425.00
1884................(1,006)	6,236	75.00	95.00	110.00	150.00	300.00
1885................(1,105)	12,261	75.00	90.00	110.00	140.00	300.00
1886................(1,016)	6,016	75.00	90.00	110.00	140.00	300.00
1887................(1,043)	8,543	75.00	90.00	110.00	145.00	300.00
1888................(1,079)	16,580	70.00	85.00	100.00	125.00	300.00
1889................(1,779)	30,729	70.00	85.00	100.00	120.00	250.00

QUARTER EAGLES

($2.50 GOLD PIECES)

Authorized by the Act of April 2, 1792, they weighed 67.5 grains, $916\frac{2}{3}$ fine until the weight was changed to 64.5 grains, fineness 899.225, by the Act of June 28, 1834. The Act of January 18, 1837 established fineness at .900. Most dates before 1834 are rare. The first issue was struck in 1796, most of which had no stars on the obverse.

Proofs of some dates prior to 1855 are known to exist, and all are rare.

CAPPED BUST TO RIGHT 1796-1807

FINE—Hair worn smooth on high spots. E PLURIBUS UNUM weak but readable.

VERY FINE—Some wear on high spots.

EXTRA FINE—Only slight wear on hair and cheek.

	Quan. Minted	Fine	V. Fine	E. Fine	Unc.
1796 No stars on obverse...............	963	$2,900	$5,500	$6,250	$7,750

QUARTER EAGLES

1796
with
Stars

1797

	Quan. Minted	Fine	V. Fine	E. Fine	Unc.
1796 Stars on obverse	432	$2,950	$5,500	$6,250	$8,250
1797	427	1,125	2,000	2,500	3,250
1798	1,094	1,250	2,000	2,500	4,750

1802
over
1

1806
over
4

1806
over
5

	Quan. Minted	Fine	V. Fine	E. Fine	Unc.
1802 over 1	3,035	550.00	925.00	1,250	2,250
1804 13-Star reverse	} 3,327	600.00	925.00	1,250	1,925
1804 14-Star reverse		600.00	950.00	1,350	2,000
1805	1,781	550.00	950.00	1,350	1,900
1806 over 4	} 1,616	750.00	1,600	2,000	2,650
1806 over 5		650.00	1,600	2,000	3,000
1807	6,812	475.00	750.00	950.00	1,500

CAPPED BUST TO LEFT, Large Size 1808

FINE—E PLURIBUS UNUM and LIBERTY on headband
readable but weak.
VERY FINE—Motto and LIBERTY clear.
EXTRA FINE—All details of hair are plain.

1808	2,710	2,000	4,250	5,250	7,000

Reduced Size 1821-1834

Those dated 1829 through 1834 are smaller in diameter than the 1821-
1827 pieces. They also have smaller letters, dates and stars.

1821

1826
over
25

1821	6,448	425.00	900.00	1,500	2,750
1824 over 21	2,600	475.00	975.00	1,400	2,400
1825	4,434	575.00	1,250	1,600	2,500
1826 over 25	760	675.00	1,275	1,750	3,400
1827	2,800	550.00	900.00	1,250	2,250
1829	3,403	400.00	800.00	950.00	1,350

QUARTER EAGLES

	Quan. Minted	Fine	V. Fine	E. Fine	Unc.
1830	4,540	$400.00	$600.00	$800.00	$1,100
1831	4,520	400.00	600.00	800.00	1,100
1832	4,400	400.00	600.00	800.00	1,100
1833	4,160	400.00	600.00	800.00	1,100
1834 (Motto)	4,000	1,250	2,000	2,600	4,250

LIBERTY CAP REMOVED — MOTTO REMOVED FROM REVERSE

In 1834 the quarter eagle was redesigned. A ribbon binding the hair, bearing the word LIBERTY, replaces the Liberty cap. The motto was omitted from the reverse. In 1840 a coronet and smaller head were designed to conform in appearance with that of the larger gold coins.

FINE—LIBERTY readable and complete. Curl under ear outlined but no detail.

VERY FINE—LIBERTY plain. Hair curl has detail.

EXTRA FINE—Small amount of wear on top of hair and below L in LIBERTY. Wear evident on wing tips and neck of eagle.

1834 No Motto	112,234	80.00	100.00	125.00	200.00
1835	131,402	65.00	85.00	110.00	200.00
1836	547,986	65.00	85.00	110.00	200.00
1837	45,080	85.00	110.00	135.00	225.00
1838	47,030	85.00	110.00	135.00	225.00
1838C	7,880	165.00	250.00	325.00	450.00
1839	27,021	80.00	100.00	125.00	225.00
1839C	18,140	135.00	200.00	260.00	400.00
1839D	13,674	160.00	220.00	285.00	450.00
1839O	17,781	100.00	140.00	190.00	300.00

1839 over 8 varieties exist for P, C and D mints.

CORONET TYPE 1840-1907

New Small Head

1840	18,859	60.00	85.00	120.00	175.00
1840C	12,822	95.00	150.00	225.00	350.00
1840D	3,532	150.00	250.00	350.00	675.00
1840O	33,580	52.50	72.50	90.00	140.00
1841 Proofs only	Shuford Sale 1968 Proof $18,000.00				
1841C	10,281	175.00	210.00	265.00	400.00
1841D	4,164	185.00	320.00	370.00	465.00
1842	2,823	135.00	260.00	310.00	400.00
1842C	6,729	135.00	185.00	225.00	350.00
1842D	4,643	145.00	225.00	285.00	425.00
1842O	19,800	50.00	75.00	90.00	125.00
1843	100,546	50.00	67.50	72.50	90.00

QUARTER EAGLES

	Quan. Minted	Fine	V. Fine	E. Fine	Unc.
1843C Small date	} 26,064	$165.00	$475.00	$725.00	$1,500
1843C Large date		80.00	110.00	135.00	175.00
1843D Small date	36,209	95.00	125.00	160.00	225.00
1843O Small date	288,002	45.00	55.00	65.00	85.00
1843O Large date	76,000	75.00	115.00	130.00	175.00
1844	6,784	100.00	150.00	185.00	250.00
1844C	11,622	110.00	145.00	175.00	235.00
1844D	17,332	95.00	125.00	150.00	225.00
1845	91,051	45.00	55.00	70.00	95.00
1845D	19,460	80.00	130.00	165.00	250.00
1845O	4,000	135.00	215.00	260.00	325.00
1846	21,598	45.00	57.50	70.00	95.00
1846C	4,808	140.00	225.00	285.00	375.00
1846D	19,303	95.00	150.00	185.00	240.00
1846O	66,000	45.00	55.00	80.00	100.00
1847	29,814	52.50	62.50	75.00	100.00
1847C	23,226	85.00	135.00	190.00	265.00
1847D	15,784	90.00	160.00	250.00	325.00
1847O	124,000	42.50	55.00	72.50	80.00
1848	7,489	325.00	575.00	800.00	1,100

CALIF. GOLD QUARTER EAGLE

CAL. above eagle on Reverse

In 1848 about two hundred and thirty ounces of gold were sent to Secretary of War Marcy by Col. R. B. Mason, Military Governor of California. The gold was turned over to the mint and made into quarter eagles. The distinguishing mark "C A L." was punched above the eagle on the reverse side, while the coins were in the die.

	Quan. Minted	Fine	V. Fine	E. Fine	Unc.
1848 CAL above eagle (2 Proofs known)	1,389	2,250	3,200	4,250	6,000
1848C	16,788	105.00	130.00	190.00	325.00
1848D	13,771	120.00	160.00	225.00	365.00
1849	23,294	40.00	52.50	80.00	115.00
1849C	10,220	90.00	135.00	185.00	280.00
1849D	10,945	115.00	185.00	240.00	325.00
1850	252,923	40.00	50.00	62.50	75.00
1850C	9,148	100.00	170.00	225.00	300.00
1850D	12,148	100.00	140.00	180.00	260.00
1850O	84,000	40.00	50.00	60.00	75.00
1851	1,372,748	40.00	50.00	60.00	75.00
1851C	14,923	110.00	150.00	240.00	360.00
1851D	11,264	120.00	160.00	250.00	380.00
1851O	148,000	40.00	50.00	60.00	75.00
1852	1,159,681	40.00	45.00	52.50	65.00
1852C	9,772	110.00	150.00	190.00	285.00
1852D	4,078	220.00	300.00	375.00	450.00
1852O	140,000	40.00	45.00	60.00	75.00
1853	1,404,668	40.00	45.00	55.00	65.00

QUARTER EAGLES

	Quan. Minted	Fine	V. Fine	E. Fine	Unc.	Proof
1853D	3,178	$325.00	$450.00	$600.00	$975.00	
1854	596,258	40.00	45.00	55.00	65.00	
1854C	7,295	100.00	150.00	225.00	375.00	
1854D	1,760	1,100	1,600	2,200	2,950	
1854O	153,000	40.00	45.00	55.00	65.00	
1854S	246	......	4,750	6,000	8,000	
1855	235,480	40.00	45.00	60.00	75.00	$4,400
1855C	3,677	275.00	375.00	485.00	700.00	
1855D	1,123	425.00	750.00	1,500	2,500	
1856	384,240	40.00	45.00	52.50	65.00	4,000
1856C	7,913	110.00	165.00	235.00	325.00	
1856D	874	750.00	1,500	2,750	4,500	
1856O	21,100	40.00	45.00	60.00	75.00	
1856S	71,120	40.00	45.00	70.00	100.00	
1857	214,130	40.00	45.00	55.00	65.00	2,750
1857D	2,364	325.00	450.00	575.00	725.00	
1857O	34,000	40.00	45.00	60.00	70.00	
1857S	69,200	42.50	55.00	75.00	105.00	
1858	47,377	40.00	47.50	57.50	70.00	1,900
1858C	9,056	145.00	185.00	240.00	350.00	
1859	39,444	40.00	45.00	55.00	70.00	1,250
1859D	2,244	260.00	375.00	480.00	700.00	
1859S	15,200	55.00	75.00	100.00	150.00	
1860 .... (112)	22,675	40.00	45.00	55.00	70.00	1,250
1860C	7,469	135.00	185.00	215.00	300.00	
1860S	35,600	50.00	80.00	110.00	150.00	
1861 .... (90)	1,283,878	40.00	45.00	52.50	65.00	1,250
1861S	24,000	45.00	55.00	75.00	140.00	
1862 .... (35)	98,543	40.00	45.00	55.00	75.00	1,400
1862 over 1		....			2,600	
1862S	8,000	80.00	120.00	165.00	225.00	
1863 Proofs only ...... (30)	30	....				5,000
1863S	10,800	65.00	95.00	115.00	175.00	
1864 .... (50)	2,874	225.00	340.00	385.00	475.00	1,500
1865 .... (25)	1,545	265.00	365.00	425.00	525.00	1,500
1865S	23,376	40.00	50.00	75.00	125.00	
1866 .... (30)	3,110	135.00	210.00	250.00	325.00	1,000
1866S	38,960	40.00	47.50	60.00	80.00	
1867 .... (50)	3,250	125.00	175.00	215.00	325.00	950.00
1867S	28,000	42.50	55.00	70.00	90.00	
1868 .... (25)	3,625	110.00	145.00	190.00	275.00	1,050
1868S	34,000	42.50	55.00	75.00	110.00	
1869 .... (25)	4,345	85.00	120.00	145.00	210.00	1,050
1869S	29,500	42.50	55.00	65.00	80.00	
1870 .... (35)	4,555	80.00	110.00	140.00	195.00	900.00
1870S	16,000	47.50	60.00	75.00	110.00	
1871 .... (30)	5,350	80.00	120.00	150.00	220.00	850.00
1871S	22,000	60.00	75.00	85.00	100.00	
1872 .... (30)	3,030	110.00	150.00	185.00	250.00	850.00
1872S	18,000	50.00	60.00	70.00	90.00	
1873 Closed 3 .... (25)	178,025	37.50	47.50	60.00	75.00	950.00
1873 Open 3		37.50	47.50	60.00	75.00	

QUARTER EAGLES

	Quan. Minted	Fine	V. Fine	E. Fine	Unc.	Proof
1873S	27,000	$42.50	$50.00	$60.00	$75.00	
1874 (20)	3,940	95.00	125.00	175.00	240.00	$1,100
1875 (20)	420	350.00	600.00	900.00	1,350	3,250
1875S	11,600	50.00	85.00	115.00	175.00	
1876 (45)	4,221	100.00	130.00	165.00	240.00	950.00
1876S	5,000	60.00	85.00	110.00	150.00	
1877 (20)	1,652	200.00	275.00	350.00	485.00	1,450
1877S	35,400	40.00	45.00	55.00	75.00	
1878 (20)	286,260	40.00	45.00	50.00	65.00	1,100
1878S	178,000	40.00	45.00	50.00	65.00	
1879 (30)	88,990	40.00	45.00	50.00	65.00	750.00
1879S	43,500	42.50	52.50	60.00	75.00	
1880 (36)	2,996	135.00	175.00	200.00	260.00	950.00
1881 (51)	691	235.00	375.00	465.00	675.00	1,300
1882 (67)	4,067	135.00	175.00	225.00	295.00	950.00
1883 (82)	2,002	160.00	220.00	265.00	325.00	1,000
1884 (73)	2,023	160.00	220.00	265.00	325.00	1,000
1885 (87)	887	215.00	395.00	475.00	585.00	1,250
1886 (88)	4,088	90.00	125.00	175.00	250.00	700.00
1887 (122)	6,282	85.00	110.00	120.00	150.00	700.00
1888 (97)	16,098	50.00	65.00	80.00	100.00	600.00
1889 (48)	17,648	50.00	75.00	90.00	125.00	625.00
1890 (93)	8,813	75.00	90.00	110.00	140.00	600.00
1891 (80)	11,040	52.50	70.00	80.00	100.00	550.00
1892 (105)	2,545	100.00	135.00	160.00	240.00	650.00
1893 (106)	30,106	45.00	60.00	70.00	85.00	600.00
1894 (122)	4,122	75.00	110.00	130.00	165.00	650.00
1895 (119)	6,119	60.00	90.00	110.00	140.00	550.00
1896 (132)	19,202	40.00	60.00	70.00	90.00	550.00
1897 (136)	29,904	40.00	60.00	70.00	80.00	500.00
1898 (165)	24,165	40.00	60.00	70.00	80.00	450.00
1899 (150)	27,350	40.00	60.00	70.00	80.00	450.00
1900 (205)	67,205	40.00	60.00	65.00	75.00	400.00
1901 (223)	91,323	40.00	55.00	60.00	65.00	400.00
1902 (193)	133,733	40.00	50.00	55.00	65.00	400.00
1903 (197)	201,257	40.00	50.00	55.00	65.00	400.00
1904 (170)	160,960	40.00	50.00	55.00	65.00	400.00
1905* (144)	217,944	40.00	50.00	55.00	65.00	400.00
1906 (160)	176,490	40.00	50.00	55.00	65.00	400.00
1907 (154)	336,448	40.00	50.00	55.00	65.00	400.00

*Pieces dated 1905S are counterfeit.

INDIAN HEAD TYPE 1908-1929

The new type represents a departure from all preceding coin types in the United States series. Bela Lyon Pratt was the designer of this and the half eagle piece. The coin has no raised milling and the main devices and legends are incuse.

FINE—Knot in haircord must show, small feathers on top of head will be faint.

VERY FINE—Haircord knot distinct. Feathers at top of head clear. Cheekbone worn.

EXTRA FINE—Cheekbone, war bonnet and headband feathers slightly worn.

QUARTER EAGLES

	Quan. Minted	Fine	V. Fine	E. Fine	Unc.	Matte Proof
1908............(236)	565,057	$35.00	$40.00	$45.00	$75.00	$600.00
1909............(139)	441,899	35.00	40.00	45.00	60.00	675.00
1910............(682)	492,682	35.00	40.00	45.00	60.00	525.00
1911............(191)	704,191	35.00	40.00	45.00	60.00	575.00
1911D...............55,680		225.00	325.00	370.00	450.00	
1912............(197)	616,197	32.50	37.50	42.50	50.00	650.00
1913............(165)	722,165	32.50	37.50	42.50	50.00	650.00
1914............(117)	240,117	37.50	45.00	50.00	60.00	750.00
1914D..............448,000		35.00	42.50	47.50	55.00	
1915............(100)	606,100	32.50	37.50	42.50	50.00	675.00
1925D..............578,000		32.50	37.50	42.50	50.00	
1926..............446,000		32.50	37.50	42.50	50.00	
1927..............388,000		32.50	37.50	42.50	50.00	
1928..............416,000		32.50	37.50	42.50	50.00	
1929..............532,000		32.50	37.50	42.50	50.00	

THREE-DOLLAR GOLD PIECES
1854-1889

The three-dollar gold piece was authorized by Act of February 21, 1853. The coin was first struck in 1854. It was never popular and saw very little circulation.

The coin weighs 77.4 grains, .900 fine. The head on the obverse represents an Indian princess with hair tightly curling over the neck, head crowned with a circle of feathers, the band of which is inscribed LIBERTY. A wreath of tobacco, wheat, corn and cotton occupies the field of the reverse, with the denomination and date within it. No change of type was made during the life of this denomination.

In the year 1854 only, the word DOLLARS is in much smaller letters than in years 1855 through 1889.

FINE—Top of headdress worn flat. Full LIBERTY. Beads above band partially worn.

VERY FINE—Eyebrow, hair about forehead and ear and bottom curl are worn smooth. Curled feather-ends have faint details showing.

EXTRA FINE—Only trace of wear above and to right of eye. Slight wear on top of curled feathers.

	Quan. Minted	Fine	V. Fine	E. Fine	Unc.	Proof
1854.....................138,618		$170.00	$225.00	$280.00	$350.00	————
1854D.......................1,120		975.00	1,800	2,250	3,000	
1854O......................24,000		180.00	250.00	290.00	365.00	
1855.......................50,555		175.00	225.00	275.00	350.00	————
1855S.......................6,600		175.00	260.00	325.00	475.00	
1856.......................26,010		165.00	230.00	285.00	340.00	————
1856S Small, medium and large S varieties exist........34,500		175.00	240.00	290.00	375.00	
1857.......................20,891		170.00	225.00	275.00	350.00	————
1857S......................14,000		180.00	260.00	310.00	385.00	
1858.......................2,133		260.00	395.00	475.00	850.00	2,550
1859.......................15,638		175.00	240.00	285.00	350.00	1,450

THREE-DOLLAR GOLD PIECES

	Quan. Minted	Fine	V. Fine	E. Fine	Unc.	Proof
1860.................(119)	7,155	$180.00	$260.00	$300.00	$390.00	$1,300
1860S..(2,592 melted at Mint)	7,000	200.00	265.00	315.00	400.00	
1861.................(113)	6,072	200.00	250.00	290.00	375.00	1,850
1862.................(35)	5,785	200.00	250.00	290.00	375.00	1,850
1863.................(39)	5,039	200.00	265.00	325.00	410.00	1,900
1864.................(50)	2,680	240.00	350.00	450.00	700.00	1,900
1865.................(25)	1,165	240.00	400.00	525.00	800.00	1,900
1866.................(30)	4,030	200.00	260.00	300.00	375.00	1,750
1867.................(50)	2,650	200.00	265.00	310.00	400.00	1,750
1868.................(25)	4,875	200.00	260.00	300.00	375.00	1,750
1869.................(25)	2,525	200.00	275.00	335.00	425.00	1,750
1870.................(35)	3,535	200.00	275.00	325.00	400.00	1,750
1870S (Unique)................2			———			
1871.................(30)	1,330	240.00	325.00	390.00	500.00	1,900
1872.................(30)	2,030	225.00	325.00	375.00	450.00	1,900
1873 Open 3.........(25)	25	....				3,500
1873 Closed 3 (All restrikes)...........					1,800	2,500
1874.................(20)	41,820	175.00	225.00	290.00	350.00	2,200
1875 Proofs only.......(20)	20......R. L. Miles Sale 1968 $25,000.00					
1876 Proofs only......(45)	45......Charles Jay Sale 1967 $7,250.00					
1877.................(20)	1,488	360.00	650.00	850.00	1,200	3,250
1878.................(20)	82,324	175.00	225.00	285.00	350.00	2,250
1879.................(30)	3,030	200.00	275.00	320.00	395.00	1,500
1880.................(36)	1,036	225.00	325.00	375.00	500.00	1,500
1881.................(54)	554	325.00	550.00	675.00	950.00	2,100
1882.................(76)	1,576	200.00	300.00	375.00	485.00	1,400
1883.................(89)	989	250.00	375.00	450.00	525.00	1,400
1884.................(106)	1,106	235.00	325.00	425.00	575.00	1,400
1885.................(109)	910	250.00	375.00	550.00	725.00	2,000
1886.................(142)	1,142	210.00	350.00	475.00	650.00	1,400
1887.................(160)	6,160	200.00	275.00	325.00	375.00	1,300
1888.................(290)	5,291	200.00	275.00	325.00	375.00	1,100
1889.................(129)	2,429	225.00	300.00	375.00	460.00	1,100

FOUR-DOLLAR GOLD OR "STELLA"

These pattern coins were first suggested by the Hon. John A. Kasson, then U.S. Minister to Austria; and it was through the efforts of Dr. W. W. Hubbell, who patented the goloid metal used in making the goloid metric dollars, that we have these beautiful and interesting pieces.

There are two distinct types in both years of issue. Barber designed the flowing hair type, and Morgan the coiled hair. They were struck in gold, aluminum, copper and white metal. Only those struck in gold are listed.

	Proof			Proof
1879 Flowing hair (415)....	$6,000		1880 Flowing hair (15).....	———
1879 Coiled hair (10).......	———		1880 Coiled hair (10).......	———

HALF EAGLES — 1795-1929
($5.00 GOLD PIECES)

The half eagle was the first gold coin actually struck for the United States. The $5.00 piece was authorized to be coined by the Act of April 2, 1792 and the first type weighed 135 grains, 916⅔ fine. The weight was changed by Act of June 28, 1834 to 129 grains, 899.225 fine. Fineness became .900 by Act of January 18, 1837.

There are many varieties among the early dates caused by changes in the number of stars, style of eagle, overdates, and differences in the size of figures in the dates. Those dated prior to 1807 do not bear any mark of value. The 1822 half eagle is considered the most valuable regular issue coin of the entire United States series. Proofs of some dates prior to 1855 are known to exist, and all are rare. The half eagle was the only U.S. denomination struck in each of the seven mints.

FINE—Hair worn smooth but with distinct outline. After 1797 E PLURIBUS UNUM is faint but readable.
VERY FINE—Slight to noticeable wear on high spots such as hair, turban, eagle's head and wings.
EXTRA FINE—Slight wear on hair and highest part of cheek.

Small Eagle   Large Eagle

	Quan. Minted	Fine	V. Fine	E. Fine	Unc.
1795 Small eagle	8,707	$1,250	$1,500	$1,900	$2,500
1795 Large or heraldic eagle		1,800	2,400	3,750	5,250

	Quan. Minted	Fine	V. Fine	E. Fine	Unc.
1796 over 95 Small eagle	6,196	1,200	1,600	2,300	2,800

	Quan. Minted	Fine	V. Fine	E. Fine	Unc.
1797 over 95 Lg. or heraldic eagle - All	3,609	1,400	1,900	2,650	3,500

HALF EAGLES

1797 - 15 Stars

16 Stars

1799

	Quan. Minted	Fine	V. Fine	E. Fine	Unc.
1797 15 Stars, small eagle	⎫	$1,200	$2,000	$3,150	$4,000
1797 16 Stars, small eagle	⎬ 3,609	1,250	2,100	3,250	4,000
1797 16 Stars, large eagle	⎭				
1798 Sm. eagle (5 known) All kinds	24,867				
1798 Lg. or heraldic eagle, sm. 8 in date		325.00	410.00	525.00	750.00
1798 Lg. eagle, lg. 8, 13 star reverse		450.00	750.00	1,050	1,500
1798 Lg. eagle, lg. 8, 14 star reverse		600.00	950.00	1,250	1,600
1799	7,451	425.00	525.00	700.00	1,000

1802 over 1   1803 over 2

Small 8

Large 8

1800	37,628	400.00	550.00	675.00	850.00
1802 over 1	53,176	450.00	575.00	625.00	750.00
1803 over 2	33,506	450.00	575.00	625.00	750.00
1804 Small 8	⎫	450.00	575.00	625.00	750.00
1804 Large 8	⎬ 30,475	450.00	575.00	625.00	750.00
1805	33,183	450.00	575.00	625.00	750.00

Pointed
6

Round Top
6

1806 Pointed top 6	⎫ 64,093	400.00	550.00	625.00	750.00
1806 Round top 6	⎭	400.00	550.00	625.00	750.00
1807	32,488	400.00	550.00	625.00	750.00

HALF EAGLES

LIBERTY FACING LEFT — ROUND CAP — SMALLER EAGLE
VALUE 5D. USED FOR FIRST TIME

FINE—*LIBERTY readable but partly weak.*
VERY FINE—*Headband edges slightly worn. LIBERTY is bold.*
EXTRA FINE—*Slight wear on highest portions of hair. 80% of major curls are plain.*

	Quan. Minted	Fine	V. Fine	E. Fine	Unc.
1807	51,605	$435.00	$525.00	$625.00	$700.00

1808 over 7   **Normal Date**

	Quan. Minted	Fine	V. Fine	E. Fine	Unc.
1808 8 over 7	55,578	375.00	460.00	525.00	625.00
1808		375.00	460.00	525.00	625.00
1809 9 over 8	33,875	385.00	480.00	550.00	650.00

Small Date   **Large Date**   **Small 5**   **Tall 5**

	Quan. Minted	Fine	V. Fine	E. Fine	Unc.
1810 Small date, small 5		800.00	1,200	2,000	—
1810 Small date, tall 5	100,287	400.00	500.00	575.00	675.00
1810 Large date, small 5		375.00	450.00	550.00	625.00
1810 Large date, tall 5		375.00	450.00	550.00	625.00
1811 Small 5	99,581	375.00	450.00	550.00	625.00
1811 Large 5		375.00	450.00	650.00	800.00
1812	58,087	400.00	500.00	575.00	650.00

NEW TYPE — LARGER HEAD

	Quan. Minted	Fine	V. Fine	E. Fine	Unc.
1813	95,428	350.00	450.00	650.00	825.00
1814 over 13	15,454	450.00	525.00	675.00	900.00
1815	635				6,500
1818	48,588	475.00	575.00	700.00	975.00
1819	51,723	3,750	5,000	6,500	8,500

HALF EAGLES

| Curved-Base 2 | Square-Base 2 | Small Letters | Large Letters |

	Quan. Minted	Fine	V. Fine	E. Fine	Unc.
1820 Curved-base 2, small letters...	}263,806	$400.00	$675.00	$825.00	$1,000
1820 Curved-base 2, large letters...		450.00	750.00	1,050	1,400
1820 Square-base 2....................		450.00	750.00	1,050	1,250
1821............................	34,641	950.00	1,700	3,000	4,750

| 1822 | 1825 over 21 | 1825 over 24 |

	Quan. Minted	Fine	V. Fine	E. Fine	Unc.
1822 (3 known).....................	17,796	......	—	—	—
1823............................	14,485	700.00	925.00	1,500	2,000
1824............................	17,340	2,400	3,500	5,750	7,750
1825 over 21.....................	}29,060	850.00	1,300	2,000	3,000
1825 over 24.....................		......	......	—	—
1826............................	18,069	1,150	2,100	2,900	3,800
1827............................	24,913	2,400	3,500	5,750	7,000

| 1828 over 27 | Large Date | Small Date |

	Quan. Minted	Fine	V. Fine	E. Fine	Unc.
1828 over 27.....................	}28,029	1,250	2,000	3,750	5,250
1828............................		1,850	2,700	4,500	6,000
1829 Large date..................	}57,442				
1829 Small date..................		...1963 Florida Sale $21,500.00			

The half eagles dated 1829 through 1834 are smaller in diameter than the earlier pieces. They also have smaller letters, dates and stars.

HALF EAGLES

Small 5D	Large 5D	12 Stars, Curved-Base 2	13 Stars, Square-Base 2

	Quan. Minted	Fine	V. Fine	E. Fine	Unc.
1830 Small 5 D - All kinds	126,351	$650.00	$950.00	$1,400	$2,350
1830 Large 5 D		650.00	950.00	1,400	2,350
1831	140,594	550.00	850.00	1,200	1,750
1832 Curved-base 2, 12 stars - All k.	157,487				
1832 Square-base 2, 13 stars		1,400	2,250	3,100	4,300
1833	193,630	600.00	900.00	1,300	2,100

Plain 4			Crosslet 4		

1834 Plain 4 - Both kinds	50,141	750.00	975.00	1,300	2,050
1834 Crosslet 4		800.00	975.00	1,400	2,350

NO MOTTO ON REVERSE

As on the quarter dollar of 1831, the motto E PLURIBUS UNUM was omitted from the new, reduced size half eagle in 1834, presumably for lack of space. The new motto IN GOD WE TRUST was nevertheless artistically added to the reverse in the form of a scroll in 1866.

1834 Plain 4 - Both kinds	658,028	60.00	80.00	175.00	300.00
1834 Crosslet 4		150.00	200.00	270.00	350.00
1835	371,534	60.00	80.00	130.00	200.00
1836	553,147	65.00	80.00	130.00	200.00
1837	207,121	65.00	80.00	130.00	200.00
1838	286,588	65.00	80.00	130.00	200.00
1838C	17,179	225.00	400.00	550.00	700.00
1838D	20,583	200.00	350.00	490.00	675.00

CORONET TYPE, no motto above eagle 1839-1866

FINE—*LIBERTY readable, but partly weak. Neck hair worn, but outlines clear.*

VERY FINE—*LIBERTY bold. Major lines show in neck hair.*

EXTRA FINE—*Neck hair details clear. Slight wear on top and lower part of coronet, and hair.*

HALF EAGLES

	Quan. Minted	Fine	V.Fine	E.Fine	Unc.
1839	118,143	$50.00	$60.00	$75.00	$200.00
1839C	17,205	150.00	250.00	350.00	500.00
1839D	18,939	150.00	250.00	350.00	525.00
1840	137,382	50.00	60.00	75.00	150.00
1840C	18,992	125.00	150.00	185.00	350.00
1840D	22,896	125.00	150.00	185.00	350.00
1840O	40,120	100.00	125.00	150.00	300.00
1841	15,833	90.00	115.00	150.00	300.00
1841C	21,467	125.00	175.00	225.00	350.00
1841D	30,495	125.00	175.00	225.00	325.00
1841O (2 known)	50				

Small Letters		Large Letters	

	Quan. Minted	Fine	V.Fine	E.Fine	Unc.
1842 Small letters - All kinds	27,578	50.00	85.00	150.00	225.00
1842 Large letters		50.00	85.00	150.00	225.00
1842C Small date - All kinds	28,184	100.00	150.00	200.00	500.00
1842C Large date		100.00	125.00	160.00	300.00
1842D Small date - All kinds	59,608	100.00	125.00	160.00	300.00
1842D Large date		150.00	350.00	450.00	550.00
1842O	16,400	95.00	110.00	140.00	275.00
1843	611,205	45.00	55.00	65.00	100.00
1843C	44,201	90.00	125.00	175.00	275.00
1843D	98,452	90.00	125.00	175.00	275.00
1843O Small letters	19,075	60.00	75.00	90.00	175.00
1843O Large letters	82,000	60.00	75.00	90.00	175.00
1844	340,330	50.00	60.00	80.00	150.00
1844C	23,631	95.00	125.00	160.00	275.00
1844D	88,982	95.00	125.00	160.00	250.00
1844O	364,000	55.00	75.00	90.00	225.00
1845	417,099	50.00	60.00	75.00	100.00
1845D	90,629	95.00	110.00	150.00	250.00
1845O	41,000	85.00	110.00	150.00	250.00
1846	395,942	50.00	60.00	75.00	100.00
1846C	12,995	95.00	125.00	175.00	300.00
1846D	80,294	95.00	125.00	175.00	325.00
1846O	58,000	75.00	90.00	150.00	200.00
1847	915,981	45.00	55.00	65.00	80.00
1847C	84,151	90.00	115.00	150.00	225.00
1847D	64,405	90.00	115.00	150.00	250.00
1847O	12,000	85.00	125.00	175.00	250.00
1848	260,775	50.00	60.00	75.00	100.00
1848C	64,472	95.00	125.00	175.00	250.00
1848D	47,465	95.00	140.00	195.00	275.00
1849	133,070	50.00	60.00	75.00	110.00

HALF EAGLES

	Quan. Minted	Fine	V. Fine	E. Fine	Unc.	Proof
1849C	64,823	$95.00	$125.00	$175.00	$250.00	
1849D	39,036	95.00	125.00	185.00	275.00	
1850	64,491	50.00	60.00	75.00	100.00	
1850C	63,591	95.00	125.00	175.00	250.00	
1850D	43,984	95.00	125.00	175.00	275.00	
1851	377,505	50.00	60.00	75.00	100.00	
1851C	49,176	95.00	125.00	175.00	300.00	
1851D	62,710	100.00	135.00	185.00	275.00	
1851O	41,000	65.00	75.00	95.00	175.00	
1852	573,901	50.00	60.00	75.00	100.00	
1852C	72,574	95.00	135.00	185.00	300.00	
1852D	91,584	95.00	135.00	175.00	275.00	
1853	305,770	45.00	55.00	65.00	85.00	
1853C	65,571	95.00	125.00	175.00	275.00	
1853D	89,678	95.00	125.00	175.00	300.00	
1854	160,675	45.00	55.00	65.00	80.00	
1854C	39,283	95.00	125.00	175.00	250.00	
1854D	56,413	95.00	125.00	175.00	275.00	
1854O	46,000	95.00	115.00	150.00	235.00	
1854S Wolfson Sale	268			16,500 ———		
1855	117,098	45.00	55.00	65.00	80.00	$3,200
1855C	39,788	95.00	125.00	175.00	250.00	
1855D	22,432	110.00	140.00	195.00	325.00	
1855O	11,100	135.00	180.00	225.00	350.00	
1855S	61,000	75.00	90.00	125.00	175.00	
1856	197,990	45.00	55.00	65.00	90.00	3,200
1856C	28,457	95.00	125.00	175.00	250.00	
1856D	19,786	125.00	150.00	175.00	300.00	
1856O	10,000	165.00	240.00	375.00	550.00	
1856S	105,100	55.00	65.00	80.00	110.00	
1857	98,188	45.00	55.00	65.00	80.00	2,950
1857C	31,360	95.00	125.00	175.00	250.00	
1857D	17,046	110.00	140.00	195.00	300.00	
1857O	13,000	100.00	125.00	165.00	275.00	
1857S	87,000	60.00	75.00	90.00	150.00	
1858	15,136	125.00	150.00	175.00	275.00	1,800
1858C	38,856	95.00	125.00	175.00	225.00	
1858D	15,362	110.00	150.00	175.00	275.00	
1858S	18,600	90.00	125.00	150.00	225.00	
1859	16,814	90.00	150.00	200.00	300.00	1,400
1859C	31,847	125.00	175.00	225.00	300.00	
1859D	10,366	125.00	175.00	250.00	350.00	
1859S	13,220	90.00	110.00	150.00	200.00	
1860	(62) 19,825	80.00	90.00	125.00	200.00	975.00
1860C	14,813	125.00	150.00	185.00	300.00	
1860D	14,635	135.00	175.00	225.00	350.00	
1860S	21,200	70.00	85.00	110.00	150.00	
1861	(66)688,150	45.00	55.00	65.00	85.00	850.00
1861C	6,879	350.00	450.00	650.00	900.00	
1861D	1,597	1,250	1,600	2,350	3,000	
1861S	18,000	75.00	90.00	125.00	200.00	
1862	(35) 4,465	150.00	225.00	300.00	400.00	850.00
1862S	9,500	125.00	175.00	225.00	400.00	

HALF EAGLES

	Quan. Minted	Fine	V. Fine	E. Fine	Unc.	Proof
1863 .... (30)	2,472	$225.00	$300.00	$400.00	$650.00	$950.00
1863S	17,000	95.00	125.00	175.00	250.00	
1864 .... (50)	4,220	200.00	250.00	325.00	550.00	1,400
1864S	3,888	300.00	450.00	850.00	1,200	
1865 .... (25)	1,295	250.00	325.00	400.00	700.00	1,000
1865S	27,612	80.00	125.00	175.00	200.00	
1866S	9,000	125.00	150.00	175.00	400.00	

MOTTO OVER EAGLE 1866-1908

FINE—All letters in motto IN GOD WE TRUST readable.

VERY FINE — Half of hairlines above coronet missing. Hair curls under ear evident, but worn. Motto and its ribbon sharp.

EXTRA FINE—Small amount of wear on top of hair and below L in LIBERTY. Wear evident on wing tips and neck of eagle.

	Quan. Minted	Fine	V. Fine	E. Fine	Unc.	Proof
1866 .... (30)	6,730	175.00	250.00	300.00	425.00	800.00
1866S	34,920	125.00	250.00	300.00	400.00	
1867 .... (50)	6,920	125.00	200.00	275.00	350.00	700.00
1867S	29,000	80.00	100.00	125.00	250.00	
1868 .... (25)	5,725	125.00	175.00	225.00	300.00	850.00
1868S	52,000	80.00	100.00	125.00	250.00	
1869 .... (25)	1,785	200.00	300.00	375.00	700.00	1,450
1869S	31,000	80.00	100.00	125.00	250.00	
1870 .... (35)	4,035	125.00	175.00	225.00	300.00	1,050
1870CC	7,675	550.00	700.00	850.00	1,250	
1870S	17,000	75.00	110.00	175.00	210.00	
1871 .... (30)	3,230	160.00	275.00	375.00	500.00	1,050
1871CC	20,770	175.00	250.00	350.00	550.00	
1871S	25,000	70.00	100.00	150.00	200.00	
1872 .... (30)	1,690	275.00	425.00	600.00	700.00	1,200
1872CC	16,980	175.00	250.00	375.00	600.00	
1872S	36,400	55.00	90.00	160.00	200.00	
1873 Closed 3 .... (25)	} 112,505	50.00	60.00	70.00	100.00	900.00
1873 Open 3		40.00	45.00	50.00	55.00	
1873CC	7,416	200.00	300.00	400.00	600.00	
1873S	31,000	55.00	90.00	140.00	190.00	
1874 .... (20)	3,508	160.00	300.00	375.00	475.00	1,100
1874CC	21,198	150.00	200.00	275.00	400.00	
1874S	16,000	50.00	65.00	100.00	140.00	
1875 .... (20)	220		1,500	2,500	3,500	5,000
1875CC	11,828	175.00	275.00	400.00	550.00	
1875S	9,000	85.00	135.00	210.00	275.00	
1876 .... (45)	1,477	250.00	350.00	475.00	600.00	1,000
1876CC	6,887	200.00	290.00	350.00	550.00	
1876S	4,000	100.00	150.00	225.00	350.00	
1877 .... (20)	1,152	225.00	450.00	725.00	900.00	1,500
1877CC	8,680	225.00	300.00	400.00	550.00	
1877S	26,700	50.00	75.00	110.00	150.00	
1878 .... (20)	131,740	40.00	45.00	50.00	55.00	1,200

HALF EAGLES

	Quan. Minted	Fine	V. Fine	E. Fine	Unc.	Proof
1878CC....................	9,054	$450.00	$600.00	$750.00	$1,300	
1878S....................	144,700	40.00	45.00	50.00	55.00	
1879..............(30)	301,950	40.00	45.00	50.00	55.00	$700.00
1879CC....................	17,281	125.00	200.00	275.00	350.00	
1879S....................	426,200	40.00	45.00	50.00	55.00	
1880..............(36)	3,166,436	40.00	45.00	50.00	55.00	625.00
1880CC....................	51,017	80.00	100.00	140.00	200.00	
1880S....................	1,348,900	40.00	45.00	50.00	55.00	
1881..............(42)	5,708,802	40.00	45.00	50.00	55.00	500.00
1881CC....................	13,886	85.00	115.00	140.00	225.00	
1881S....................	969,000	40.00	45.00	50.00	55.00	
1882..............(48)	2,514,568	40.00	45.00	50.00	55.00	500.00
1882CC....................	82,817	75.00	90.00	115.00	150.00	
1882S....................	969,999	40.00	45.00	50.00	55.00	
1883..............(61)	233,461	40.00	45.00	50.00	55.00	550.00
1883CC....................	12,958	90.00	110.00	145.00	200.00	
1883S....................	83,200	40.00	45.00	50.00	55.00	
1884..............(48)	191,078	40.00	45.00	50.00	55.00	1,000
1884CC....................	16,402	90.00	110.00	145.00	175.00	
1884S....................	177,000	40.00	45.00	50.00	55.00	
1885..............(66)	601,506	40.00	45.00	50.00	55.00	500.00
1885S....................	1,211,500	40.00	45.00	50.00	55.00	
1886..............(72)	388,432	40.00	45.00	50.00	55.00	475.00
1886S....................	3,268,000	40.00	45.00	50.00	55.00	
1887 Proofs only.....(87)	87	....				2,750
1887S....................	1,912,000	40.00	45.00	50.00	55.00	
1888..............(95)	18,296	50.00	60.00	70.00	90.00	750.00
1888S....................	293,900	40.00	45.00	50.00	55.00	
1889..............(45)	7,565	175.00	225.00	275.00	450.00	875.00
1890..............(88)	4,328	200.00	250.00	325.00	450.00	800.00
1890CC....................	53,800	55.00	65.00	80.00	110.00	
1891..............(53)	61,413	40.00	45.00	50.00	55.00	600.00
1891CC....................	208,000	50.00	60.00	75.00	90.00	
1892..............(92)	753,572	40.00	45.00	50.00	55.00	475.00
1892CC....................	82,968	50.00	60.00	75.00	95.00	
1892O....................	10,000	350.00	550.00	700.00	875.00	
1892S....................	298,400	40.00	45.00	50.00	75.00	
1893..............(77)	1,528,197	40.00	45.00	50.00	55.00	475.00
1893CC....................	60,000	55.00	65.00	75.00	110.00	
1893O....................	110,000	55.00	65.00	75.00	110.00	
1893S....................	224,000	40.00	45.00	50.00	55.00	
1894..............(75)	957,955	40.00	45.00	50.00	55.00	550.00
1894O....................	16,600	60.00	75.00	90.00	125.00	
1894S....................	55,900	40.00	45.00	60.00	85.00	
1895..............(81)	1,345,936	40.00	45.00	50.00	55.00	475.00
1895S....................	112,000	40.00	45.00	50.00	55.00	
1896..............(103)	59,063	40.00	45.00	50.00	55.00	475.00
1896S....................	155,400	40.00	45.00	50.00	55.00	
1897..............(83)	867,883	40.00	45.00	50.00	55.00	475.00
1897S....................	354,000	40.00	45.00	50.00	55.00	
1898..............(75)	633,495	40.00	45.00	50.00	55.00	475.00
1898S....................	1,397,400	40.00	45.00	50.00	55.00	
1899..............(99)	1,710,729	40.00	45.00	50.00	55.00	475.00
1899S....................	1,545,000	40.00	45.00	50.00	55.00	

HALF EAGLES

	Quan. Minted	Fine	V. Fine	E. Fine	Unc.	Proof
1900............(230)	1,405,730	$40.00	$45.00	$50.00	$55.00	$475.00
1900S...................	329,000	40.00	45.00	50.00	55.00	
1901............(140)	616,040	40.00	45.00	50.00	55.00	475.00
1901S...................	3,648,000	40.00	45.00	50.00	55.00	
1902............(162)	172,562	40.00	45.00	50.00	55.00	475.00
1902S...................	939,000	40.00	45.00	50.00	55.00	
1903............(154)	227,024	40.00	45.00	50.00	55.00	475.00
1903S...................	1,855,000	40.00	45.00	50.00	55.00	
1904............(136)	392,136	40.00	45.00	50.00	55.00	475.00
1904S...................	97,000	45.00	55.00	60.00	95.00	
1905............(108)	302,308	40.00	45.00	50.00	55.00	475.00
1905S...................	880,700	40.00	45.00	50.00	55.00	
1906............(85)	348,820	40.00	45.00	50.00	55.00	475.00
1906D..................	320,000	40.00	45.00	50.00	55.00	
1906S...................	598,000	40.00	45.00	50.00	55.00	
1907............(92)	626,192	40.00	45.00	50.00	55.00	475.00
1907D..................	888,000	40.00	45.00	50.00	55.00	
1908...................	421,874	40.00	45.00	50.00	55.00	

INDIAN HEAD TYPE 1908-1929

This type conforms to the quarter eagle of the same date. The incuse designs and lettering make this a unique series, along with the quarter eagle, in our United States coinage.

The scarcer mint marks when well struck command higher prices.

FINE—The knot in hair cord must show but small feathers on top of head will be faint.

VERY FINE—Noticeable wear on large middle feathers and tip of eagle's wing.

EXTRA FINE—Cheekbone, war bonnet and headband feathers slightly worn. Feathers on eagle's upper wing show considerable wear.

						Matte Proof
1908............(167)	578,012	50.00	60.00	70.00	80.00	750.00
1908D..................	148,000	50.00	65.00	75.00	85.00	
1908S..................	82,000	85.00	150.00	225.00	400.00	
1909............(78)	627,138	50.00	65.00	75.00	80.00	800.00
1909D..................	3,423,560	50.00	65.00	75.00	80.00	
1909O*.................	34,200	150.00	225.00	325.00	450.00	
1909S..................	297,200	50.00	65.00	75.00	125.00	
1910............(250)	604,250	50.00	65.00	75.00	80.00	800.00
1910D..................	193,600	50.00	65.00	75.00	125.00	
1910S..................	770,200	50.00	65.00	75.00	90.00	
1911............(139)	915,139	50.00	65.00	75.00	80.00	800.00
1911D..................	72,500	75.00	95.00	150.00	250.00	

*Beware spurious "O" mint mark.

HALF EAGLES

	Quan. Minted	Fine	V. Fine	E. Fine	Unc.	Matte Proof
1911S	1,416,000	$50.00	$65.00	$75.00	$90.00	
1912 (144)	790,144	50.00	65.00	70.00	80.00	
1912S	392,000	50.00	65.00	75.00	90.00	
1913 (99)	916,000	50.00	65.00	70.00	80.00	$800.00
1913S	408,000	50.00	65.00	75.00	125.00	
1914 (125)	247,125	50.00	65.00	70.00	80.00	900.00
1914D	247,000	50.00	65.00	70.00	85.00	
1914S	263,000	50.00	65.00	75.00	125.00	
1915* (75)	588,075	50.00	65.00	70.00	80.00	1,000
1915S	164,000	50.00	65.00	70.00	110.00	
1916S	240,000	60.00	70.00	80.00	110.00	
1929	662,000	1,000	1,300	1,450	1,600	

*Pieces dated 1915D are counterfeit.

EAGLES ($10.00 Gold Pieces)

Coinage authority including specified weights and fineness of the eagle conforms to that of the half eagle. The small eagle reverse was used until 1797 when the large, heraldic eagle replaced it. The early dates have variations in the number of stars, the rarest date being 1798. No eagles were struck from 1805 to 1837. Proofs of some dates prior to 1855 are known to exist, and all are rare.

FINE—Details on turban and head obliterated.

VERY FINE—Neck hairlines and details under turban and over forehead are worn but distinguishable.

EXTRA FINE—Definite wear on hair to left of eye and strand of hair across and around turban, also on eagle's wing tips.

	Quan. Minted	Fine	V. Fine	E. Fine	Unc.
1795	5,583	$1,100	$1,500	$1,900	3,000
1796	4,146	900.00	1,300	1,800	2,700
1797 Small eagle	2,466	950.00	1,500	1,950	3,000

	Quan. Minted	Fine	V. Fine	E. Fine	Unc.
1797 Large eagle	12,089	800.00	1,100	1,300	1,500

EAGLES

1798 over 97 9 Stars Left, 4 Right	1798 over 97 7 Stars Left, 6 Right	1799

	Quan. Minted	Fine	V. Fine	E. Fine	Unc.
1798 8 over 7, 9 stars left, 4 right	900	$1,300	$1,750	$2,600	$3,500
1798 8 over 7, 7 stars left, 6 right	842	2,400	3,400	5,750	8,750
1799	37,449	550.00	750.00	1,000	1,200
1800	5,999	600.00	800.00	1,000	1,200
1801	44,344	550.00	750.00	950.00	1,200
1803	15,017	600.00	800.00	1,000	1,200
1804	3,757	800.00	1,000	1,300	1,750

CORONET TYPE, no motto above eagle 1838-1866

In 1838 the weight and diameter of the eagle were reduced and the obverse and reverse were redesigned. Liberty now faces left and the word LIBERTY is placed on the coronet. A more natural appearing eagle is used on the reverse. The value, TEN D., is shown for the first time on this denomination.

FINE—LIBERTY readable but may be slightly worn.

VERY FINE—Hairlines above coronet partly worn. Curls under ear worn but defined.

EXTRA FINE—Small amount of wear on top of hair and below L in LIBERTY. Wear evident on wing tips and neck of eagle.

The Liberty head style of 1838 and 1839 (large letters) differs from that used for subsequent issues.

1838	7,200	375.00	550.00	800.00	1,000
1839 Large letters	25,801	300.00	400.00	650.00	900.00
1839 Small letters	12,447	400.00	650.00	850.00	1,100
1840	47,338	55.00	65.00	75.00	225.00
1841	63,131	55.00	65.00	75.00	200.00
1841O	2,500	300.00	400.00	525.00	1,000
1842 Small date	81,507	55.00	65.00	75.00	175.00
1842 Large date		55.00	65.00	75.00	175.00
1842O	27,400	60.00	75.00	90.00	225.00
1843	75,462	55.00	60.00	65.00	125.00

EAGLES

	Quan. Minted	Fine	V. Fine	E. Fine	Unc.	Proof
1843O	175,162	$55.00	$60.00	$65.00	$125.00	
1844	6,361	150.00	225.00	300.00	575.00	
1844O	118,700	55.00	60.00	75.00	150.00	
1845	26,153	55.00	60.00	75.00	150.00	
1845O	47,500	55.00	60.00	65.00	150.00	
1846	20,095	55.00	65.00	80.00	200.00	
1846O	81,780	55.00	65.00	75.00	150.00	
1847	862,258	55.00	60.00	65.00	100.00	
1847O	571,500	55.00	60.00	65.00	120.00	
1848	145,484	55.00	60.00	65.00	125.00	
1848O	35,850	55.00	60.00	65.00	150.00	
1849	653,618	55.00	60.00	65.00	100.00	
1849O	23,900	75.00	85.00	100.00	225.00	
1850	291,451	55.00	60.00	65.00	110.00	
1850O	57,500	65.00	75.00	95.00	225.00	
1851	176,328	55.00	60.00	65.00	100.00	
1851O	263,000	55.00	60.00	65.00	120.00	
1852	263,106	55.00	60.00	65.00	95.00	
1852O	18,000	65.00	100.00	125.00	250.00	
1853	201,253	55.00	60.00	65.00	95.00	
1853O	51,000	65.00	75.00	85.00	175.00	
1854	54,250	55.00	60.00	65.00	100.00	
1854O	52,500	65.00	85.00	95.00	225.00	
1854S	123,826	55.00	60.00	80.00	150.00	
1855	121,701	55.00	60.00	65.00	100.00	$5,000
1855O	18,000	85.00	110.00	165.00	350.00	
1855S	9,000	125.00	160.00	200.00	300.00	
1856	60,490	55.00	60.00	65.00	100.00	3,000
1856O	14,500	75.00	90.00	125.00	275.00	
1856S	68,000	55.00	60.00	75.00	175.00	
1857	16,606	85.00	100.00	140.00	300.00	3,000
1857O	5,500	200.00	300.00	375.00	600.00	
1857S	26,000	75.00	90.00	125.00	300.00	
1858*	2,521	2,750	3,750	4,300	6,200	———
1858O	20,000	85.00	100.00	150.00	275.00	
1858S	11,800	70.00	85.00	125.00	225.00	
1859	16,093	90.00	125.00	175.00	275.00	1,600
1859O	2,300	160.00	195.00	250.00	550.00	
1859S	7,000	125.00	175.00	225.00	400.00	
1860 (50)	15,105	75.00	85.00	100.00	200.00	1,600
1860O	11,100	75.00	85.00	125.00	250.00	
1860S	5,000	250.00	325.00	400.00	650.00	
1861 (69)	113,233	55.00	60.00	75.00	95.00	1,500
1861S	15,500	65.00	75.00	85.00	225.00	
1862 (35)	10,995	95.00	150.00	225.00	300.00	1,550
1862S	12,500	90.00	140.00	200.00	350.00	
1863 (30)	1,248	350.00	550.00	750.00	1,000	1,800
1863S	10,000	125.00	200.00	225.00	450.00	
1864 (50)	3,580	225.00	275.00	350.00	700.00	1,600
1864S	2,500	300.00	475.00	850.00	1,150	
1865 (25)	4,005	250.00	350.00	475.00	750.00	1,600
1865S All kinds	16,700	250.00	350.00	475.00	1,000	

*Beware removed mint mark.

	Quan. Minted	Fine	V. Fine	E. Fine	Unc.	Proof
1865S over inverted 186...........						
1866S All kinds............	20,000	$150.00	$250.00	$325.00	$475.00	

MOTTO OVER EAGLE 1866-1907

FINE—All letters in LIBERTY are complete.

VERY FINE—Half of hairlines over coronet visible. Curls under ear worn but defined. IN GOD WE TRUST and its ribbon are sharp.

EXTRA FINE—Small amount of wear on top of hair and below L in LIBERTY. Wear evident on wing tips and neck of eagle.

		Quan. Minted	Fine	V. Fine	E. Fine	Unc.	Proof
1866	(30)	3,780	125.00	275.00	325.00	650.00	$1,150
1866S			100.00	200.00	275.00	475.00	
1867	(50)	3,140	125.00	200.00	275.00	400.00	1,100
1867S		9,000	100.00	150.00	200.00	300.00	
1868	(25)	10,655	85.00	110.00	150.00	250.00	1,250
1868S		13,500	85.00	110.00	150.00	275.00	
1869	(25)	1,855	250.00	400.00	525.00	675.00	1,250
1869S		6,430	125.00	200.00	275.00	450.00	
1870	(35)	4,025	200.00	300.00	375.00	500.00	1,100
1870CC		5,908	250.00	350.00	500.00	800.00	
1870S		8,000	125.00	175.00	225.00	375.00	
1871	(30)	1,820	200.00	300.00	475.00	600.00	2,200
1871CC		7,185	250.00	400.00	525.00	750.00	
1871S		16,500	75.00	100.00	175.00	200.00	
1872	(30)	1,650	225.00	310.00	450.00	600.00	1,750
1872CC		5,500	250.00	400.00	525.00	700.00	
1872S		17,300	70.00	100.00	175.00	250.00	
1873	(25)	825	500.00	900.00	1,500	2,000	2,500
1873CC		4,543	275.00	450.00	600.00	800.00	
1873S		12,000	75.00	110.00	200.00	275.00	
1874	(20)	53,160	50.00	65.00	85.00	110.00	2,000
1874CC		16,767	125.00	175.00	250.00	350.00	
1874S		10,000	80.00	135.00	200.00	300.00	
1875	(20)	120	650.00	1,000	1,500	2,000	4,000
1875CC		7,715	200.00	350.00	475.00	550.00	
1876	(45)	732	350.00	650.00	850.00	1,050	1,750
1876CC		4,696	250.00	375.00	475.00	600.00	
1876S		5,000	160.00	250.00	300.00	350.00	
1877	(20)	817	500.00	900.00	1,250	1,450	2,500
1877CC		3,332	250.00	375.00	475.00	625.00	
1877S		17,000	55.00	75.00	110.00	175.00	
1878	(20)	73,800	45.00	50.00	75.00	80.00	1,600
1878CC		3,244	300.00	450.00	550.00	900.00	
1878S		26,100	45.00	50.00	75.00	90.00	
1879	(30)	384,770	45.00	50.00	75.00	90.00	1,150
1879CC		1,762	600.00	850.00	1,000	1,400	

EAGLES

	Quan. Minted	Fine	V. Fine	E. Fine	Unc.	Proof
1879O	1,500	$550.00	$675.00	$950.00	$1,200	
1879S	224,000	45.00	50.00	75.00	90.00	
1880	(36) 1,644,876	45.00	50.00	75.00	90.00	$1,000
1880CC	11,190	85.00	100.00	140.00	200.00	
1880O	9,200	65.00	90.00	150.00	215.00	
1880S	506,250	45.00	50.00	65.00	75.00	
1881	(40) 3,877,260	45.00	50.00	65.00	75.00	1,000
1881CC	24,015	85.00	100.00	125.00	175.00	
1881O	8,350	65.00	100.00	160.00	210.00	
1881S	970,000	45.00	50.00	75.00	90.00	
1882	(40) 2,324,480	45.00	50.00	75.00	90.00	1,000
1882CC	6,764	95.00	150.00	185.00	225.00	
1882O	10,820	50.00	75.00	100.00	160.00	
1882S	132,000	45.00	50.00	65.00	80.00	
1883	(40) 208,740	45.00	50.00	65.00	80.00	1,000
1883CC	12,000	85.00	125.00	165.00	200.00	
1883O	800	675.00	1,100	1,500	2,000	
1883S	38,000	55.00	80.00	110.00	165.00	
1884	(15) 76,905	45.00	50.00	65.00	80.00	1,800
1884CC	9,925	90.00	120.00	165.00	250.00	
1884S	124,250	45.00	50.00	65.00	80.00	
1885	(65) 253,527	45.00	50.00	55.00	65.00	900.00
1885S	228,000	45.00	50.00	55.00	65.00	
1886	(60) 236,160	45.00	50.00	55.00	65.00	900.00
1886S	826,000	45.00	50.00	55.00	65.00	
1887	(80) 53,680	50.00	55.00	65.00	75.00	850.00
1887S	817,000	45.00	50.00	55.00	65.00	
1888	(75) 132,996	50.00	55.00	65.00	80.00	850.00
1888O	21,335	55.00	65.00	75.00	125.00	
1888S	648,700	55.00	60.00	65.00	70.00	
1889	(45) 4,485	150.00	250.00	325.00	475.00	950.00
1889S	425,400	45.00	50.00	60.00	70.00	
1890	(63) 58,043	45.00	50.00	60.00	70.00	850.00
1890CC	17,500	60.00	65.00	75.00	135.00	
1891	(48) 91,868	45.00	50.00	60.00	70.00	850.00
1891CC	103,732	55.00	60.00	70.00	95.00	
1892	(72) 797,552	45.00	50.00	60.00	70.00	950.00
1892CC	40,000	60.00	70.00	85.00	125.00	
1892O	28,688	55.00	60.00	65.00	85.00	
1892S	115,500	50.00	55.00	65.00	80.00	
1893	(55) 1,840,895	45.00	50.00	60.00	70.00	950.00
1893CC	14,000	65.00	75.00	90.00	175.00	
1893O	17,000	55.00	60.00	65.00	85.00	
1893S	141,350	45.00	50.00	60.00	70.00	
1894	(43) 2,470,778	45.00	50.00	60.00	70.00	1,000
1894O	107,500	50.00	55.00	65.00	80.00	
1894S	25,000	55.00	70.00	85.00	200.00	
1895	(56) 567,826	45.00	50.00	60.00	70.00	950.00
1895O	98,000	45.00	50.00	60.00	75.00	
1895S	49,000	45.00	50.00	60.00	75.00	
1896	(78) 76,348	45.00	50.00	60.00	70.00	950.00
1896S	123,750	45.00	50.00	60.00	70.00	
1897	(69) 1,000,159	45.00	50.00	60.00	70.00	850.00

EAGLES

	Quan. Minted	Fine	V. Fine	E. Fine	Unc.	Proof
1897O	42,500	$50.00	$55.00	$65.00	$80.00	
1897S	234,750	45.00	50.00	60.00	70.00	
1898	(67) 812,197	45.00	50.00	60.00	70.00	$850.00
1898S	473,600	45.00	50.00	60.00	70.00	
1899	(86) 1,262,305	45.00	50.00	60.00	70.00	850.00
1899O	37,047	50.00	55.00	65.00	80.00	
1899S	841,000	45.00	50.00	60.00	70.00	
1900	(120) 293,960	45.00	50.00	60.00	70.00	850.00
1900S	81,000	45.00	50.00	60.00	75.00	
1901	(85) 1,718,825	45.00	50.00	60.00	70.00	850.00
1901O	72,041	55.00	60.00	65.00	85.00	
1901S	2,812,750	45.00	50.00	60.00	70.00	
1902	(113) 82,513	45.00	50.00	60.00	70.00	850.00
1902S	469,500	45.00	50.00	60.00	70.00	
1903	(96) 125,926	45.00	50.00	60.00	70.00	850.00
1903O	112,771	45.00	50.00	60.00	70.00	
1903S	538,000	45.00	50.00	60.00	70.00	
1904	(108) 162,038	45.00	50.00	60.00	70.00	850.00
1904O	108,950	45.00	50.00	60.00	75.00	
1905	(86) 201,078	45.00	50.00	60.00	70.00	850.00
1905S	369,250	45.00	50.00	60.00	75.00	
1906	(77) 165,497	45.00	50.00	60.00	70.00	850.00
1906D	981,000	45.00	50.00	60.00	75.00	
1906O	86,895	50.00	55.00	65.00	80.00	
1906S	457,000	45.00	50.00	60.00	75.00	
1907 All kinds	(74) 1,203,973	45.00	50.00	60.00	70.00	850.00
1907D	1,030,000	45.00	50.00	60.00	75.00	
1907S	210,500	55.00	60.00	65.00	85.00	

INDIAN HEAD TYPE, no motto 1907-1908

Augustus Saint-Gaudens, considered by many the greatest of modern sculptors, introduced a new high standard of art in United States coins evidenced by his eagle and double eagle types of 1907. The obverse of the eagle shows the head of Liberty crowned with an Indian war bonnet while an impressively majestic eagle dominates the reverse side. A departure from older standards is found on the edge of the piece, where 46 raised stars are arranged signifying the states of the Union, instead of a lettered or reeded edge. (48 stars 1912 and later.)

The first eagles struck had no motto IN GOD WE TRUST as did the later issues starting in 1908. President Theodore Roosevelt personally objected to the use of the Deity's name on coins. The motto was restored to the coins by Act of Congress in 1908.

FINE—Feathers on bonnet show definite wear. Full LIBERTY.

VERY FINE—Bonnet feathers worn near band. Hair high points show wear.

EXTRA FINE—Slight wear on cheekbone and headdress feathers. Eagle's eye and left wing will show slight wear.

EAGLES

No Motto   With Motto

	Quan. Minted	Fine	V. Fine	E. Fine	Unc.	Proof
1907 Wire edge (rim), periods before and after legends 500					$2,300	$3,500
1907 Same, no stars on edge (unique)						
1907 Rolled edge, periods 42		. . . . .R. L. Miles Sale 1968 $8,250.00				
1907 No periods. 239,406	$65.00	$70.00	$85.00	100.00	
1908 No motto. 33,500	65.00	70.00	85.00	125.00	
1908D No motto. 210,000	65.00	70.00	85.00	110.00	

With Motto IN GOD WE TRUST, 1908-1933

	Quan. Minted	Fine	V. Fine	E. Fine	Unc.	Matte Proof
1908 . . . .(116)	341,486	65.00	70.00	80.00	90.00	1,350
1908D	836,500	65.00	70.00	80.00	90.00	
1908S	59,850	75.00	100.00	150.00	300.00	
1909 . . . .(74)	184,863	65.00	70.00	80.00	90.00	1,350
1909D	121,540	65.00	70.00	80.00	90.00	
1909S	292,350	65.00	75.00	90.00	125.00	
1910 . . . .(204)	318,704	65.00	70.00	80.00	90.00	1,350
1910D 2,356,640		65.00	70.00	80.00	90.00	
1910S	811,000	65.00	70.00	80.00	110.00	
1911 . . . .(95)	505,595	65.00	70.00	80.00	90.00	1,350
1911D	30,100	75.00	100.00	150.00	225.00	
1911S	51,000	75.00	100.00	135.00	200.00	
1912 . . . .(83)	405,083	65.00	70.00	80.00	90.00	1,350
1912S	300,000	65.00	70.00	80.00	90.00	
1913 . . . .(71)	442,071	65.00	70.00	80.00	90.00	1,350
1913S	66,000	65.00	75.00	95.00	135.00	
1914 . . . .(50)	151,050	65.00	70.00	80.00	90.00	1,500
1914D	343,500	65.00	70.00	80.00	90.00	
1914S	208,000	65.00	70.00	80.00	90.00	
1915 . . . .(75)	351,075	65.00	70.00	80.00	90.00	1,350
1915S	59,000	75.00	100.00	140.00	200.00	
1916S	138,500	70.00	90.00	120.00	175.00	
1920S	126,500	2,000	2,750	3,500	4,750	
1926 1,014,000		65.00	70.00	80.00	90.00	
1930S	96,000	1,750	2,250	2,500	3,250	
1932 4,463,000		65.00	70.00	80.00	90.00	
1933	312,500	2,500	3,200	4,000	5,500	

DOUBLE EAGLES ($20.00 Gold Pieces) — 1849-1933

This largest of all regular United States issues was authorized to be coined by the Act of March 3, 1849. Its weight was 516 grains, .900 fine. The 1849 double eagle is a unique pattern and reposes in the Mint collection. The rarest date obtainable is 1883. The 1861S reverse design by Paquet was withdrawn soon after striking. Very few specimens are known.

FINE—LIBERTY worn but readable. All hairlines show considerable wear.
VERY FINE—LIBERTY is bold. Jewels on crown defined. Lower half worn flat. Hair worn about ear.
EXTRA FINE—Trace of wear on rounded prongs of crown and down hair curls. Minor bag marks.

1861S Paquet Reverse

	Quan. Minted	Fine	V. Fine	E. Fine	Unc.	Proof
1849	1		U.S. Mint Collection			——
1850	1,170,261	$125.00	$160.00	$225.00	$500.00	
1850O	141,000	125.00	160.00	225.00	500.00	
1851	2,087,155	100.00	125.00	175.00	250.00	
1851O	315,000	125.00	160.00	225.00	400.00	
1852	2,053,026	100.00	125.00	175.00	250.00	
1852O	190,000	125.00	160.00	225.00	400.00	
1853	1,261,326	90.00	110.00	150.00	225.00	
1853O	71,000	165.00	225.00	300.00	500.00	
1854	757,899	90.00	110.00	150.00	225.00	
1854O	3,250	1,500	2,000	2,750	4,000	
1854S	141,468	125.00	150.00	185.00	450.00	
1855	364,666	90.00	110.00	150.00	225.00	
1855O	8,000	375.00	500.00	650.00	950.00	
1855S	879,675	90.00	110.00	150.00	225.00	
1856	329,878	90.00	110.00	150.00	200.00	
1856O	2,250	3,250	4,500	5,250	7,000	
1856S	1,189,750	100.00	125.00	155.00	275.00	
1857	439,375	100.00	110.00	150.00	225.00	
1857O	30,000	175.00	250.00	325.00	475.00	
1857S	970,500	90.00	110.00	150.00	200.00	
1858	211,714	100.00	125.00	175.00	250.00	$4,000
1858O	35,250	200.00	350.00	475.00	600.00	
1858S	846,710	90.00	110.00	150.00	200.00	
1859	43,597	150.00	200.00	250.00	400.00	3,500
1859O	9,100	350.00	525.00	800.00	1,100	
1859S	636,445	100.00	125.00	175.00	250.00	
1860	(59) 577,670	100.00	125.00	175.00	225.00	2,400
1860O	6,600	650.00	900.00	1,200	1,750	
1860S	544,950	90.00	110.00	150.00	195.00	
1861	(66) 2,976,453	85.00	100.00	115.00	150.00	2,400

DOUBLE EAGLES

	Quan. Minted	Fine	V. Fine	E. Fine	Unc.	Proof
1861O	5,000	$400.00	$525.00	$750.00	$1,050	
1861S	768,000	90.00	110.00	150.00	225.00	
1861—A.C. Paquet rev. (Ex. Rare).					———	
1861S—A.C. Paquet rev.						
(Tall letters)			2,500	3,000	4,500	
1862 (35)	92,133	150.00	225.00	300.00	425.00	2,350
1862S	854,173	90.00	110.00	150.00	275.00	
1863 (30)	142,790	150.00	225.00	325.00	450.00	2,350
1863S	966,570	90.00	110.00	150.00	225.00	
1864 (50)	204,285	95.00	125.00	175.00	300.00	2,350
1864S	793,660	90.00	110.00	150.00	225.00	
1865 (25)	351,200	125.00	160.00	190.00	250.00	2,350
1865S	1,042,500	85.00	110.00	140.00	200.00	
1866S		300.00	450.00	575.00	950.00	

Motto above eagle, value TWENTY D. 1866-1876

	Quan. Minted	Fine	V. Fine	E. Fine	Unc.	Proof
1866 (30)	698,775	100.00	125.00	175.00	300.00	2,350
1866S	842,250	85.00	110.00	150.00	225.00	
1867 (50)	251,065	100.00	120.00	160.00	200.00	2,350
1867S	920,750	85.00	110.00	150.00	225.00	
1868 (25)	98,600	125.00	160.00	190.00	250.00	2,350
1868S	837,500	85.00	110.00	140.00	175.00	
1869 (25)	175,155	100.00	120.00	160.00	225.00	2,350
1869S	686,750	90.00	110.00	150.00	200.00	
1870 (35)	155,185	100.00	125.00	175.00	275.00	2,350
1870CC	3,789	4,250	6,500	8,500	10,500	
1870S	982,000	90.00	110.00	150.00	200.00	
1871 (30)	80,150	125.00	150.00	175.00	300.00	2,350
1871CC	14,687	400.00	550.00	725.00	1,100	
1871S	928,000	85.00	110.00	140.00	175.00	
1872 (30)	251,880	100.00	120.00	160.00	225.00	2,400
1872CC	29,650	150.00	300.00	425.00	600.00	
1872S	780,000	85.00	110.00	140.00	175.00	
1873 Closed 3 (25)	1,709,825	275.00	400.00	575.00	750.00	2,500
1873 Open 3		85.00	100.00	120.00	150.00	
1873CC Closed 3	22,410	175.00	300.00	450.00	700.00	
1873S	1,040,600	85.00	100.00	120.00	150.00	
1874 (20)	366,800	80.00	90.00	115.00	135.00	2,500
1874CC	115,085	90.00	110.00	150.00	200.00	
1874S	1,214,000	80.00	90.00	120.00	150.00	
1875 (20)	295,740	80.00	90.00	115.00	135.00	2,500

DOUBLE EAGLES

	Quan. Minted	Fine	V. Fine	E. Fine	Unc.	Proof
1875CC	111,151	$90.00	$110.00	$150.00	$200.00	
1875S	1,230,000	80.00	90.00	110.00	125.00	
1876	(45) 583,905	80.00	90.00	110.00	125.00	$2,500
1876CC	138,441	85.00	100.00	140.00	175.00	
1876S	1,597,000	80.00	90.00	110.00	125.00	

TWENTY DOLLARS

	Quan. Minted	Fine	V. Fine	E. Fine	Unc.	Proof
1877	(20) 397,670	75.00	80.00	90.00	100.00	2,600
1877CC	42,565	100.00	150.00	200.00	325.00	
1877S	1,735,000	75.00	80.00	90.00	100.00	
1878	(20) 543,645	75.00	80.00	90.00	100.00	2,600
1878CC	13,180	175.00	225.00	275.00	450.00	
1878S	1,739,000	75.00	80.00	90.00	100.00	
1879	(30) 207,630	75.00	80.00	90.00	100.00	2,600
1879CC	10,708	250.00	350.00	450.00	700.00	
1879O	2,325	500.00	750.00	900.00	1,250	
1879S	1,223,800	75.00	80.00	90.00	100.00	
1880	(36) 51,456	85.00	100.00	140.00	175.00	2,350
1880S	836,000	75.00	80.00	90.00	100.00	
1881	(40) 2,260	600.00	850.00	1,250	1,500	3,000
1881S	727,000	75.00	80.00	90.00	100.00	
1882	(40) 630	600.00	1,250	2,000	2,800	4,000
1882CC	39,140	100.00	120.00	160.00	225.00	
1882S	1,125,000	75.00	80.00	90.00	100.00	
1883 Proofs only	(40) 40					9,000
1883CC	59,962	125.00	160.00	190.00	250.00	
1883S	1,189,000	85.00	100.00	120.00	140.00	
1884 Proofs only	(71) 71					7,000
1884CC	81,139	125.00	160.00	190.00	250.00	
1884S	916,000	85.00	95.00	110.00	135.00	
1885	(77) 828	750.00	1,250	1,750	2,000	4,500
1885CC	9,450	250.00	375.00	450.00	650.00	
1885S	683,500	85.00	95.00	110.00	135.00	
1886	(106) 1,106	850.00	1,250	2,100	3,500	4,500
1887 Proofs only	(121) 121					5,000
1887S	283,000	85.00	100.00	140.00	175.00	
1888	(105) 226,266	85.00	100.00	140.00	175.00	3,200
1888S	859,600	75.00	80.00	90.00	100.00	
1889	(41) 44,111	100.00	125.00	165.00	275.00	2,600
1889CC	30,945	100.00	125.00	165.00	300.00	
1889S	774,700	75.00	80.00	90.00	100.00	
1890	(55) 75,995	85.00	95.00	110.00	150.00	2,500

DOUBLE EAGLES

	Quan. Minted	Fine	V. Fine	E. Fine	Unc.	Proof
1890CC	91,209	$90.00	$110.00	$150.00	$200.00	
1890S	802,750	65.00	70.00	75.00	85.00	
1891 (52)	1,442	375.00	600.00	825.00	1,000	$2,600
1891CC	5,000	300.00	400.00	500.00	650.00	
1891S	1,288,125	65.00	70.00	75.00	85.00	
1892 (93)	4,523	300.00	500.00	700.00	900.00	2,500
1892CC	27,265	125.00	160.00	190.00	250.00	
1892S	930,150	75.00	80.00	90.00	100.00	
1893 (59)	344,339	85.00	95.00	110.00	135.00	2,100
1893CC	18,402	150.00	200.00	250.00	350.00	
1893S	996,175	65.00	70.00	75.00	85.00	
1894 (50)	1,368,990	65.00	70.00	75.00	85.00	2,200
1894S	1,048,550	75.00	80.00	90.00	100.00	
1895 (51)	1,114,656	75.00	80.00	90.00	100.00	2,500
1895S	1,143,500	65.00	70.00	75.00	85.00	
1896 (128)	792,663	65.00	70.00	75.00	85.00	2,300
1896S	1,403,925	65.00	70.00	75.00	85.00	
1897 (86)	1,383,261	65.00	70.00	75.00	85.00	2,300
1897S	1,470,250	65.00	70.00	75.00	85.00	
1898 (75)	170,470	85.00	95.00	110.00	150.00	2,300
1898S	2,575,175	65.00	70.00	75.00	85.00	
1899 (84)	1,669,384	65.00	70.00	75.00	85.00	2,300
1899S	2,010,300	65.00	70.00	75.00	85.00	
1900 (124)	1,874,584	65.00	70.00	75.00	85.00	2,300
1900S	2,459,500	65.00	70.00	75.00	85.00	
1901 (96)	111,526	75.00	80.00	90.00	100.00	2,400
1901S	1,596,000	65.00	70.00	75.00	85.00	
1902 (114)	31,254	90.00	110.00	150.00	200.00	2,400
1902S	1,753,625	65.00	70.00	75.00	85.00	
1903 (158)	287,428	65.00	70.00	75.00	85.00	2,100
1903S	954,000	65.00	70.00	75.00	85.00	
1904 (98)	6,256,797	65.00	70.00	75.00	85.00	2,400
1904S	5,134,175	65.00	70.00	75.00	85.00	
1905 (90)	59,011	90.00	110.00	150.00	200.00	2,600
1905S	1,813,000	65.00	70.00	75.00	85.00	
1906 (94)	69,690	90.00	110.00	140.00	190.00	2,500
1906D	620,250	75.00	80.00	90.00	100.00	
1906S	2,065,750	65.00	70.00	75.00	85.00	
1907 (78)	1,451,864	65.00	70.00	75.00	85.00	2,500
1907D	842,250	75.00	80.00	90.00	100.00	
1907S	2,165,800	65.00	70.00	75.00	85.00	

SAINT-GAUDENS TYPE

A few experimental pieces were struck having an extremely high relief. They are easily distinguished from the ones issued later for general circulation, which also have a very high relief.

The field of the rare experimental pieces is excessively concave and connects directly with the edge without any border, giving it a sharp knifelike appearance; Liberty's skirt shows two folds on the side of her right leg; the Capitol building in the background at left is very small; the sun, on the reverse side, has 14 rays, as opposed to the regular high relief coins that have only 13 rays extending from the sun.

11,250 high relief pieces were struck for general circulation. The relief is somewhat lower but both have the date 1907 in Roman numerals. Flat-relief double eagles were issued later in 1907 with Arabic numerals.

DOUBLE EAGLES

Proof

1907 Ex. high relief, plain edge (Unique)..........................———
1907 Ex. high relief, lettered edge — New York Sale, 1961......$18,250.00

VERY FINE—Minor wear on legs and toes. Eagle's left wing and breast feathers worn.

EXTRA FINE—Drapery lines on chest visible. Wear on right breast, knee and below. Eagle's feathers on breast and right wing are bold.

	Quan. Minted	V. Fine	Ex. Fine	Unc.	Proof
1907 High relief, Roman numerals (MCMVII), wire rim.....	11,250	$475.00	$725.00	$950.00	$2500.00
1907 Same, flat rim...........		475.00	725.00	950.00	2500.00

Arabic
Numerals

No
Motto

1907 Large letters on edge (Proof only) Unique...................				———
1907 Small letters on edge......361,667	90.00	100.00	125.00	
1908.....................4,271,551	85.00	95.00	110.00	
1908D......................663,750	85.00	95.00	120.00	

With motto IN GOD WE TRUST, 1908-1933

Matte
Proof

1908.................(101) 156,359	70.00	80.00	100.00	2400.00

DOUBLE EAGLES

	Quan. Minted	V. Fine	Ex. Fine	Unc.	Matte Proof
1908D....................	349,500	$ 70.00	$100.00	$125.00	
1908S....................	22,000	150.00	250.00	600.00	
1909 9 over 8............	}161,282	100.00	135.00	200.00	
1909 Norm. date...(67)		85.00	110.00	175.00	$2,500
1909D....................	52,500	125.00	175.00	350.00	
1909S....................	2,774,925	65.00	80.00	100.00	
1910............(167)	482,167	65.00	75.00	85.00	2,400
1910D....................	429,000	65.00	75.00	85.00	
1910S....................	2,128,250	70.00	85.00	100.00	
1911............(100)	197,350	70.00	85.00	110.00	2,500
1911D....................	846,500	65.00	75.00	85.00	
1911S....................	775,750	75.00	85.00	110.00	
1912............(74)	149,824	110.00	150.00	200.00	2,500
1913............(58)	168,838	65.00	80.00	110.00	2,700
1913D....................	393,500	65.00	80.00	100.00	
1913S....................	34,000	125.00	175.00	275.00	
1914............(70)	95,320	85.00	110.00	125.00	2,800
1914D....................	453,000	65.00	75.00	85.00	
1914S....................	1,498,000	70.00	80.00	95.00	
1915............(50)	152,050	90.00	100.00	125.00	2,800
1915S....................	567,500	70.00	85.00	100.00	
1916S....................	796,000	90.00	100.00	125.00	
1920.....................	228,250	65.00	80.00	100.00	
1920S....................	558,000	850.00	1,450	2,000	
1921.....................	528,500	1,750	2,400	3,500	
1922.....................	1,375,500	65.00	75.00	85.00	
1922S....................	2,658,000	125.00	175.00	250.00	
1923.....................	566,000	65.00	75.00	85.00	
1923D....................	1,702,250	65.00	75.00	95.00	
1924.....................	4,323,500	65.00	75.00	85.00	
1924D....................	3,049,500	140.00	185.00	250.00	
1924S....................	2,927,500	225.00	325.00	425.00	
1925.....................	2,831,750	65.00	75.00	85.00	
1925D....................	2,938,500	350.00	475.00	700.00	
1925S....................	3,776,500	150.00	250.00	350.00	
1926.....................	816,750	65.00	75.00	85.00	
1926D....................	481,000	450.00	650.00	850.00	
1926S....................	2,041,500	175.00	250.00	400.00	
1927.....................	2,946,750	65.00	75.00	85.00	
1927D....................	180,000	New York Sale 1969.....$32,000.00			
1927S....................	3,107,000	500.00	650.00	1,000	
1928.....................	8,816,000	65.00	75.00	85.00	
1929.....................	1,779,750	800.00	1,250	1,750	
1930S....................	74,000	1,500	2,000	3,500	
1931.....................	2,938,250	1,000	1,500	2,000	
1931D....................	106,500	1,500	2,000	3,500	
1932.....................	1,101,750	1,000	1,500	3,000	

1933 None placed in circulation.

COMMEMORATIVE
COINS

Commemorative coins have been popular since the days of the Greeks and Romans. In the beginning they served to record and honor important events and in the absence of newspapers they proved highly useful in passing along news of the day.

Many modern nations have issued commemorative coins and such pieces are highly esteemed by collectors. Yet no nation has surpassed our own country when it comes to commemorative coins and in this we have reason to be proud.

The unique position occupied by commemoratives in United States coinage is largely due to the fact that with few exceptions they are the only coins that have a real historical significance. The progress and advance of people in the New World are presented in an interesting and instructive manner on the commemorative issues. Such a record of facts artistically presented on our gold and silver memorial issues appeals strongly to the collector who favors the historical side of numismatics. It is the historical features of the commemoratives, in fact, which create interest among many people who would otherwise have little interest in coins.

Commemorative issues are considered for coinage by two committees of Congress — The Committee on Banking and Currency of the Senate, and the Committee on Banking and Currency of the House. Congress is guided to a great extent by the reports of these committees when passing upon bills authorizing commemorative coins.

These special coins are usually issued either to commemorate events or to help pay for monuments or celebrations that commemorate historical persons, places or things. The commemorative coins are offered in most instances by a commission in charge of the event to be commemorated, and sold at a price in advance of the face value of the piece.

During a half century over fifty different types of commemorative coins have been issued in the United States. A complete type set of commemorative half dollars consists of forty-eight pieces. The addition of mint mark varieties makes a total of 142 coins in the series.

No commemorative coins were struck from 1940 to 1945, and none since 1954.

Unless otherwise stated, the coinage figures given represent the total outstanding coinage. In many cases, larger quantities were minted but were not all sold. The unsold coins were usually returned to the mint and melted, although some were placed in circulation at face value.

Note: The Commemorative section following is arranged alphabetically.

COMMEMORATIVE SILVER — Isabella, Lafayette

ISABELLA QUARTER DOLLAR

In 1893 the Board of Lady Managers of the Columbian Exposition petitioned for a souvenir quarter-dollar. Authority was granted March 3, 1893. The coin known as the Isabella quarter was designed by C. E. Barber. These souvenir quarters were sold for $1.00. The obverse has
the crowned bust of Queen Isabella of Spain. The kneeling female on the reverse with distaff and spindle is emblematic of woman's industry.

		Quan. Minted	Ex. Fine	Unc.
1893	Columbian Exposition, Chicago	24,214	$52.50	$85.00

LAFAYETTE DOLLAR

The heads of Washington and Lafayette appear on this commemorative issue, which was the first commemorative coin of one dollar denomination, and the first authorized United States coin to bear a portrait of one of our presidents. The dies were prepared by C. E. Barber. The statue on the reverse is similar to the monument of General Lafayette which was erected in Paris as a gift of the American people. The coins were sold by the Lafayette Memorial Commission for $2.00 each.

1900	Lafayette Dollar	36,026	90.00	180.00

ALABAMA CENTENNIAL

The Alabama half dollars were authorized in 1920 for the centennial which was celebrated in 1919, but they were not struck until 1921. The coins, designed by Laura Gardin Fraser, were offered first during President Harding's visit to Birmingham, October 26, 1921. The St. Andrews cross, an emblem on the state flag, appears on a part of the issue between the figures 22 indicating the twenty-second state of the Union. The obverse has busts of W. W. Bibb, first governor of Alabama, and T. E. Kilby, governor at the time of the centennial. This is the first instance of the use of a living person's portrait on a United States coin.

2x2 in field

		Quan. Minted	Ex. Fine	Unc.
1921	Alabama Centennial, with 2 x 2 in field of obverse	6,006	$37.50	$65.00
1921	Alabama Centennial, no 2 x 2	59,038	27.50	50.00

ALBANY, NEW YORK CHARTER

The two hundred and fiftieth anniversary of the granting of a charter to the city of Albany was the occasion for a commemorative half dollar. The reverse design shows Governor Dongan, Peter Schuyler and Robert Livingston. The obverse has a beaver which is gnawing on a maple branch. Gertrude K. Lathrop of Albany was the designer.

1936	Albany, New York	17,671	27.50	50.00

BATTLE OF ANTIETAM

A souvenir half dollar was designed by William Marks and struck in 1937 to commemorate the seventy-fifth anniversary of the famous Civil War battle to thwart Lee's invasion of Maryland. The opposing generals McClellan and Lee are featured on the obverse while the Burnside Bridge, an important tactical objective, is shown on the reverse. The Battle of Antietam on September 17, 1862, was one of the bloodiest single-day battles of the war with total losses of about 25,000 men.

1937	Battle of Antietam 1862-1937	18,028	42.50	80.00

ARKANSAS CENTENNIAL

This souvenir issue marked the one hundredth anniversary of the admission of Arkansas into the Union. Edward Everett Burr designed the piece and models were prepared by Emily Bates of Arkansas. Although 1936 was the centennial year the first of several issues was brought out in 1935 from all three mints. During 1936 a new design was authorized by Congress. The late Senator Joseph T. Robinson consented to have his portrait placed on the obverse side of the coins which were struck in January 1937 at the Philadelphia Mint. The 1937 and 1938 issues were the same as those of 1935 except for the dates. They were sold by the distributors at $8.75 per set of three coins. The obverse shows accolated heads of an Indian chief of 1836 and an American girl of 1936.

		Quan. Minted		Unc.
1935	Arkansas Centennial	13,012		
1935D	Same type D mint	5,505	Set	$ 42.50
1935S	Same type S mint	5,506		
1936	Arkansas Centennial, same as 1935 — date 1936 on rev	9,660		
1936D	Same type D mint	9,660	Set	42.50
1936S	Same type S mint	9,662		
1937	Arkansas Centennial (same as 1935)	5,505		
1937D	Same type D mint	5,505	Set	42.50
1937S	Same type S mint	5,506		
1938	Arkansas Centennial (same as 1935)	3,156		
1938D	Same type D mint	3,155	Set	65.00
1938S	Same type S mint	3,156		
1939	Arkansas Centennial (same as 1935)	2,104		
1939D	Same type D mint	2,104	Set	
1939S	Same type S mint	2,105		310.00
	Single, type coin			15.00

BAY BRIDGE SAN FRANCISCO-OAKLAND

The opening of the San Francisco Bay Bridge was the occasion for a special souvenir fifty-cent piece. The designs were the work of Jacques Schnier, a San Francisco artist. A California grizzly bear dominates the obverse. The famous bridge is shown on the reverse. The coins were struck at the San Francisco Mint in November 1936. The bear depicted was Monarch II.

	Quan. Minted	Ex. Fine	Unc.
1936 San Francisco-Oakland Bay Bridge S mint	71,424	14.00	23.50

COMMEMORATIVE SILVER — Boone

DANIEL BOONE BICENTENNIAL

This coin, issues for which covered several dates, was struck to commemorate the two hundredth anniversary of the famous frontiersman's birth. The commemorative date, 1934, was removed after the first issue. The change of date to 1935 for the next year's coinage brought about the addition of 1934 above the words PIONEER YEAR. Coinage covered several years similar to the schedule for the Texas issues. The models for this coin were prepared by Augustus Lukeman. The obverse bears a portrait of Daniel Boone. The reverse shows Boone with Chief Black Fish.

		Quan. Minted		Unc.
1934	Daniel Boone Bicentennial	10,007		$ 24.00
1935	Same type	10,010		
1935D	Same type D mint	5,005	Set	47.50
1935S	Same type S mint	5,005		

1935	Daniel Boone Bicentennial same as 1934 but small 1934 added on reverse	10,008		
1935D	Same type D mint	2,003	Set	300.00
1935S	Same type S mint	2,004		
1936	Daniel Boone Bicentennial (same as 1934)	12,012		
1936D	Same type D mint	5,005	Set	47.50
1936S	Same type S mint	5,006		
1937	Daniel Boone Bicentennial (same as 1934)	9,810		
1937D	Same type D mint	2,506	Set	170.00
1937S	Same type S mint	2,506		
1938	Daniel Boone Bicentennial (same as 1934)	2,100		
1938D	Same type D mint	2,100	Set	300.00
1938S	Same type S mint	2,100		
	Single, type coin			17.50

BRIDGEPORT, CONNECTICUT CENTENNIAL

In commemoration of the one hundredth anniversary of the incorporation of the city of Bridgeport a special fifty-cent piece was authorized May 15, 1936. Henry Kreiss designed this coin which somewhat resembles the Connecticut Tercentenary issue. The head of P. T. Barnum, who was Bridgeport's best known citizen, occupies the obverse. An ultra-modernistic eagle dominates the reverse.

		Quan. Minted	Ex. Fine	Unc.
1936	Bridgeport, Conn., Centennial............	25,015	$16.50	$27.50

CALIFORNIA DIAMOND JUBILEE

The California half dollar was designed by Jo Mora, a noted California sculptor. The obverse bears a kneeling figure of a forty-niner. The reverse shows a walking grizzly bear, the state emblem. The celebration for which these coins were struck marked the seventy-fifth anniversary of the admission of California into the Union. The jubilee was held in 1925.

1925S California Diamond Jubilee.............. 86,594	16.00	25.00

CINCINNATI MUSICAL CENTER

Although the head of Stephen Foster, "America's Troubadour," dominates the obverse of this special issue the anniversary celebrated bears no relation to him. The coins, designed by Constance Ortmayer of Washington, D. C., were struck to commemorate the fiftieth anniversary in 1936 of Cincinnati as a center of music. The coins were struck at the three mints and were sold only in sets at $7.75, the highest initial cost of a new type

1936	Cincinnati Musical Center................ 5,005		
1936D	Same type D............................ 5,005	Set	375.00
1936S	Same type S............................ 5,006		
	Single, type coin.............................		127.50

COMM. SILVER — Cleveland, Columbia, S. C., Columbian

CLEVELAND GREAT LAKES EXPOSITION

A special coinage of fifty-cent pieces was authorized in commemoration of the centennial celebration of Cleveland, Ohio on the occasion of the Great Lakes Exposition held there in 1936. The designs were prepared by Brenda Putnam. Although half the coinage was struck in 1937 all were dated 1936. The obverse has a bust of Moses Cleaveland and the reverse displays a map of the Great Lakes region with a compass pointed at Cleveland. Nine Great Lakes cities are marked by stars.

		Quan. Minted	Ex. Fine	Unc.
1936	Cleveland, Great Lakes Exposition	50,030	$10.00	$18.00

COLUMBIA, SOUTH CAROLINA SESQUICENTENNIAL

Souvenir half dollars were authorized to help finance the extensive celebrations marking the sesquicentennial of the founding of Columbia in 1786. A. Wolfe Davidson designed the coin which was struck at all three mints and sold only in sets. The obverse bears the figure of Justice with sword and scales. At the left is the Capitol of 1786 and at the right the Capitol of 1936. A palmetto tree, the state emblem, is the reverse device.

1936	Columbia, S. C., Sesquicentennial	9,007	
1936D	Same type D mint	8,009	} Set 150.00
1936S	Same type S mint	8,007	
	Single, type coin		50.00

COLUMBIAN EXPOSITION HALF DOLLAR

The first United States commemorative coin was the Columbian half dollar. C. E. Barber designed the obverse showing the bust of Columbus; and G. T. Morgan designed the reverse having a representation of Columbus' flagship the Santa Maria above two hemispheres. The coins were sold for $1.00 each at the World's Columbian Exposition in Chicago during 1893. A great many remained unsold and a substantial quantity was later released for circulation at face value.

1892	Columbian Exposition, Chicago	950,000	3.00	8.50
1893	Same type	1,550,405	2.50	6.00

COMMEMORATIVE SILVER — Connecticut, Delaware, Elgin

CONNECTICUT TERCENTENARY

In commemoration of the three hundredth anniversary of the founding of the Colony of Connecticut a souvenir half dollar was struck. Henry Kreiss designed the coin. The famous "Charter Oak" is the main device on the obverse. According to tradition the Royal Charter was secreted in the tree during the reign of James II who wished to revoke it. The Charter was produced after the king's overthrow in 1688 and the Colony continued under its protection.

		Quan. Minted	Ex. Fine	Unc.
1935	Connecticut Tercentenary	25,018	$25.00	$52.50

DELAWARE TERCENTENARY

The three hundredth anniversary of the landing of the Swedes in Delaware was the occasion for a souvenir issue of half dollars. The colonists landed on a spot which is now Wilmington and established a church which is the oldest Protestant church still used for worship. Their ship "Kalmar Nyckel" is shown on the obverse of the coin and the old Swedes church is on the reverse. Designs were chosen from a competition which was won by Carl L. Schmitz. This coin was authorized in 1936, struck in 1937 and dated 1938 on the obverse and 1936 on the reverse. The anniversary was celebrated in 1938 both in Sweden and America. A two kroner coin was issued in Sweden to commemorate the same event.

1936	Delaware Tercentenary	20,993	24.00	47.50

ELGIN, ILLINOIS CENTENNIAL

The one hundredth anniversary of the founding of Elgin was marked by a special issue of half dollars in 1936. The proceeds were devoted to financing a Pioneer Memorial statue, which is depicted on the reverse of the coin. The year 1673 bears no relation to the event but refers to the year in which Joliet and Marquette entered Illinois Territory. The designs were prepared by Trygve Rovelstad who also designed the Memorial.

1936	Elgin, Illinois, Centennial	20,015	20.00	37.50

COMMEMORATIVE SILVER — Gettysburg, Grant, Hawaiian

BATTLE OF GETTYSBURG

On June 16, 1936 Congress authorized a coinage of fifty-cent pieces in commemoration of the Battle of Gettysburg. The models were prepared by Frank Vittor, a Philadelphia sculptor. Portraits of a Union and a Confederate veteran are shown on the obverse. Two shields representing the Union and Confederate armies separated by a double-bladed fasces are on the reverse.

	Quan. Minted	Ex. Fine	Unc.
1936 Battle of Gettysburg 1863-1938	26,928	$ 25.00	$ 44.00

GRANT MEMORIAL

This coin was struck during 1922 as a centenary souvenir of Ulysses S. Grant's birth. A star which appeared on the first issues was later removed, creating a second variety. The star has no particular significance. Laura Gardin Fraser designed both the Grant half dollar and gold dollar. The reverse shows a log cabin in Point Pleasant, Ohio, where Grant lived as a boy.

(Fake stars have flattened spot on reverse.)

1922	Grant Memorial. Star in obverse field	4,256	60.00	125.00
1922	Same, no star	67,405	13.00	25.00

HAWAIIAN SESQUICENTENNIAL

This small issue was struck to commemorate the 150th anniversary of the rediscovery of the Hawaiian Islands by Captain James Cook in 1778. The design was sketched by Juliette May Fraser of Honolulu and executed by Chester Beach. Captain Cook is shown on the obverse and a native chief on the reverse. The coins were distributed in 1928 and sold for $2.00 each, the highest initial sale price up to that time.

1928	Hawaiian Sesquicentennial	9,958	250.00	465.00
1928	Hawaiian Sesquicentennial — sandblast proof presentation piece	50		———

COMMEMORATIVE SILVER — Hudson, Huguenot, Iowa

HUDSON, NEW YORK SESQUICENTENNIAL

This souvenir half dollar marked the one hundred and fiftieth anniversary of the founding of Hudson, New York, which was named after the explorer Hendrik Hudson. The designs by Chester Beach show Hudson's flagship the "Half Moon" on the obverse and the seal of the City of Hudson on the reverse. Details of the seal include representations of Neptune with trident on a spouting whale and a mermaid blowing a conch shell.

		Quan. Minted	Ex. Fine	Unc.
1935	Hudson, N. Y. Sesquicentennial	10,008	$135.00	$245.00

HUGUENOT-WALLOON TERCENTENARY

Settling of the Huguenots and Walloons in the New World was the occasion commemorated by this issue. New Netherlands, now New York, was founded in 1624 by a group of Dutch colonists. The persons represented on the obverse were not directly concerned with the occasion, however. They are Admiral Coligny and William the Silent. The reverse shows the vessel "Nieu Nederland." G. T. Morgan prepared the models for this coin.

1924	Huguenot-Walloon Tercentenary	142,080	15.00	29.50

IOWA CENTENNIAL

This half dollar, commemorating the one hundredth anniversary of Iowa's statehood, was designed by Adam Pietz of Philadelphia. The obverse shows the Iowa state seal and the reverse has the first stone capitol building at Iowa City. This issue was sold

first to the residents of Iowa and only a small remainder to others. The entire issue was disposed of in a few weeks.

1946	Iowa Centennial	100,057	15.00	24.50

LEXINGTON-CONCORD SESQUICENTENNIAL

The two famous battles fought in 1775 are commemorated on this coin. A statue of the familiar Minute Man is depicted on the obverse, and the old Belfry at Lexington is the reverse device. Chester Beach designed the coin. The famous statue by Daniel Chester French located in Concord was used for the design.

		Quan. Minted	Ex. Fine	Unc.
1925	Lexington-Concord Sesquicentennial	162,013	$ 8.00	$17.00

LINCOLN-ILLINOIS CENTENNIAL

The obverse was designed by G. T. Morgan and the reverse by J. R. Sinnock. The obverse shows the head of Lincoln taken from the statue by Andrew O'Connor in Springfield, Illinois. The reverse is based on the Illinois State Seal. This coin was authorized to commemorate the one hundredth anniversary of the admission of Illinois into the Union, the first souvenir piece for such an event.

1918	Illinois Centennial	100,058	15.00	28.50

LONG ISLAND TERCENTENARY

This souvenir issue was authorized to commemorate the three hundredth anniversary of the first white settlement on Long Island which was at Jamaica Bay by Dutch colonists. The design was prepared by Howard Kenneth Weinman, son of the sculptor A. A. Weinman, who designed the regular Liberty standing type half dollar. Accolated heads depicting a Dutch settler and an Indian are shown on the obverse, while a Dutch sailing vessel is the reverse device. This was the first issue for which a date was specified (1936) irrespective of the year minted or issued.

1936	Long Island Tercentenary	81,826	11.00	17.50

[199]

COMMEMORATIVE SILVER — Lynchburg, Maine, Maryland

LYNCHBURG, VIRGINIA SESQUICENTENNIAL

The issuance of a charter to the city of Lynchburg in 1786 was commemorated in 1936 by a special coinage of half dollars. The models for the coin were prepared by Charles Keck. The obverse bears a portrait of Senator Carter Glass, a native of Lynchburg and former Secretary of the Treasury, who objected to the idea of using portraits of living men on coins. Despite his protests his likeness was incorporated on the coin. The reverse shows Liberty standing, with the old Lynchburg courthouse in the background.

	Quan. Minted	Ex. Fine	Unc.
1936 Lynchburg, Va., Sesquicentennial.........	20,013	$20.00	$38.00

MAINE CENTENNIAL

Congress authorized the Maine Centennial half dollar May 10, 1920, to be sold at the Centennial celebration at Portland. They were received too late for this event and were sold by the state Treasurer until all were sold. Anthony de Francisci modeled this coin according to specifications furnished him. The latin word DIRIGO means: I direct. The obverse device is the arms of the state of Maine.

1920 Maine Centennial.....................	50,028	17.00	28.00

MARYLAND TERCENTENARY

The three hundredth anniversary of the founding of the Maryland Colony by Cecil Calvert (known as Lord Baltimore) was the occasion for this special coin. The profits from the sale of this issue were used to finance the celebration in Baltimore during 1934. Hans Schuler designed the coin which shows the facing head of Lord Baltimore on the obverse and the arms of Maryland on the reverse, reminiscent of the Maryland colonial pieces.

1934 Maryland Tercentenary................	25,015	20.00	36.00

COMM. SILVER — Missouri, Monroe, New Rochelle

MISSOURI CENTENNIAL

The one hundredth anniversary of the admission of Missouri to the Union was celebrated at Sedalia during August, 1921. To mark the occasion Congress authorized the coinage of a fifty-cent piece. Robert Aitken designed the piece which shows the bust of a frontiersman on the obverse, and another frontiersman and Indian on the reverse. The first coins struck show 2★4 incused, indicating that Missouri was the twenty-fourth star in the flag. The type without the star was struck later, but was the first to be sold.

2★4 in field

		Quan. Minted	Ex. Fine	Unc.
1921	Missouri Centennial 2★4 in field of obverse	5,000	$80.00	$155.00
1921	Missouri Centennial, no 2★4	15,428	75.00	142.50

MONROE DOCTRINE CENTENNIAL

The motion picture industry promoted this issue in conjunction with a motion picture exposition in June 1923. The obverse shows the heads of James Monroe and John Quincy Adams who were identified with the Monroe Doctrine. The Western Hemisphere is portrayed on the reverse by two female figures. Chester Beach prepared the models for this coin.

1923S Monroe Doctrine Centennial	274,077	9.00	17.50

NEW ROCHELLE, NEW YORK

To observe the founding of New Rochelle in 1688 by French Huguenots, a special half dollar was issued in 1938. The title to the land which the Huguenots purchased from John Pell provided that a fattened calf be given away every year on June 20th. This will explain the appearance of the calf and figure representing John Pell on the obverse of the coin. The fleur-de-lis which is shown on the reverse is adopted from the Seal of the city. Both sides of the coin were designed by Gertrude K. Lathrop.

		Quan. Minted	Ex. Fine	Unc.
1938	New Rochelle, N. Y. 1688-1938............15,266		$32.50	$65.00

NORFOLK, VIRGINIA BICENTENNIAL

To provide funds for the celebration of Norfolk's anniversary of its growth from a township in 1682 to a royal borough in 1736, Congress first passed a law for the striking of medals. The proponents, however, being dissatisfied finally succeeded in winning authority for half dollars commemorating the 300th anniversary of the original Norfolk land grant and the 200th anniversary of the establishment of the borough. William Marks Simpson and his wife Marjorie Emory Simpson designed the piece. The obverse shows the Seal of the City of Norfolk with a three-masted ship as the central device. The reverse features the Royal Mace of Norfolk presented by Lieutenant Governor Dinwiddie in 1753.

1936	Norfolk, Va., Bicentennial................16,936	35.00	57.50

OREGON TRAIL MEMORIAL

This memorial coin was struck in commemoration of the Oregon trail and in memory of the pioneers, many of whom lie buried along the famous 2,000 mile highway of history. James Earle Fraser and his wife, Laura Gardin Fraser, prepared the designs. The original issue was struck at Philadelphia and San Francisco in 1926. The coin was reissued in 1928 (released in 1933) 1933, 1934, 1936, and 1938. The 1933 half dollar was the first commemorative coin struck at the Denver Mint.

1926	Oregon Trail Memorial..................47,955	8.00	16.50
1926S	Same type S mint......................83,055	8.00	16.50
1928	Oregon Trail Memorial (same as 1926)......6,028		18.50
1933D	Oregon Trail Memorial, same type, D mint..5,008		37.00
1934D	Oregon Trail Memorial, same type, D mint..7,006		17.50
1936	Oregon Trail Memorial (same as 1926) 10,006		16.50
1936S	Same type S mint........................5,006		20.00
1937D	Oregon Trail Memorial D mint (same as 1926).12,008		16.50
1938	Oregon Trail Memorial (same as 1926).......6,006		
1938D	Same type D mint........................6,005	Set	47.50
1938S	Same type S mint........................6,006		
1939	Oregon Trail (same as 1926)................3,004		
1939D	Same type D mint........................3,004	Set	125.00
1939S	Same type S mint........................3,005		
	Single, type coin.............................		16.00

COMMEMORATIVE SILVER — Panama-Pacific, Pilgrim

PANAMA-PACIFIC EXPOSITION

This half dollar was designed by C. E. Barber. The exposition held in San Francisco in 1915 celebrated the opening of the Panama Canal. The coins were struck at the San Francisco Mint and were sold at $1.00 each during the exposition. The Panama-Pacific coins have the distinction of being the first commemorative coins to carry the motto. IN GOD WE TRUST appears above the eagle. A representation of Columbia with the golden gate in the background is the principal feature of the obverse.

	Quan. Minted	Ex. Fine	Unc.
1915S Panama-Pacific Exposition	27,134	$45.00	$90.00

PILGRIM TERCENTENARY

To commemorate the landing of the Pilgrims at Plymouth, Massachusetts in 1620, Congress authorized a special half dollar May 12, 1920. Cyrus E. Dallin, a Boston sculptor, executed the designs furnished him by the Commission. The obverse has a portrait of Governor Bradford. The reverse shows the "Mayflower." The first issue had no date on the obverse. The coins struck in 1921 show that date in addition to 1620-1920. There was a large coinage of both issues and not all were sold. A total of 128,000 were returned to the mint and melted.

1920 Pilgrim Tercentenary	152,112	10.00	21.50

1921 Same type	20,053	20.00	65.00

COMM. SILVER — Rhode Island, Roanoke, Robinson

RHODE ISLAND, TERCENTENARY PROVIDENCE

The three hundredth anniversary of Roger Williams' founding of Providence was the occasion for this special half dollar in 1935. The designs were the work of Arthur Graham Carey and John Howard Benson. The obverse shows Roger Williams in a canoe being welcomed by an Indian. The reverse has the anchor of Hope with a shield and mantling in the background. Although the founding of Providence was being celebrated, no mention of the city is to be found on the coin.

		Quan. Minted	Ex. Fine	Unc.
1936	Rhode Island Tercentenary	20,013		
1936D	Same type D mint	15,010	Set	$56.00
1936S	Same type S mint	15,011		
	Single, type coin		$ 8.00	20.00

ROANOKE ISLAND, NORTH CAROLINA

A celebration was held in Old Fort Raleigh in 1937 to commemorate the three hundred and fiftieth anniversary of Sir Walter Raleigh's "Lost Colony" and the birth of Virginia Dare, the first white child born on the American Continent. A special half dollar was minted for the occasion which was designed by William Marks Simpson of Baltimore. The obverse bears a portrait of Sir Walter Raleigh and the reverse has a figure representing Eleanor Dare holding the child Virginia Dare.

1937	Roanoke Island, N. C., 1587-1937	29,030	17.00	30.00

ROBINSON-ARKANSAS CENTENNIAL

A new obverse design for the Arkansas Centennial coin was authorized by the Act of June 26, 1936. Senator Joseph T. Robinson is the subject for the new issue designed by Henry Kreiss. The reverse, designed by Everett Burr, was unchanged. The law specified a change in the reverse, because of the fact that the obverse side is that which bears the date. From a numismatic viewpoint, however, the side which has the portrait is usually considered the obverse. Thus in this instance, the side with the eagle device is considered the reverse.

1936	Arkansas Centennial (Robinson)	25,265	16.00	26.00

COMM. SILVER — San Diego, Sesquicentennial, Spanish Trail

SAN DIEGO-CALIFORNIA-PACIFIC EXPOSITION

Congress approved the coinage of souvenir half dollars for the exposition May 3, 1935. Robert Aitken designed the coin which was struck at the San Francisco Mint. The same type with date 1936 was struck at the Denver Mint, under authority of the special Recoinage Act of May 6, 1936, which specified that 180,000 pieces could be recoined with the date 1936 irrespective of the year of issue. The obverse displays a seated female with spear and a bear in the left background. The reverse shows the observation tower and the State of California building at the Exposition.

	Quan. Minted	Ex. Fine	Unc.
1935S San Diego, California-Pacific Exp. S mint...70,132		$10.00	$16.50
1936D San Diego, California-Pacific Exposition			
D mint (same as 1935)................30,092		11.00	18.50

SESQUICENTENNIAL OF AMERICAN INDEPENDENCE

The one hundred and fiftieth anniversary of the signing of the Declaration of Independence was the occasion for an International Fair held in Philadelphia in 1926. To help raise funds for financing the fair special issues of half dollars and quarter-eagles were authorized by Congress. For the first time a portrait of a president appeared on a coin struck during his lifetime. President Coolidge and Washington are depicted on the obverse of the half-dollar. The reverse bears an accurate model of the Liberty Bell. John R. Sinnock, Chief Engraver of the United States mint, designed the sesquicentennial coins. The dies were in very low relief causing much loss of detail in the coin.

1926 Sesquicentennial of American			
Independence......................141,120		9.00	17.50

OLD SPANISH TRAIL

This coin commemorated the four hundredth anniversary of the overland trek of the Cabeza de Vaca Expedition through the gulf states in 1535. L. W. Hoffecker designed the coin models which were prepared by

COMMEMORATIVE SILVER — Stone Mountain, Texas

Edmund J. Senn. The explorer's name literally translated means "head of a cow," therefore this device was chosen for the obverse. The reverse bears a yucca tree and a map showing the Old Spanish Trail.

		Quan. Minted	Ex. Fine	Unc.
1935	Old Spanish Trail 1535-1935	10,008	$130.00	$225.00

STONE MOUNTAIN MEMORIAL

The models for this coin were prepared by Gutzon Borglum. The first coins were struck at Philadelphia January 21, 1925, General Thomas "Stonewall" Jackson's birthday. General Robert E. Lee and Jackson, mounted, are shown on the obverse. The reverse has an eagle and the words MEMORIAL TO THE VALOR OF THE SOLDIER OF THE SOUTH. The funds received from the sale of this large issue of half dollars were devoted to the expense of carving figures of Confederate leaders and soldiers on Stone Mountain in Georgia. The work was never completed.

1925	Stone Mountain Memorial	1,314,709	6.00	11.50

TEXAS CENTENNIAL

This issue commemorated the independence of Texas. The first of several dates was offered in 1934. The later dates were struck at all three mints. The models were prepared by Pompeo Coppini. The reverse shows the kneeling figure of winged Victory, and on each side, medallions with portraits of General Sam Houston and Stephen Austin, founders of the Republic and State of Texas. The large five-pointed star behind the eagle on the obverse carries out the "Lone star" tradition.

1934	Texas Centennial	61,463		19.00
1935	Texas Centennial (same as 1934)	9,996		
1935D	Same type D mint	10,007	Set	50.00
1935S	Same type S mint	10,008		
1936	Texas Centennial (same as 1934)	8,911		
1936D	Same type D mint	9,039	Set	50.00
1936S	Same type S mint	9,055		
1937	Texas Centennial (same as 1934)	6,571		
1937D	Same type D mint	6,605	Set	50.00
1937S	Same type S mint	6,637		
1938	Texas Centennial (same as 1934)	3,780		
1938D	Same type D mint	3,775	Set	115.00
1938S	Same type S mint	3,814		
	Single, type coin			17.50

FORT VANCOUVER CENTENNIAL

Dr. John McLaughlin, shown on the obverse of this coin, built Fort Vancouver on the Columbia River in 1825. The sale of the coins at $1.00 each helped to finance the pageant staged for the celebration. Laura Gardin Fraser prepared the models for this coin which was minted in San Francisco. The S Mint mark was omitted. The reverse has a pioneer settler in buckskin suit with a musket in his hands. Fort Vancouver is in the background.

		Quan. Minted	Ex. Fine	Unc.
1925	Fort Vancouver Centennial	14,994	$50.00	$87.50

VERMONT SESQUICENTENNIAL

This souvenir issue commemorates the 150th Anniversary of the Battle of Bennington and the Independence of Vermont. Authorized in 1925 it was not coined until 1927. The models were prepared by Charles Keck. The obverse shows the head of Ira Allen, founder of Vermont. The reverse bears a catamount on a pedestal.

1927	Vermont Sesquicentennial (Bennington)	28,142	24.00	37.50

BOOKER T. WASHINGTON MEMORIAL

The great Negro educator was memorialized in this half dollar. Issued from all mints, it received wide distribution from the start. The reverse has the legend FROM SLAVE CABIN TO HALL OF FAME. His log cabin birthplace is shown beneath. Designed by Isaac Scott Hathaway, as was the Washington-Carver half dollar issued under the same authority.

COMM. SILVER — Washington-Carver

		Quan. Minted	Ex. Fine	Unc.
1946	Booker T. Washington	*1,000,546		
1946D	Same type D mint	200,113	Set	$12.00
1946S	Same type S mint	500,279		
1947	Same type as 1946	100,017		
1947D	Same type D mint	100,017	Set	16.00
1947S	Same type S mint	100,017		
1948	Same type as 1946	8,005		
1948D	Same type D mint	8,005	Set	22.00
1948S	Same type S mint	8,005		
1949	Same type as 1946	6,004		
1949D	Same type D mint	6,004	Set	37.00
1949S	Same type S mint	6,004		
1950	Same type as 1946	6,004		
1950D	Same type D mint	6,004	Set	32.00
1950S	Same type S mint	512,091		
1951	Same type as 1946	510,082		
1951D	Same type D mint	7,004	Set	32.00
1951S	Same type S mint	7,004		
	Single, type coin			3.75

*Minted; quantity melted unknown.

WASHINGTON-CARVER

Designed by Isaac Scott Hathaway, this coin shows the conjoined busts of two prominent Negro Americans. Booker T. Washington was a lecturer, educator, and principal of Tuskegee Institute. He urged training to advance independence and efficiency for his race. George Washington Carver was an agricultural chemist who worked to improve the economy of the south. He spent his life teaching crop improvement and new uses for soybeans, peanuts, sweet potatoes and cotton waste.

Money obtained from the sale of these commemoratives was to be used "to oppose the spread of communism among Negroes in the interest of national defense."

1951	Washington-Carver	110,018		
1951D	Same type D mint	10,004	Set	12.00
1951S	Same type S mint	10,004		
1952	Same type as 1951	2,006,292		
1952D	Same type D mint	8,006	Set	19.00
1952S	Same type S mint	8,006		
1953	Same type as 1951	8,003		
1953D	Same type D mint	8,003	Set	21.50
1953S	Same type S mint	108,020		
1954	Same type as 1951	12,006		
1954D	Same type D mint	12,006	Set	12.00
1954S	Same type S mint	122,024		
	Single, type coin			3.75

COMMEMORATIVE SILVER — Wisconsin, York

WISCONSIN TERRITORIAL CENTENNIAL

The one hundredth anniversary of the Wisconsin Territorial government was the occasion for a special half dollar issue. The original design was made by David Parsons, a University of Wisconsin student. Benjamin Hawkins, a New York artist, made changes to conform with technical requirements. The obverse has the Territorial Seal, which includes a forearm holding a pickaxe over a mound of lead ore, and the inscription 4th DAY OF JULY ANNO DOMINI 1836. The reverse shows a badger on a log typifying the early fur trade, and the state emblem.

		Quan. Minted	Ex. Fine	Unc.
1936	Wisconsin Centennial	25,015	$17.50	$35.00

YORK COUNTY, MAINE TERCENTENARY

A souvenir half dollar was authorized by Congress upon the three hundredth anniversary of the founding of York County, Maine. Brown's Garrison on the Saco River was the site of a town which was settled in 1636. The designs were made by Walter H. Rich of Portland. The reverse design shows a stockade and the obverse has an adaptation of the York County seal. The oversize border inscriptions have been the basis for much adverse criticism.

1936	York County, Maine Centennial	25,015	16.00	28.00

COMMEMORATIVE GOLD—
Grant, Lewis & Clark, Louisiana Purchase

GRANT MEMORIAL GOLD DOLLARS

Like the half-dollar commemorative coins the gold dollars were issued first with a star which was removed for the later issues. The designs by Laura Gardin Fraser are the same as for the half-dollar coinage.

		Quan. Minted	Ex. Fine	Unc.
1922	Grant Memorial Dollar with star	5,016	$150.00	$250.00
1922	Grant Memorial Dollar without star	5,000	160.00	262.50

LEWIS AND CLARK EXPOSITION

The Lewis and Clark Centennial Exposition was held in Portland, Oregon in 1905. A souvenir issue of gold dollars was struck to mark the event with the dates 1904 and 1905. The two famous explorers are represented on each side of the coin which was designed by C. E. Barber. A bronze memorial of the Indian guide, Sacagawea, who assisted in the famous expedition was erected in Portland, Oregon and financed by the sale of these coins.

1904	Lewis and Clark Exposition Dollar	10,025	160.00	300.00
1905	Lewis and Clark Exposition Dollar	10,041	160.00	310.00

LOUISIANA PURCHASE EXPOSITION

The first souvenir gold coins were authorized for the Louisiana Purchase Exposition held in St. Louis in 1904. There are two varieties of gold dollars — one with the head of Jefferson who was president when the Louisiana Territory was purchased from France; and the other President William McKinley who sanctioned the Exposition. The reverse is the same for each variety. The designs were by C. E. Barber.

*1903	Louisiana Purchase Jefferson Dollar	17,500	37.50	75.00
*1903	Louisiana Purchase McKinley Dollar	17,500	37.50	75.00

*Proofs exist of each type.

McKINLEY MEMORIAL GOLD DOLLARS

The sale of the McKinley dollars aided in paying for a memorial building at Niles, Ohio, the martyred president's birthplace. The obverse showing a profile of McKinley was designed by C. E. Barber and the reverse with the memorial building designed by G. T. Morgan.

	Quan. Minted	Ex. Fine	Unc.
1916 McKinley Memorial Dollar	9,977	$ 35.00	$ 70.00
1917 McKinley Memorial Dollar	10,000	67.50	135.00

PANAMA-PACIFIC EXPOSITION

Charles Keck designed the gold dollar, the obverse of which has the head of a man representing a Panama Canal laborer. Two dolphins encircle ONE DOLLAR on the reverse.

1915S Panama-Pacific Exposition Dollar	15,000	37.50	67.50

The quarter-eagle was the work of Charles E. Barber and George T. Morgan. It was the first commemorative coin of this denomination. The obverse shows Columbia with a caduceus in her left hand seated on a hippocampus typifying the use of the Panama Canal. An American eagle with raised wings is shown on the reverse.

1915S Panama-Pacific Exposition $2.50	6,749	160.00	300.00

The fifty-dollar gold piece was designed by Robert Aitken and was issued in round and octagonal form. The obverse bears the helmeted head of Minerva; the owl, symbol of wisdom, is on the reverse. The octagonal issue has eight dolphins in the angles on both sides. The devices are smaller on the octagonal variety.

	Quan. Minted	Ex. Fine	Unc.
1915S Panama-Pacific $50 Round................483			$5,000.00
1915S Panama-Pacific $50 Octagonal..............645			4,250.00

PHILADELPHIA SESQUICENTENNIAL—QUARTER EAGLES

The obverse of this special gold issue has a standing female figure symbolic of Liberty, holding in one hand a scroll representing the Declaration of Independence and in the other the Torch of Freedom. The reverse bears a representation of Independence Hall in Philadelphia. The coin was designed by J. R. Sinnock.

	Quan. Minted	Ex. Fine	Unc.
1926 Philadelphia Sesquicentennial $2.50........46,019		30.00	57.50

BIBLIOGRAPHY

Bullowa, David M., The Commemorative Coinage of the U. S., 1938.
Mosher, Stuart, U. S. Commemorative Coins (1892-1939), 1940.
Slabaugh, Arlie., United States Commemorative Coins, 1962.

PRIVATE OR TERRITORIAL GOLD COINS

The words "Private Gold," used with reference to coins struck outside of the United States Mint, are a general term. In the sense that no state or territory had authority to coin money, private gold simply refers to those interesting necessity pieces of various shapes, denominations and degrees of intrinsic worth which were circulated in isolated areas of our country by individuals, assayers, bankers, etc. Some will use the words "Territorial" and "State" to cover certain issues because they were coined and circulated in a Territory or State. While the state of California properly sanctioned the ingots stamped by F. D. Kohler as state assayer, in no instance were any of the gold pieces struck by authority of any of the territorial governments.

The stamped ingots put out by Augustus Humbert, the United States assayer of gold, were not recognized at the United States Mint as an official issue of coins, but simply as ingots, though Humbert placed the value and fineness on the pieces as an official agent of the federal government.

Private coins were circulated in most instances because of a shortage of regular coinage. In the western states particularly, money became so scarce that the very commodity which the pioneers had come so far to acquire was converted into a local medium of exchange.

Ephraim Brasher's New York doubloon of 1787 described on page 40 also falls into this class.

BIBLIOGRAPHY — Private Gold Coinage

Adams, Edgar H., Private Gold Coinage of California.................1913
Adams, Edgar H., Official Premium Lists, Private Territorial Gold.....1909
Griffin, Clarence, The Bechtlers and Bechtler Coinage and Gold
    Mining in North Carolina (1814-1830)...........................1922
Lee, Ed. M., California Gold Quarters, Halves and Dollars............1939
Renz, Dr. Russell H., Private Gold Coinage of The United States......1938

TEMPLETON REID

Georgia 1830

Gold pieces were struck by Templeton Reid, a goldsmith and assayer, in Lumpkin County, Georgia, in 1830. The designs and denominations of these coins were well known, but almost nothing has been learned about Templeton Reid. Denominations struck were $2.50, $5.00 and $10.00.

	Fine
1830 $2.50..	———
1830 $5.00..	———

TEMPLETON REID — GEORGIA

1830 TEN DOLLARS. . . . .

Unc.

(No Date) TEN DOLLARS — Waldorf Sale 1966 . . . . $29,000.00

TEMPLETON REID
San Francisco, California 1849

The later Templeton Reid issues were made in California in 1849. It is supposed that he moved his coining equipment to California when gold was discovered there. The California issues were in denominations of ten and twenty-five dollars. The twenty-five dollar issue is unique in design and denomination.

Fine

1849 TEN DOLLAR GOLD (Mint Collection) . . . . Unique

1849 TWENTY-FIVE DOLLARS GOLD . . . . Unknown

The only specimen known of this piece was stolen from the Cabinet of the U.S. Mint on August 16, 1858. It was never recovered.

THE BECHTLERS
Rutherford County, N. C. 1830-1852

Two skilled German metallurgists, Christopher Bechtler and his son, August Bechtler, and later Christopher Bechtler, Junior, a nephew of Christopher the elder, operated a "private" mint at Rutherfordton, North Carolina. Rutherford county in which Rutherfordton is located was the principal source of the nation's gold supply from 1790 to 1840.

The coins minted by the Bechtlers were of only three denominations, but they cover a wide variety of weights and sizes.

[214]

THE BECHTLERS

The Bechtlers have the distinction of producing the first gold dollar in the United States. The government mint did not release the first regular series until 1849.

The inscription "Aug. 1, 1834" on one variety of the five-dollar piece has a special significance. The Secretary of the Treasury recommended to the Director of the Mint that the gold coins of the reduced weight bear the date "Aug. 1, 1834." Instead of this, however, a new U.S. gold design was used (the motto was omitted). Christopher Bechtler evidently acted on the official recommendation to avoid any difficulty with Treasury authorities.

CHRISTOPHER BECHTLER

	V. Fine	Ex. Fine	Unc.
ONE DOLLAR CAROLINA, 28 gr. N reversed.......	$115.00	$135.00	$225.00
ONE DOLLAR N. CAROLINA, 28 gr., without star ...	400.00	575.00	775.00

ONE DOLLAR N. CAROLINA, 30 gr.	175.00	225.00	335.00
$2.50 CAROLINA, 67 gr. 21 carats..............	335.00	375.00	475.00

$2.50 CAROLINA, 70 gr. 20 carats..............	335.00	400.00	500.00
$2.50 GEORGIA, 64 gr. 22 carats...............	335.00	375.00	475.00
$2.50 GEORGIA, 64 gr. 22 carats — even 22.......	625.00	700.00	900.00

$2.50 NORTH CAROLINA, 75 gr. 20 carats.			
RUTHERFORD in a circle. Border of lg. beads..	700.00	725.00	950.00
$2.50 NORTH CAROLINA, without 75 G	700.00	725.00	950.00

THE BECHTLERS

	V. Fine	Ex. Fine	Unc.
$2.50 NORTH CAROLINA, without 75 G, CAROLINA above 250 instead of GOLD......			(Unique)
$2.50 NORTH CAROLINA, 20 carats on obv. 75 gr. on rev. Border finely serrated......	$1,375	$1,500	——

	V. Fine	Ex. Fine	Unc.
5 DOLLARS CAROLINA, RUTHERFORD, 140 gr. 20 carats. Date August 1, 1834. Plain or reeded edges.......................	375.00	425.00	575.00
5 DOLLARS CAROLINA, 134 gr. 21 carats..........	350.00	400.00	500.00

	V. Fine	Ex. Fine	Unc.
5 DOLLARS GEORGIA, RUTHERFORD. 128 gr. 22 carats..........................	425.00	550.00	750.00
5 DOLLARS GEORGIA, RUTHERF. 128 gr. 22 carats..	350.00	400.00	500.00
5 DOLLARS CAROLINA, RUTHERF. 140 gr. 20 carats. Date August 1, 1834........	350.00	400.00	500.00

Without
150 G

	V. Fine	Ex. Fine	Unc.
5 DOLLARS NORTH CAROLINA, 150 gr. 20 carats...	750.00	850.00	1,250
5 DOLLARS. Same as last variety without 150 G...	2,000	2,500	3,500

THE BECHTLERS
AUGUST BECHTLER
1842-1852

	V. Fine	Ex. Fine	Unc.
1 DOLLAR CAROLINA, 27 gr. 21 carats...........	$115.00	$150.00	$275.00
5 DOLLARS CAROLINA, 134 gr. 21 carats.........	300.00	375.00	475.00

5 DOLLARS CAROLINA, 128 gr. 22 carats.........	300.00	375.00	475.00
5 DOLLARS CAROLINA, 141 gr. 20 carats.........	350.00	450.00	550.00

(Restrikes in "proof" exist from original dies.)

NORRIS, GRIEG & NORRIS
San Francisco 1849

Edgar H. Adams considered this piece the first of the California private gold coins. A newspaper account dated May 31, 1849, described a five-dollar gold coin, struck at Benicia City, though with the imprint San Francisco. It mentioned the private stamp of Norris, Grieg and Norris. The initials N. G. and N. were not identified until 1902 when the coins of Augustus Humbert were sold.

	Fine	V. Fine	Ex. Fine	Unc.
1849 HALF EAGLE — Plain Edge........	$350.00	$500.00	$750.00	$1,000
1849 HALF EAGLE — Reeded Edge......	350.00	500.00	750.00	1,000

A recently discovered specimen is dated 1850, with STOCKTON beneath date.
1850 HALF EAGLE (Unique)................................... ——

MOFFAT & CO.
San Francisco 1849-1853

The firm of Moffat and Company was perhaps the most important of the California private coiners. The assay office they conducted was semi-official in character. The successors to this firm, Curtis, Perry and Ward, later established the United States Branch mint of San Francisco.

In June or July, 1849, Moffat & Co. began to issue small rectangular pieces of gold owing to lack of coin in the locality, in values from $9.43 to $264. The $9.43, $14.25 and $16.00 varieties are the only types known today.

$14.25 Ingot 1849

The only specimen known of the $9.43 ingot is in the National Coin Collection.

$9.43 Ingot (Unique)... ——
$14.25 Ingot (Unique).. ——
$16.00 Ingot (Beware of spurious specimens)...................... ——

The dies for the $10 piece were cut by a Bavarian, Albert Kuner. The words MOFFAT & CO. appear on the coronet of Liberty instead of the word LIBERTY as in regular United States issues.

	Fine	V. Fine	Ex. Fine	Unc.
1849 FIVE DOL. (All varieties)..........	$200.00	$300.00	$375.00	$575.00
1850 FIVE DOL. (All varieties)..........	200.00	325.00	475.00	750.00
1849 TEN DOL.	375.00	500.00	750.00	——
1849 TEN D.	500.00	750.00	1,000	——

United States Assay Office
AUGUSTUS HUMBERT
U. S. Assayer 1851

Augustus Humbert, a New York watch-case maker, was appointed United States Assayer, and he placed his name and the government stamp on the ingots of gold issued by Moffat & Co. The assay office was a temporary expedient to accommodate the Californians until the establishment of a permanent branch mint.

The fifty-dollar piece was accepted as legal tender on a par with standard U.S. gold coins and was known variously as a slug, quintuple eagle or five-eagle piece. It was officially termed an ingot.

LETTERED EDGE VARIETIES

	Fine	V. Fine	Ex. Fine	Unc.
1851 50 D C 880 THOUS., no 50 on Reverse. Sunk in Edge: AUGUSTUS HUMBERT UNITED STATES ASSAYER OF GOLD CALIFORNIA 1851	$2,000	$2,500	$3,500	——

Rev. Rays From Central Star

1851 50 D C Similar to last variety, but 50 on Reverse	2,250	2,750	3,750	——
1851 Similar to last variety, but 887 THOUS	2,250	2,750	3,750	——
1851 50 D C 887 THOUS., no 50 on Reverse	2,500	3,000	3,500	——
1851 50 D C 880 THOUS. Rev. Rays from Central Star (Unique)				——

REEDED EDGE VARIETIES

	Fine	V. Fine	Ex. Fine	Unc.
1851 FIFTY DOLLS 880 THOUS.				
"Target" Reverse.............	$1,400	$1,875	$2,500	——
1851 FIFTY DOLLS 887 THOUS.				
"Target" Reverse.............	1,400	1,750	2,250	——
1852 FIFTY DOLLS. 887 THOUS..........	1,400	1,875	2,500	——

The withdrawal of the discredited private coins of $5, $10 and $20 denominations as a result of the new U.S. Assay operations caused a new turn of affairs for Californians.

The fractional currency coins of almost every nation were pressed into service by the Californians, but the supply was too small to help to any extent. Moffat & Co. proceeded in January, 1852 to issue a new ten-dollar piece bearing the stamp MOFFAT & CO.

1852 TEN D. MOFFAT & CO. (Wide Date).	550.00	750.00	950.00	——
1852 TEN D. MOFFAT & CO. (Close Date).	450.00	650.00	850.00	——

	Fine	V. Fine	Ex. Fine	Unc.
1852 TWENTY DOLS. 1852 over 1	$1,875	$2,500	$3,500	——

1852 TEN DOLS. 1852 over 1	300.00	400.00	600.00	——
1852 TEN DOLS.	275.00	350.00	475.00	——

UNITED STATES ASSAY OFFICE OF GOLD

1852

The firm of Moffat & Co. dissolved and a new reorganized company known as the United States Assay Office of Gold, composed of Curtis, Perry and Ward took over the contract.

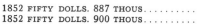

1852 FIFTY DOLLS. 887 THOUS.	1,400	1,750	2,225	——
1852 FIFTY DOLLS. 900 THOUS.	1,400	1,875	2,500	——

UNITED STATES ASSAY OFFICE

		Fine	V. Fine	Ex. Fine	Unc.
TEN DOLS				TEN D.	
1852 TEN DOLS 884 THOUS		$300.00	$400.00	$475.00	$600.00
1853 TEN D. 884 THOUS		600.00	750.00	1,000	——

	Fine	V. Fine	Ex. Fine	Unc.
1853 TEN D. 900 THOUS	550.00	700.00	1,000	——

	Fine	V. Fine	Ex. Fine	Unc.
1853 TWENTY D. 884 THOUS	1,250	1,750	2,000	——

	Fine	V. Fine	Ex. Fine	Unc.
1853 TWENTY D. 900 THOUS	300.00	400.00	500.00	650.00

U. S. ASSAY — MOFFAT

The last Moffat issue was the 1853 Twenty-dollar piece which is very similar to the U.S. Double Eagle of that period. It was struck after the retirement of Mr. Moffat from the Assay Office.

	Fine	V. Fine	Ex. Fine	Unc.
1853 TWENTY D.	$450.00	$600.00	$750.00	——

CINCINNATI MINING & TRADING CO.

The origin and location of this company are unknown.

	Fine	Unc.
1849 FIVE DOLLARS....................................	——	——
1849 TEN DOLLARS.....................................	——	——

MASSACHUSETTS AND CALIFORNIA COMPANY
San Francisco 1849

This company was believed to have been organized in Northampton, Mass. in May 1849.

1849 FIVE D. — Waldorf Sale 1964........................Proof $8,750.00

MINERS' BANK
San Francisco 1849

The institution of Wright & Co., exchange brokers located in Portsmouth Square, San Francisco, was known as the Miners' Bank.

A ten-dollar piece was issued in the autumn of 1849, but the coins were not readily accepted because they were worth less than face value. The firm dissolved January 14, 1850. Unlike most issues, the gold in these coins was alloyed with copper.

	V. Fine	Ex. Fine	Unc.
(1849) TEN. D.	$2,000	$2,500	$3,500

J. S. ORMSBY
Sacramento 1849

The initials J. S. O. which appear on certain issues of California privately coined gold pieces represent the firm of J. S. Ormsby & Co. They struck both five- and ten-dollar denominations, all undated.

	Fine	Unc.
(1849) 5 DOLLS.	——	——
(1849) 10 DOLLS.	——	——

PACIFIC COMPANY
San Francisco 1849

The origin of the Pacific Co. is very uncertain. All data regarding the firm is based on conjecture.

Edgar H. Adams wrote that he believed that the coins bearing the stamp of the Pacific Company were produced by the coining firm of Broderick and Kohler. The coins were probably handstruck, with the aid of a sledgehammer.

PACIFIC COMPANY

1849 5 DOLLARS
Waldorf Sale, 1964
Ex. Fine.......$18,000.00

1849 10 DOLLARS
Waldorf Sale, 1964
Ex. Fine.......$24,000.00

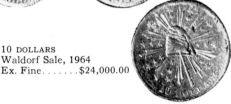

F. D. KOHLER
California State Assayer 1850

The State Assay Office was authorized April 12, 1850. Governor Burnett appointed F. D. Kohler that year who thereupon sold his assaying business to Baldwin & Co. He served at both San Francisco and Sacramento Offices. The State Assay Offices were discontinued at the time the U.S. Assay Office was established Feb. 1, 1951.

Ingots issued ranged from $36.55 to $150.

	Fine
$36.55 Sacramento...........	——
$37.31 San Francisco.........	——
$40.07 San Francisco.........	——
Note: $40.07 stolen from the Mint Cabinet in 1858 and was never recovered.	
$41.68 San Francisco.........	——
$45.34 San Francisco.........	——
$50.00 San Francisco.........	——
$54.09 San Francisco.........	——

DUBOSQ & COMPANY
San Francisco 1850

Theodore Dubosq, a Philadelphia jeweler, took melting and coining machinery to San Francisco in 1849.

	Fine	Unc.
1850 FIVE D.	——	——
1850 TEN D.	——	——

BALDWIN & COMPANY

San Francisco 1850

George C. Baldwin and Thomas S. Holman were in the jewelry business in San Francisco and were known as Baldwin & Co. They were the successors to F. D. Kohler & Co., taking over their machinery and other equipment in May, 1850.

	Fine	V. Fine	Ex. Fine	Unc.
1850 FIVE DOL.	$800.00	$1,050	$1,350	——
1850 TEN DOLLARS — Horseman type				
Public Auction Sale, 1963			Unc.	$7,500.00

1851 TEN D.	2,500	3,000	4,000	——

The Baldwin & Co. $20 piece was the first of that denomination issued in California.

Baldwin coins were believed to have contained about twenty-thousandths copper alloy.

	Fine	Unc.
1851 TWENTY D.	——	——

SCHULTZ & COMPANY

San Francisco 1851

The firm located in back of Baldwin's establishment conducted a brass foundry beginning in 1851. Judge G. W. Schultz and William T. Garratt were partners in the enterprise.

1851 FIVE D — Walton Sale 1963 . . . . V. Fine $8,250.00
Waldorf Sale 1964 . . . . Fine   3,800.00

DUNBAR & COMPANY

San Francisco 1851

Edward E. Dunbar conducted the California Bank in San Francisco. Mr. Dunbar later returned to New York and organized the famous Continental Bank Note Co.

1851 FIVE D — Walton Sale 1963 . . . . Ex. Fine $11,250.00

WASS, MOLITOR & COMPANY

San Francisco 1852-1855

The gold smelting and assaying plant of Wass, Molitor & Co. was composed of two Hungarian patriots Count S. C. Wass and A. P. Molitor. They maintained an excellent laboratory and complete apparatus for analysis and coinage of gold.

Large Head, Pointed Bust

	Fine	V. Fine	Ex. Fine	Unc.
1852 FIVE DOLLARS Small head with rounded bust	$650.00	$900.00	$1,250	——
1852 FIVE DOLLARS Large head with pointed bust	500.00	800.00	1,000	——

WASS, MOLITOR & COMPANY

The company struck five-, ten-, twenty- and fifty-dollar coins. In 1852 in addition to the five-dollar piece illustrated above they produced a ten-dollar piece similar in design to the five-dollar denomination. The difference is in the reverse legend which reads: s.m.v. (Standard Mint Value) CALIFORNIA GOLD TEN D.

| Large Head | | Small Head | |

	Fine	V. Fine	Ex. Fine	Unc.
1852 TEN D. Large Head..............	$350.00	$450.00	$650.00	——
1852 TEN D. Small Head..............	1,000	1,500	——	——

No pieces were coined in 1853 or 1854, but they brought out the twenty-dollar and fifty-dollar pieces in 1855. A considerable number of the fifty-dollar coins were made. There was a ten-dollar piece issued in 1855 also, with a somewhat different design of the Liberty head.

| 1855 TEN D. .... | 650.00 | 850.00 | 1,250 | —— |

| Large Head | | Small Head | |

| 1855 TWENTY DOL. Large Head........ | —— | —— | —— | —— |
| 1855 TWENTY DOL. Small Head......... | 1,000 | 1,500 | —— | —— |

WASS, MOLITOR & COMPANY

	Fine	V. Fine	Ex. Fine	Unc.
1855 50 DOLLARS........	$2,500	$3,500	$4,500	——

KELLOGG & COMPANY
San Francisco 1854-1855

John G. Kellogg came to San Francisco October 12, 1849, from Auburn, New York. At first he was employed by Moffat and Company, and remained with that organization when control passed to Curtis, Perry and Ward. When the United States Assay Office was discontinued December 14, 1853, Mr. Kellogg became associated with G. F. Richter, who had been an assayer in the government assay office. These two set up business as Kellogg & Richter December 19, 1853.

When the U. S. Assay Office ceased operations a period ensued during which no private firm was striking gold. The new San Francisco branch mint did not produce coins for some months after Curtis & Perry took the contract for the government. The lack of coin was again keenly felt by business men who petitioned Kellogg & Richter to "supply the vacuum" by issuing private coin.

Their plea was soon answered, for on February 9, 1854, Kellogg & Co. placed their first twenty-dollar piece in circulation.

| 1854 TWENTY D. .... | 350.00 | 400.00 | 500.00 | —— |

The 1855 twenty-dollar piece is similar to that dated 1854. The letters on the reverse side are larger and the arrows longer on one 1854 variety. There are several die varieties of both issues.

[229]

KELLOGG & COMPANY

	Fine	V. Fine	Ex. Fine	Unc.
1855 TWENTY D.	$375.00	$425.00	$525.00	——

The firm dissolved late in 1854 and reorganized as Kellogg & Humbert. The latter partner was Augustus Humbert, for some time identified as U. S. Assayer.

Regardless of the fact that the branch mint was then producing coins, Kellogg & Humbert issued coins in 1855 in a quantity greater than before.

1855 FIFTY DOLLS.	——	——	——	——

CALIFORNIA SMALL
DENOMINATION GOLD PIECES

California Gold quarters, halves and dollars were struck from 1852 to 1882, when the U. S. Government passed a law forbidding private coinage. The impetus of the gold rush created a shortage of "small change," and private companies supplied these coins for the 30-year period in direct proportion to the need.

Shapes were both octagonal and round, and the genuine coins bear one of the following — "cents," "Dol," "Doll" or "Dollar" on the reverse. Obverses are of three main types — Liberty Head, Indian Head and Washington Head. The reverses are also of three main types — Wreath, Beaded Circle and Eagle. Coins with the word "cents" or the Washington Head or the Eagle Reverse are more scarce and command premium prices of about twice regular values.

CALIFORNIA SMALL DENOMINATION GOLD PIECES

Typical Obverses   Typical Reverses

	Fine	V. Fine	Unc.	Proof*
25¢ Octagonal	$ 17.50	$ 22.50	$ 32.50	$ 40.00
25¢ Round	17.50	22.50	32.50	40.00
50¢ Octagonal	18.50	25.00	35.00	42.50
50¢ Round	18.50	25.00	35.00	42.50
$1.00 Octagonal	50.00	65.00	95.00	120.00
$1.00 Round	300.00	350.00	450.00	650.00

*Not actually struck as proofs, but proof-like in appearance and quality.

OREGON EXCHANGE COMPANY
Oregon City, 1849
THE BEAVER COINS OF OREGON

Upon the discovery of gold in California there was a great exodus of settlers who joined in the hunt for the precious metal. Soon returning gold seekers offered their gold dust, which became the accepted medium of exchange. As in other western areas of that time the uncertain qualities of the gold and weighing devices tended to irk the tradespeople and petitions were made to the legislature for a standard gold coin issue.

On February 16, 1849, the legislature passed an act providing for a mint and specified five- and ten-dollar gold coins without alloy. Oregon City, the largest city in the territory with a population of about 1000, was designated as the location for the mint. At the time this act was passed Oregon had been brought into the United States as a territory by act of Congress. When the new governor arrived March second, he declared the coinage act unconstitutional.

The public-spirited people, however, continued to work for a convenient medium of exchange and soon took matters into their own hands by starting a private mint. Eight men of affairs whose names were Kilborne, Magruder, Taylor, Abernethy, Willson, Rector, Campbell and Smith set up the Oregon Exchange Company.

The coins struck were of virgin gold as specified in the original act. Ten-dollar dies were made later, and were of finer design and workmanship.

	Fine	V. Fine	Ex. Fine	Unc.
1849 5 D	$2,000	$2,500	$3,500	——

OREGON EXCHANGE COMPANY

1849 TEN D — Walton Sale, 1963.....................V. Fine $10,500.00

MORMON GOLD PIECES

Salt Lake City, Utah 1849-1860

The first name given to the organized Mormon Territory was the "State of Deseret," the latter word meaning "honey bee." The beehive, which is shown on the reverse of the five-dollar 1860 piece, was a favorite device of the followers of Joseph Smith and Brigham Young. The clasped hands appear on most Mormon coins and exemplify strength in unity. "Holiness to the Lord" was an inscription frequently used.

Brigham Young was the instigator of the coinage system and personally supervised the mint which was housed in a little adobe building in Salt Lake City.

The mint was inaugurated late in 1849 as a public convenience.

	Fine	V. Fine	Ex. Fine	Unc.
1849 TWO AND HALF DO...............	$550.00	$750.00	$900.00	——
1849 FIVE DOLLARS...................	400.00	475.00	575.00	——

1849 TEN DOLLARS — Walton Sale, 1963.................Fine $14,000.00

MORMON GOLD PIECES

1849 TWENTY DOLLARS — Public Auction Sale, 1965 . . . . . V. Fine $6,500.00

The Mormon twenty-dollar piece was the first of that denomination to be coined in this country.

1850 FIVE DOLLARS

Fine	$425.00
V. Fine	500.00
Ex. Fine	600.00
Unc	———

1860 5D

V. Fine	$1150.00
Ex. Fine	1500.00
Unc	1750.00

COLORADO GOLD PIECES
Clark, Gruber & Co. — Denver 1860-1861

Clark, Gruber and Co. was a well-known private minting firm in Denver, Colo. in the early sixties.

CLARK & CO. 1860

	Fine	V. Fine	Ex. Fine	Unc.
1860 2½D	$300.00	$400.00	$475.00	$600.00
1860 5D	400.00	475.00	575.00	700.00

COLORADO GOLD PIECES

CLARK, GRUBER & CO. 1860-1861

	Fine	V. Fine	Ex. Fine	Unc.
1860 TEN D............................	$750.00	$1,150	$1,500	$2,000
1860 TWENTY D — Public Auction Sale, 1963............Ex. Fine $5,000.00				

The $2.50 and five-dollar pieces of 1861 follow closely the designs of the 1860 issues. The main difference is found in the legends. The reverse side now has CLARK GRUBER & CO. DENVER. PIKES PEAK is on the coronet of Liberty.

	Fine	V. Fine	Ex. Fine	Unc.
1861 2½D.........................	300.00	400.00	500.00	650.00
1861 FIVE D.......................	400.00	500.00	600.00	750.00
1861 TEN D........................	400.00	475.00	575.00	——

	Fine	V. Fine	Ex. Fine	Unc.
1861 TWENTY D....................	1,000	1,250	1,750	——

JOHN PARSONS & COMPANY
Tarryall Mines — Colorado 1861

Very little is known regarding the mint of John Parsons and Co., although it is reasonably certain that it operated in the South Park of Colorado, near Tarryall, in the summer of 1861.

JOHN PARSONS & COMPANY

1860 20 DOLS. Gold Ingot.................................... ——

Pikes Peak Gold

	Fine	Unc.
(1861) Undated 2½ D...............................	——	——
(1861) Undated FIVE D...............................	——	——

J. J. CONWAY & COMPANY
Georgia Gulch, Colorado, 1861

Records show that the Conway Mint operated for a short while in 1861.
As in all gold mining areas the value of gold dust caused disagreement among
the merchants and the miners. The firm of J. J. Conway & Co. solved this
difficulty by bringing out their gold pieces in August, 1861.

(1861) Undated 2½ DOLL'S — Waldorf Sale, 1964......Ex. Fine $13,500.00

	Fine	Unc.
(1861) Undated FIVE DOLLARS........................	——	——
(1861) Undated FIVE DOLLARS, Similar.		
Variety without numeral 5 on reverse.............	——	——

(1861) Undated
    TEN DOLLARS.. ——

Old Red Books Never Die

Reports reach us more and more that many collectors are assembling yearly editions of this catalog and occasionally we hear from proud owners who have complete sets. These individuals are truly fortunate, for they have a generation of coin values to check, to study, and to give them an understanding of what makes our American coin market what it is today.

The growth of coin collecting since World War II has been phenomenal. The modern method of collecting coins in series from current circulation has been widespread in this country, aided and abetted by the popular coin folder. We have created a *modus operandi* unlike that of any other nation or of any other time in history. Other countries, notably Canada, Great Britain and some Commonwealth nations, have slowly adopted this pattern, but collectors in the United States already have a generation of experience behind them. We have established a system that is interesting and economically significant. Needless to say, the *Guide Book of United States Coins* (Red Book) serves as both a needed tool and a permanent record of market performance for the American collecting fraternity.

This growth, though there have been occasional value retreats in some areas, has been fairly constant in nearly every United States coin series. The beginner usually grows into his numismatic world by starting with recent United States cents. He soon widens his field to late-date nickels, dimes, and higher denominations. Later, his attention turns backward to obsolete types, reaching the 1790's. It is then only a short step to early Americana, private gold, tokens and the rest.

The old editions of the Red Book take on a special meaning to those collectors who are looking for a concise and accurate record of past performance. For the most part, a search through old editions proves exciting and rewarding, and in some few instances, a little disappointing. Our objective in including this department in the catalog is to demonstrate with a few tables how some answers can be obtained that are not found elsewhere. Adjacent pages contain performance tables of over 60 selected coins spread over five denomination categories, cents to half dollars. Much can be learned, even from such a brief format, about how "personality" coins got where they are today.

It is hoped that these tables will encourage readers to start a search for past editions so as to check independently coins of their own special interest — not necessarily the glamor specimens. Perhaps only a half dozen old editions, three or four years apart, could serve this purpose for many. We feel obliged to state that all past editions of this catalog are out of print and no longer available through the publisher. The only sources are friends, fellow collectors, or dealers. Those collectors who have told us of their partly formed or completed sets have emphasized how fascinating and helpful early-year

Red Books have been to them. Past records of individual coins tabulated over a span of years have told them a great deal about today's values and have helped them to anticipate the market more clearly. Acquiring scarce coins before they reach high value is not all luck. Reaching the goal of quality investment is largely based on experience, study, and keeping up to date.

The collector of United States coins who entered the hobby during the past decade is usually astounded at the low price tags certain expensive coins carried back in 1947, the first year of the Guide Book, or even in 1957, the tenth edition year. The accompanying tables of figures demonstrate the general upward trend in values as more and more collectors joined our ranks over the years. Little dramas sometimes liven the scene, like the struggle for first position between the 1931-D and 1931-S uncirculated cents. Without a year by year comparison of these two rivals we would be unaware of this curious situation. The prevalence of uncirculated grade is probably the same for each branch mint, though the mintage was 4,480,000 by Denver and 866,000 for San Francisco. Here is a classic case of how immediate withdrawal of uncirculated coins or delay in doing so can affect coin values. In this special illustration, the result is clear and lasting and the collecting fraternity still is not quite sure which of the two branch mint 1931's is scarcer in uncirculated condition (see table 1*).

The used, or circulated, 1931-D or 1931-S cents pose a different story. Their values in Good to Extra Fine are in direct normal relation to quantities minted. Refer to page 86 in this catalog for latest values and a demonstration of this fact.

Another interesting phenomenon has been the 1950-D nickel, an instance of almost complete capture of an issue at the outset. When released, a great majority of the 2,630,030 was stored away by speculators. The fact that so few have been found in circulation testifies to the thoroughness of the withdrawal. Here is an unusual example of an uncirculated specimen being commoner than the used coin. Practice prevents the lesser quality coin from commanding a higher price, however. Most transactions involving this coin are carried on in roll quantities. The table shows how this nickel has bounced around for some years. It will be interesting to see where its resting place will be in 10, 15, or 20 years. In this connection, one might mentally speculate on a possible sleeper, such as the 1951-S nickel in uncirculated. Compare this with the 1950-D nickel in the same uncirculated grade. It is likely that these two are about equal in quantity available in that condition, somewhat similar to the situation of the 1931-D and -S cents cited above. Compare these two nickels on page 95 of this book. It is not difficult to detect the effects of the bright light of publicity, all in favor of the 1950-D nickel (see table 2*).

Cases such as these illustrate the truism that coin values are based only partly on statistics. The human element is often present to influence supply and demand in strange and unpredictable ways.

Part of the romance of collecting United States series of coins is the discovery and ownership of significant die varieties. Such varieties are usually discovered several years after they are issued, have no known quantity available, but enjoy a fairly stable value and sustained popularity. Examples found in the tables are 1922 no "D" cent, 1955 double die cent, 1937-D 3-legged Buffalo nickel, 1942/41 dime, and 1918-S 8/7 quarter. Over the years, these and a limited few others have been added to the catalog when popularity and availability have been established. The special character of these coins adds flavor to the hobby. Each possesses a special aura of fascination and mystery and is treasured for its "rareness," for this kind of mistake seldom comes out of our mints.

This section of the present catalog is intended to serve as a stimulus to the reader to make his own interesting comparisons of coins and series, and to study how influences of time, quality, and quantity affect market values. Value comparisons can be made in a variety of categories. We have included a table to illustrate the rate of growth in value of Fine versus Uncirculated. One scarce coin of each denomination was selected: 1924-D cent, 1926-S nickel, 1926-S dime, 1927-S quarter, and 1923-S half dollar. They all fall within a five-year period of issue, have a small mintage, and are well back in time so as to offer a good value perspective. The answers come into focus quite readily. Our only comment is that the cent obviously has its own special result, namely, that the used coin has a better record than the uncirculated. The other four denominations in the cases cited greatly favor the uncirculated coin. We conclude that the cent has earned a special advantage, because it has been the basic coin board series that in turn has greatly influenced this equalization of values regardless of grade in low mintage dates.

Studies such as this often produce surprising answers. Results sometimes differ for coins of high or low denomination, circulated or uncirculated grade, scarce or numerous, and of old or recent vintage. In future editions we plan similar tables in other collecting areas, using average prices from all past editions of the *Guide Book of United States Coins*.

TABLE 1 — CENTS

	1909S VDB	1914D	1922 No D	1923S	1926S	1931D*	1931S*	1947S	1949S	1950S	1951S	1952	1952S	1955 Dbl. Die	1955S
1st/1947	15.00	10.00	—	9.00	6.50	3.00	1.35	.05	—	—					
2nd/1948	16.50	15.00	V.G. 3.50	11.00	6.50	3.50	1.50	.05	—	—					
3rd/1949	16.50	16.50	3.50	12.00	7.50	3.50	1.75	.05	.05	—					
4th/1951-52	12.50	20.00	3.50	15.00	6.50	3.50	1.60	.05	.05	.05	.05	.05			
5th/1952-53	13.50	27.50	3.50	17.50	7.50	4.00	1.50	.05	.05	.05	.05	.05			
6th/1953-54	13.50	35.00	3.50	20.00	8.50	4.00	1.75	.05	.05	.05	.05	.05	.05		
7th/1954-55	17.50	47.50	3.50	25.00	9.00	4.50	2.00	.05	.05	.05	.05	.05	.05		
8th/1955	20.00	65.00	4.50	32.50	12.00	5.00	3.50	.10	.15	.05	.05	.05	.05		.05
9th/1956	30.00	80.00	Fine 7.50	40.00	13.50	6.50	4.50	.15	.25	.10	.10	.05	.10		.05
10th/1957	40.00	110.00	7.50	55.00	17.50	8.50	7.00	.20	.35	.20	.15	.05	.15		.05
11th/1958	60.00	150.00	Unc. 10.00	65.00	20.00	12.50	14.00	.20	.35	.25	.25	.05	.20		.10
12th/1959	77.50	200.00	100.00	110.00	35.00	17.50	18.50	.25	.50	.35	.35	.15	.30	E.F. .50 / Unc. —	.15
13th/1960	85.00	250.00	125.00	130.00	45.00	20.00	18.00	.30	.75	.50	.60	.25	.35	E.F. .45 / Unc. .80	.25
14th/1961	97.50	275.00	165.00	140.00	55.00	28.50	21.00	.60	1.25	.75	.80	.50	.70	E.F. 55.00 / Unc. 95.00	.40
15th/1962	115.00	310.00	185.00	150.00	65.00	35.00	25.00	.50	1.15	.65	.75	.45	.65	E.F. — / Unc. —	.40
16th/1963	165.00	410.00	275.00	180.00	75.00	45.00	42.50	.65	1.50	.90	1.00	.55	.80	E.F. — / Unc. —	.50
17th/1964	310.00	500.00	325.00	200.00	80.00	60.00	72.50	.80	1.75	1.00	1.35	.60	1.00	E.F. — / Unc. —	.90
18th/1965	335.00	700.00	600.00	250.00	140.00	85.00	85.00	1.25	2.25	1.10	1.50	.70	1.25	E.F. 250.00 / Unc. 250.00	1.00
19th/1966	350.00	775.00	800.00	285.00	160.00	87.50	95.00	1.50	2.50	1.40	1.80	.85	1.25	E.F. 200.00 / Unc. 350.00	1.25
20th/1967	300.00	700.00	850.00	265.00	160.00	80.00	85.00	1.25	2.25	1.20	1.50	.75	1.00	E.F. 235.00 / Unc. 435.00	1.00
21st/1968	240.00	585.00	700.00	225.00	105.00	60.00	60.00	.75	1.50	.80	.95	.65	.65	E.F. 235.00 / Unc. 400.00	.75
22nd/1969	220.00	560.00	700.00	225.00	105.00	60.00	60.00	.75	1.50	.80	.95	.65	.65	E.F. 235.00 / Unc. 400.00	.75
23rd/1970	220.00	560.00	675.00	225.00	100.00	55.00	60.00	.70	1.50	.75	.90	.60	.60	E.F. 245.00 / Unc. 430.00	.75

*See text

TABLE 2 — NICKELS

	1924S	1926D	1926S	1937D 3 Legs	1939D	1939S	1942D	1942P	1946S	1950D*	1951S*	1952D	1955
1st/1947	22.50	3.00	35.00		1.75	1.50	1.25	.25	.10				
2nd/1948	35.00	3.75	60.00		2.25	2.25	1.25	.25	.10				
3rd/1949	35.00	4.50	65.00	6.50	2.25	2.00	1.25	.25	.25				
4th/1951-52	45.00	4.50	70.00	7.50	2.25	2.00	1.25	.25	.25	.10			
5th/1952-53	50.00	5.00	75.00	7.50	2.50	2.25	1.25	.25	.30	.15	.15	.15	
6th/1953-54	60.00	5.50	80.00	8.50	3.00	3.00	1.50	.25	.30	.35	.25	.15	
7th/1954-55	75.00	5.50	90.00	10.00	3.00	3.00	1.50	.25	.30	.35	.35	.15	
8th/1955	80.00	7.00	95.00	12.00	3.50	3.50	1.50	.25	.35	.40	.60	.15	.15
9th/1956	85.00	7.50	100.00	15.00	4.50	4.50	2.00	.30	.40	.45	.75	.20	.15
10th/1957	90.00	7.50	125.00	20.00	5.50	5.25	2.50	.30	.45	.50	.75	.25	.15
11th/1958	100.00	8.50	140.00	25.00	7.00	6.50	3.00	.40	.50	.90	.80	.30	.40
12th/1959	105.00	9.00	150.00	30.00	10.00	8.50	5.00	.45	.60	1.25	1.25	.40	.50
13th/1960	110.00	10.00	165.00	42.50	15.00	11.00	6.00	.65	.75	1.35	1.35	.50	.55
14th/1961	125.00	12.00	175.00	50.00	42.50	17.50	12.00	3.00	.90	5.50	3.75	3.75	1.25
15th/1962	135.00	22.50	210.00	60.00	40.00	17.50	13.50	3.00	.80	5.00	3.00	3.00	1.10
16th/1963	150.00	45.00	225.00	90.00	37.50	15.00	14.50	4.50	.80	6.50	3.25	3.00	1.15
17th/1964	175.00	190.00	275.00	125.00	40.00	16.00	15.00	3.50	1.35	15.00	4.50	3.50	2.00
18th/1965	250.00	250.00	325.00	180.00	50.00	20.00	18.00	12.50	2.50	22.00	6.75	4.50	4.25
19th/1966	450.00	350.00	400.00	210.00	65.00	23.50	20.00	13.25	3.00	26.00	10.00	5.50	5.00
20th/1967	550.00	370.00	430.00	225.00	60.00	21.00	20.00	13.25	3.00	22.50	10.00	5.50	4.50
21st/1968	625.00	300.00	435.00	225.00	45.00	15.00	13.50	8.50	2.00	16.00	6.25	4.00	3.00
22nd/1969	650.00	300.00	440.00	240.00	40.00	12.25	11.00	7.75	1.65	17.50	6.00	4.00	3.00
23rd/1970	675.00	315.00	440.00	220.00	40.00	11.50	11.00	8.00	1.50	16.00	5.25	3.25	2.40

*See text.

TABLE 3 — DIMES

	1916D	1921	1921D	1925D	1926S	1942/41	1949S	1950S	1951S	1952S	1955	1955D
1st/1947	65.00	37.50	6.50	5.00	7.50	Fine 4.50						
2nd/1948	75.00	50.00	8.50	5.00	10.00	Unc. 15.00						
3rd/1949	100.00	60.00	10.00	6.50	12.50	15.00	.15	.10				
4th/1951-52	100.00	60.00	9.00	6.50	15.00	15.00	.20	.15	.10			
5th/1952-53	100.00	60.00	12.50	6.50	17.50	25.00	.25	.15	.15	.15		
6th/1953-54	100.00	75.00	20.00	7.50	22.50	30.00	.25	.15	.15	.15		
7th/1954-55	125.00	85.00	30.00	9.00	30.00	40.00	.25	.15	.15	.15		
8th/1955	135.00	100.00	35.00	11.00	35.00	45.00	.50	.20	.15	.15	.15	.15
9th/1956	150.00	110.00	50.00	12.50	40.00	50.00	3.00	2.50	1.00	.75	.15	.15
10th/1957	175.00	115.00	60.00	13.50	45.00	60.00	3.50	3.50	2.50	1.00	.30	.25
11th/1958	210.00	135.00	80.00	17.50	50.00	90.00	3.50	3.50	3.00	1.00	.30	.25
12th/1959	250.00	145.00	95.00	19.50	57.50	100.00	3.75	3.50	3.00	1.10	.30	.25
13th/1960	285.00	150.00	100.00	21.00	60.00	125.00	3.50	3.25	3.00	1.10	.30	.30
14th/1961	360.00	175.00	125.00	27.50	70.00	150.00	7.50	7.50	5.00	2.00	.90	.75
15th/1962	400.00	190.00	130.00	30.00	72.50	150.00	7.50	6.50	5.00	1.75	.75	.65
16th/1963	435.00	205.00	145.00	42.50	87.50	175.00	6.00	5.50	4.00	1.75	.75	.65
17th/1964	500.00	230.00	175.00	250.00	95.00	275.00	7.00	6.50	5.75	2.00	1.25	1.00
18th/1965	625.00	275.00	225.00	300.00	150.00	360.00	15.00	12.25	11.75	4.50	2.75	2.00
19th/1966	750.00	325.00	275.00	330.00	250.00	400.00	16.00	14.50	13.00	4.50	3.50	2.40
20th/1967	750.00	325.00	275.00	330.00	250.00	425.00	16.00	14.50	13.00	4.50	3.50	2.40
21st/1968	750.00	350.00	300.00	290.00	275.00	475.00	11.00	10.00	9.00	3.00	2.25	1.60
22nd/1969	700.00	350.00	300.00	290.00	300.00	525.00	10.00	8.00	7.50	2.00	1.75	1.50
23rd/1970	675.00	375.00	325.00	300.00	320.00	525.00	13.50	9.00	7.50	2.25	2.00	1.50

TABLE 4 — QUARTERS

[242]

	1916	1918S 8/7	1919S	1927S	1932D	1932S	1936D	1948S	1949	1951S	1955D	1958
1st/1947	80.00	150.00	65.00	27.50	17.50	10.00	2.50	.75				
2nd/1948	90.00	150.00	65.00	60.00	40.00	27.50	9.00	1.25				
3rd/1949	90.00	150.00	65.00	60.00	37.50	22.50	9.00	1.25	.35			
4th/1951-52	90.00	150.00	65.00	75.00	32.50	17.50	9.00	1.25	.35	.35		
5th/1952-53	100.00	165.00	70.00	85.00	32.50	15.00	10.00	1.50	.40	.40		
6th/1953-54	100.00	185.00	75.00	90.00	35.00	16.50	11.00	1.50	.40	.40		
7th/1954-55	125.00	190.00	90.00	100.00	35.00	17.50	12.50	1.50	.50	.50		
8th/1955	135.00	200.00	100.00	110.00	37.50	20.00	17.50	1.50	.50	.50		
9th/1956	140.00	250.00	100.00	150.00	45.00	22.50	25.00	1.75	.60	.65	.50	
10th/1957	150.00	250.00	110.00	175.00	50.00	25.00	32.50	2.50	.90	1.00	.65	
11th/1958	180.00	325.00	125.00	200.00	62.50	27.50	45.00	2.50	.90	1.50	.65	
12th/1959	235.00	500.00	125.00	210.00	70.00	32.50	55.00	3.75	1.00	1.65	.65	.50
13th/1960	250.00	525.00	140.00	235.00	75.00	35.00	65.00	4.25	1.00	1.85	.70	.50
14th/1961	290.00	700.00	160.00	275.00	90.00	40.00	75.00	5.50	2.50	2.75	1.00	.60
15th/1962	400.00	900.00	190.00	390.00	100.00	42.50	95.00	6.00	4.00	2.75	1.25	.60
16th/1963	500.00	1750.00	225.00	450.00	120.00	50.00	130.00	6.50	4.75	3.00	1.25	.60
17th/1964	900.00	2500.00	250.00	550.00	150.00	60.00	160.00	8.00	5.50	3.50	2.00	.75
18th/1965	1000.00	2750.00	275.00	575.00	165.00	80.00	180.00	12.00	11.50	5.00	4.00	1.50
19th/1966	1175.00	2900.00	325.00	700.00	240.00	110.00	265.00	25.00	15.00	7.50	6.00	2.50
20th/1967	1175.00	3000.00	340.00	750.00	240.00	150.00	285.00	27.50	15.00	8.00	6.00	4.00
21st/1968	1000.00	2900.00	335.00	725.00	240.00	130.00	265.00	20.00	13.00	6.75	4.25	1.75
22nd/1969	950.00	2900.00	335.00	725.00	225.00	115.00	250.00	17.50	10.00	5.00	4.00	1.50
23rd/1970	900.00	3250.00	350.00	750.00	225.00	115.00	250.00	17.50	10.00	6.25	5.00	2.00

TABLE 5 — HALVES

	1917S Obv.	1919	1919D	1919S	1920D	1921	1921D	1921S	1938D	1949	1949S	1955
1st/1947	125.00	20.00	18.00	67.50	18.00	60.00	15.00	18.00	6.50			
2nd/1948	135.00	25.00	25.00	110.00	25.00	65.00	20.00	32.50	7.50			
3rd/1949	140.00	30.00	30.00	130.00	30.00	65.00	25.00	37.50	7.50	.75	.75	
4th/1951-52	150.00	30.00	35.00	150.00	32.50	65.00	27.50	37.50	7.50	.75	.75	
5th/1952-53	175.00	40.00	65.00	175.00	65.00	75.00	45.00	65.00	8.50	1.00	1.00	
6th/1953-54	200.00	50.00	80.00	200.00	85.00	100.00	65.00	80.00	9.00	1.25	1.25	
7th/1954-55	225.00	60.00	100.00	300.00	125.00	115.00	75.00	90.00	10.00	1.25	1.25	
8th/1955	250.00	70.00	175.00	400.00	150.00	140.00	150.00	175.00	11.00	2.75	1.75	1.00
9th/1956	300.00	75.00	200.00	450.00	175.00	165.00	160.00	190.00	15.00	4.00	2.75	1.00
10th/1957	325.00	80.00	200.00	500.00	185.00	165.00	165.00	190.00	17.50	6.00	3.50	1.75
11th/1958	360.00	80.00	200.00	485.00	190.00	190.00	200.00	215.00	22.50	6.00	3.50	1.50
12th/1959	375.00	80.00	225.00	485.00	190.00	190.00	200.00	225.00	27.50	8.00	3.50	1.50
13th/1960	385.00	87.50	275.00	475.00	195.00	200.00	210.00	245.00	32.50	10.00	3.75	1.40
14th/1961	385.00	90.00	285.00	465.00	210.00	225.00	235.00	275.00	42.50	15.00	4.75	1.50
15th/1962	385.00	90.00	285.00	465.00	210.00	225.00	235.00	275.00	45.00	17.50	5.50	1.50
16th/1963	385.00	90.00	285.00	465.00	210.00	225.00	235.00	275.00	47.50	14.50	5.50	1.50
17th/1964	385.00	100.00	310.00	465.00	225.00	250.00	250.00	290.00	60.00	16.00	6.50	1.50
18th/1965	400.00	110.00	330.00	465.00	250.00	265.00	275.00	325.00	77.50	40.00	16.00	7.00
19th/1966	400.00	135.00	350.00	490.00	280.00	300.00	350.00	380.00	135.00	45.00	26.50	12.00
20th/1967	440.00	225.00	410.00	550.00	400.00	450.00	575.00	525.00	175.00	35.00	25.00	12.00
21st/1968	450.00	265.00	485.00	625.00	450.00	650.00	850.00	900.00	200.00	27.00	20.00	11.00
22nd/1969	450.00	285.00	485.00	625.00	485.00	650.00	850.00	975.00	200.00	22.50	20.00	10.00
23rd/1970	475.00	365.00	550.00	625.00	530.00	700.00	900.00	1100.00	200.00	26.50	24.00	11.25

TABLE 6 — GROWTH

	CENT 1924D (2.52 Million)		NICKEL 1926S (.97 Million)		DIME 1926S (1.5 Million)		QUARTER 1927S (.396 Million)		HALF 1935 (2.2 Million)	
	Fine	Unc.	Fine	Unc.	Fine	Unc.	Fine	Unc.	Fine	Unc.
1st/1947	.50	8.00	6.00	35.00	2.00	7.50	5.00	27.50	2.50	18.00
2nd/1948	.60	9.00	6.00	60.00	2.00	10.00	5.00	60.00	2.50	25.00
3rd/1949	.60	9.00	3.00	65.00	1.50	12.50	5.00	60.00	2.50	30.00
4th/1951-52	.60	9.50	3.00	70.00	1.50	15.00	6.00	75.00	2.50	35.00
5th/1952-53	.60	10.00	3.00	75.00	2.50	17.50	7.50	85.00	2.50	45.00
6th/1953-54	.75	11.00	4.00	80.00	3.50	22.50	9.00	90.00	3.50	70.00
7th/1954-55	1.00	12.00	5.00	90.00	3.50	30.00	12.50	100.00	3.50	85.00
8th/1955	1.50	15.00	7.50	95.00	3.50	35.00	15.00	110.00	4.00	100.00
9th/1956	2.50	20.00	9.00	100.00	5.00	40.00	15.00	150.00	5.00	115.00
10th/1957	3.00	27.50	8.50	125.00	6.50	45.00	12.50	175.00	6.00	125.00
11th/1958	4.00	35.00	10.00	140.00	7.50	50.00	15.00	200.00	4.00	150.00
12th/1959	4.00	45.00	10.50	150.00	9.00	57.50	17.50	210.00	4.50	152.50
13th/1960	4.50	50.00	12.50	165.00	8.00	60.00	11.00	235.00	4.50	165.00
14th/1961	5.50	60.00	14.00	175.00	9.00	70.00	13.50	275.00	4.50	175.00
15th/1962	6.00	70.00	15.00	210.00	6.00	72.50	13.50	390.00	4.50	175.00
16th/1963	7.75	82.50	18.00	225.00	7.00	87.50	17.50	450.00	4.50	175.00
17th/1964	7.50	110.00	19.50	275.00	8.00	95.00	20.00	550.00	4.50	175.00
18th/1965	27.50	200.00	20.00	325.00	9.50	150.00	17.50	575.00	5.00	195.00
19th/1966	27.50	250.00	21.00	400.00	10.00	250.00	17.50	700.00	5.25	220.00
20th/1967	22.50	225.00	21.00	430.00	10.00	250.00	17.50	750.00	6.00	250.00
21st/1968	16.50	175.00	17.00	435.00	10.00	275.00	15.00	725.00	4.50	300.00
22nd/1969	16.50	175.00	17.00	440.00	10.00	300.00	15.00	725.00	4.50	350.00
23rd/1970	13.50	180.00	16.50	440.00	11.50	320.00	15.00	750.00	6.00	365.00
Growth Multiple	x27	x22.5	x2.75	x12.6	x5.75	x42.7	x3	x27.2	x2.4	x20.4

LESHER REFERENDUM DOLLARS

Coined by Joseph Lesher in 1900 and 1901 at Victor, Colorado. Used in trade to some extent, and stocked by various merchants who redeemed them in goods. Coins were numbered and a blank space left at bottom of 1901 issues, in which were stamped names of businessmen who bought them. All are quite rare, many varieties extremely rare.

1900

1901

	V. Fine	Unc.
1900 First Type, no business name	$250.00	$400.00
1900 A.B. Bumstead, with scrolls	220.00	350.00
1900 A.B. Bumstead, no scrolls	175.00	300.00
1900 Bank Type (5 known)		
1901 Imprint Type, no name	225.00	375.00
1901 Imprint Type, various names	$200-$600	$300-$1000

Feuchtwanger Cent 1837

Dr. Lewis Feuchtwanger produced a metal which was really a variety of German silver consisting of nickel, copper and some zinc. He suggested as early as 1837 to Congress that his metal be substituted for copper. He made some one-cent and three-cent trial pieces in this metal at that time.

Values: Cent..Fine $10.00; Ex. Fine $25.00   Three-Cent piece..V. Scarce

HARD TIMES
TOKENS
1834-1844

In addition to the coins issued by the United States government, numismatists include in their collections the Hard Times and Civil War tokens which circulated as money during two periods in this country's history when nearly all the minor coin was hoarded.

The Hard Times tokens were issued in the period 1834-1844 and are the size of the large U. S. cent. They were generally struck in copper and are of two general groups: political tokens whose theme centered around President Jackson's fight against the United States Bank, and those issued by merchants (tradesmen's cards). Many different varieties exist. The most common pieces are generally valued at $1.50 Good to $7.50 Ex. Fine.

CIVIL WAR TOKENS — 1861-1864

Civil War Tokens are generally divided into two groups: tradesmen's tokens, and anonymously issued pieces with political or patriotic themes. They came into existence only because of the scarcity of government coins and disappeared as soon as the bronze coins of 1864 met the public demand for small copper change.

From the outset of the Civil War, government cents were insufficient in number, widely hoarded and worth a premium over all other currencies. As a result of this scarcity of cent pieces, private copper coins were issued by many individuals. Their wide circulation was made possible by the scarcity of copper-nickel cents and the public dislike of fractional paper money.

The tradesmen's tokens were issued by various firms to provide change and advertise the dealers' wares. They usually bore an implied or an explicit promise of redemption in goods or money. The second type were simply unauthorized substitutes for government coins, produced at a profit by private manufacturers and put into general circulation through various agencies.

These tokens are of great variety in composition and design. A number were more or less faithful imitations of the copper-nickel cent. A few of this type have the word "NOT" in very small letters above the words "ONE CENT."

Many pieces, especially of the tradesmen token type, were individual in device and size, representing any caprice of design or slogan that appealed to the maker. Some were political or patriotic in character, carrying the likeness of some military leader such as McClellan or bearing such inscriptions as "Millions for contractors, not one cent for the widows." An estimated 50,000,000 or more of these pieces were issued. Approximately 10,000 different varieties have been recorded.

The legal status of the Civil War Tokens was uncertain. Mint Director Pollock thought they were illegal; however, there was no law prohibiting the issue of tradesmen's tokens or of private coins not in imitation of United States coins. A law was passed on April 22, 1864 prohibiting the issue of any one or two-cent coins, tokens, or devices for use as money, and on June 8 another law was passed which abolished private coinage of every kind.

	Fine	V. Fine	Unc.
Copper or Brass Tokens	$1.35	$ 2.50	$ 4.75
Nickel or German Silver Tokens	4.00	7.50	16.00
White Metal Tokens	3.00	6.00	12.00
Copper-Nickel Tokens	3.25	6.50	12.00
Silver Tokens	8.00	13.50	27.50

CONFEDERATE STATES OF AMERICA
Confederate 1861 Half Dollar

The half dollar struck by the Confederacy was unknown to collectors until 1879. A specimen of the coin and both dies were found in the possession of Dr. B. F. Taylor of New Orleans. Mr. E. Mason, Jr. of Philadelphia purchased Dr. Taylor's specimen and the reverse die and later sold them to J. W. Scott and Company of New York.

CONFEDERATE STATES OF AMERICA — 1861

Five hundred genuine 1861 half dollars from the New Orleans mint were acquired by J. W. Scott and Company. The reverses were planed off and then restamped with the Confederate die. These are known as restrikes. The restrikes have flattened obverses.

According to records only four originals were struck. These were made on a hand press. Original silver half dollar planchets were used, as well as the original obverse die. One of the coins was given to the Secretary of the Confederacy Memminger who passed it on to President Jefferson Davis for his approval. Another was given to Prof. Biddle of the University of Louisiana. Dr. E. Ames of New Orleans received a third specimen, the last being kept by Chief Coiner Taylor, who sold it later as mentioned above.

Lack of bullion prevented the Confederate government from proceeding with any coinage plans that might have been made.

J. W. Scott struck some tokens in white metal using the Confederate reverse die and a special die bearing the inscription

4 ORIGINALS STRUCK BY ORDER OF C. S. A. IN NEW ORLEANS 1861 *******
REV. SAME AS U.S. (FROM ORIGINAL DIE SCOTT)

Confederate Reverse   Scott Obverse

	Quan. Minted	V. Fine	Unc.
1861 HALF DOL. (Ex. Rare)	4	—	—
1861 HALF DOL. Restrike	500	$400.00	$675.00
1861 Scott Token, obverse. Confederate reverse	500	75.00	140.00

THE CONFEDERATE CENT

An order to make cents for the Confederacy was placed with Mr. Robert Lovett Jr., an engraver and die-sinker of Philadelphia, through a jewelry firm of that city. Fearing arrest by the United States government for giving assistance to the enemy, Mr. Lovett decided against delivering the coins to the Confederate government and hid the coins and dies in his cellar.

The original dies were later purchased by Capt. John W. Haseltine who made restrikes from the dies.

		Proof
1861 Cent Original (copper-nickel)	12	$2200.00
1861 Cent Restrike (copper)	55	1200.00
1861 Cent Restrike (gold)	7	2800.00
1861 Cent Restrike (silver)	12	1500.00

COINS AND TOKENS OF HAWAII

The first official coins of Hawaii were the copper cents of 1847 issued by King Kamehameha III. The five cent piece of 1881 and the eighth dollar piece of 1883 are patterns. In 1883 Kalakaua I issued silver dimes, quarters, halves and dollars bearing his bust and showing the Hawaiian coat of arms on the reverse. The plantation tokens listed here were all used as small change on the Islands.

Ten Cents 1883

One Cent — 1847

	Quan. Minted	Fine	V. Fine	Ex. Fine	Unc.	Proof
1847 Cent	100,000	$ 50.00	$ 70.00	$ 85.00	$140.00	———
1881 Five Cents		———	———	———	650.00	900.00
1883 Ten Cents	250,000	7.00	11.00	25.00	75.00	200.00
1883 Eighth Dollar (12½¢)	100,000	130.00	200.00	400.00	700.00	
1883 Quarter Dollar	500,000	6.00	8.50	11.00	20.00	200.00
1883 Half Dollar	700,000	19.00	25.00	40.00	72.50	200.00
1883 Dollar	500,000	70.00	85.00	110.00	275.00	350.00

HAWAIIAN TOKENS

Thomas Hobron Token —1879   Haiku Plantation — 1882

Wailuku Plantation — 1871   Wailuku Plantation — 1880

	Fine	Ex. Fine
Waterhouse Token 1862. Bust of Kamehameha IV	$325.00	$650.00
Wailuku Plantation Token 1871	85.00	150.00
Wailuku Plantation Token 1880	100.00	150.00
Thomas Hobron Token 1879	85.00	150.00
Haiku Plantation Token	60.00	100.00
Grove Ranch Plantation Token 1886	125.00	175.00

ALASKA RURAL REHABILITATION CORPORATION
TOKENS OF 1935

These tokens were issued by the U. S. Government for the use of the colonists of the Matanuska Valley Colonization Project to supply them with much needed Federal aid. They were redeemable only at the ARRC stores. The "Bingles", as they were called, were in use only about six months during 1935-1936 after which they were redeemed for regular U. S. money and destroyed. They were issued on a basis of family dependents. Each token is the size of the corresponding U. S. coin with the exception of the one cent piece which is octagonal. The design is the same on both sides of each denomination.

	Quantity Minted	V. Fine	Unc.
1¢ Aluminum	5,000	$15.00	$22.50
5¢ Aluminum	5,000	15.00	22.50
10¢ Aluminum	5,000	15.00	22.50
25¢ Aluminum	3,000	20.00	30.00
50¢ Aluminum	2,500	25.00	45.00
$1.00 Aluminum	2,500	40.00	70.00
$5.00 Brass	1,000	60.00	80.00
$10.00 Brass	1,000	75.00	100.00

PHILIPPINES UNDER SOVEREIGNTY OF THE U.S.

The 1903-19 issues were struck at Philadelphia and San Francisco. 1920 and after were struck at Manila. Because of World War II the 1944-45 coins were minted at Philadelphia, Denver and San Francisco.

Bronze

	E.F.	Unc.
½ Centavo 1903-08...	$1.00	$3.50
1 Centavo 1903-36...	.75	2.50

Copper-Nickel

5 Centavos 1903-28...	1.00	3.00
5 Centavos 1918 Rev. of 20 Centavos (Mule)............	45.00	80.00

Reduced Size

5 Centavos 1930-35...	1.25	4.00

Silver

10 Centavos 1903-06...	1.75	4.50
20 Centavos 1903-06...	2.50	7.00
50 Centavos 1903-06...	7.50	15.00
1 Peso 1903-06.......	8.50	15.00

Size Reduced

	E.F.	Unc.
10 Centavos 1907-35...$	1.00	$ 4.00
20 Centavos 1907-29...	2.50	6.00
20 Centavos 1928 Rev. of 5 Centavos (Mule)	20.00	50.00
50 Centavos 1907-21...	5.00	9.00
1 Peso 1907-12.......	6.00	10.00

Commonwealth Issues

Bronze

1 Centavo 1937-44...	.15	.40

Copper-Nickel

5 Centavos 1937-41...	1.00	3.00

Nickel-Silver
Same Type as Cop.-Nic.

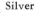

5 Centavos 1944-45...	.15	.35

Silver

10 Centavos 1937-45...	.20	.40
20 Centavos 1937-45...	.30	.50
50 Centavos 1944-45...	.80	1.00

PHILIPPINES UNDER SOVEREIGNTY OF THE U. S.

Silver Coins Commemorating the Establishment of the Commonwealth of the Philippines, 1935

Murphy and Quezon Facing Each Other

Unc.

50 Centavos 1936 (20,000 struck) $27.50

Gov. Gen. Murphy and Quezon   Roosevelt and Quezon

1 Peso 1936 Murphy and Quezon (10,000 struck) 50.00
1 Peso 1936 Roosevelt and Quezon (10,000 struck) 50.00

PUERTO RICO

The farthest island east of the Greater Antilles in the Atlantic Ocean. Ceded to the United States after the Spanish-American war, it is a self-governing Commonwealth of the United States. Major industry: sugar cultivation and processing. Capital: *San Juan*. Area: 3,435 square miles. Population: 2,210,703.

UNDER SPAIN
ALFONSO XIII
1886-1898

	Quantity Minted	Good	Fine	V.F.	Unc.
5 Centavos 1896	600,000	$ 1.50	$ 3.50	$ 6.00	$ 9.00
10 Centavos 1896	700,000	1.75	5.00	12.50	30.00
20 Centavos 1895	3,350,006	3.00	7.50	12.50	25.00
40 Centavos 1896	725,002	10.00	17.50	32.50	55.00
1 Peso 1895	8,500,021	15.00	30.00	50.00	75.00

INDEX

INDEX — *Continued*

INDEX — *Continued*

[254]

INDEX — *Continued*

The following numismatic magazines are obtainable by subscription. They are published monthly or as indicated below:

The Numismatist
Published by the American
Numismatic Association
P.O. Box 2366
Colorado Springs, Colo.   80901
(Single Copy 75¢)

Coins Magazine
Iola, Wisconsin   54945
(Single Copy 60¢)

Numismatic News (Weekly)
Iola, Wisconsin   54945
(Single Copy 25¢)

Coin World (Weekly)
P.O. Box 150
Sidney, Ohio   45365
(Single Copy 35¢)

Hobbies Magazine
1006 S. Michigan Ave.
Chicago, Ill.   60605
(Has a coin section, Single Copy 50¢)

Numismatic Scrapbook Magazine
P.O. Box 150
Sidney, Ohio   45365
(Single Copy 60¢)

COINage Magazine
16250 Ventura Blvd.
Encino, California   91316
(Single Copy 60¢)

COIN FOLDERS

A Convenient Method
of Housing Your Collection

Made in two tones of blue . . . printed in black and silver, giving a brilliant "Jewel Case" effect to your coin collection.

Made by WHITMAN   Size Folded 5¾" x 7½"

COMPLETE LIST OF STYLES
UNITED STATES

Large Cent — 1793 to 1825
Large Cent — 1826 to 1857
Indian-Eagle Cents — 1857 to 1909
Lincoln Head Cent — 1909 to 1940
Lincoln Head Cent — Starting 1941
Lincoln Memorial Cent — Starting 1959
Cents — Plain, no printing

Half Dime — 1794 to 1873
Shield Type Nickel — 1866 to 1883
Liberty Head Nickel — 1883 to 1913
Buffalo Nickel — 1913 to 1938
Jefferson Nickel — 1938 to 1961
Jefferson Nickel — Starting 1962
Nickels — Plain, no printing

Bust Type Dime — 1796 to 1837
Liberty Seated Dime — 1837 to 1862
Liberty Seated Dime — 1863 to 1891
Barber Dime — 1892 to 1916
Mercury Head Dime — 1916 to 1945
Roosevelt Dime — Starting 1946
Dimes — Plain, no printing

Liberty Seated Quarter — 1838 to 1865
Liberty Seated Quarter — 1866 to 1891
Barber Quarter — 1892 to 1905
Barber Quarter — 1906 to 1916
Lib. Standing Quarter — 1916 to 1930
Wash. Head Quarter — 1932 to 1945
Wash. Head Quarter — 1946 to 1959
Wash. Head Quarter — Starting 1960
Quarters — Plain, no printing

Lib. Seated Half Dollar — 1839 to 1850
Lib. Seated Half Dollar — 1851 to 1862
Lib. Seated Half Dollar — 1863 to 1873
Lib. Seated Half Dollar — 1873 to 1891
Barber Half Dollar — 1892 to 1903
Barber Half Dollar — 1904 to 1915
Lib. Standing Half Dollar — 1916 to 1936
Lib. Standing Half Dollar — 1937 to 1947
Ben. Franklin Half Dollar — 1948-1963
Kennedy Half Dollar — Starting 1964
Halves — Plain, no printing

Morgan Dollar — 1878 to 1883
Morgan Dollar — 1884 to 1890
Morgan Dollar — 1891 to 1897
Morgan Dollar — 1898 to 1921
Peace Dollar — 1921 to 1935
Dollars — Plain, no printing

MISCELLANEOUS

Half Cent — 1793 to 1857
Silver Three Cent — 1851 to 1873
Two Cent — Nickel Three Cent — 1864 to 1889
Type Coins, Small Denominations
Type Coins, Large Denominations
20th Century Type Coins

ONE-A-YEAR

Cents, 1909 to Date
Nickels, 1913 to Date
Dimes, 1916 to Date
Quarters, 1916 to Date

CANADA

Large Cents — 1858 to 1920
Small Cents — Starting 1920
Silver Five Cents — 1858 to 1921
Nickels — 1922-1960
Nickels — Starting 1961
Dimes — 1858 to 1936
Dimes — Starting 1937
Quarters — 1858 to 1910
Quarters — 1911 to 1952
Quarters — Starting 1953
Halves — 1870 to 1910
Halves — 1911 to 1936
Halves — 1937-1960
Halves — Starting 1961
Silver Dollars — 1935 to 1957
Silver Dollars — Starting 1958
Quarters — Plain, no printing
Halves — Plain, no printing
Canada Coin Type Collection
Dollars — Plain, no printing